D1436337

AUTOMATIC CONTROL THEORY

WILEY SERIES IN ELECTRONIC
ENGINEERING TECHNOLOGY

AUTOMATIC CONTROL THEORY

by Benjamin E. DeRoy

Electrical Engineering Laboratory, Campbell Soup Company
formerly of Technical Institute and Community College, Temple
University

JOHN WILEY & SONS, INC.

New York / London / Sydney

Library of Congress Catalog Card Number: 66-27893
Printed in the United States of America

to Dr. C. N. Weygandt and Frank E. Hagen
in partial fulfillment
of my debt of gratitude

Preface

There are two hurdles facing the instructor teaching automatic control theory to technical institute students: their mathematics and their motivation. This book attempts to solve both these problems. For mathematics it uses only that which is taught in the first year of the technical institute curriculum, and for motivation it uses hardware examples throughout in developing the theory.*

In the writing of this book two fortunate circumstances brought me into contact with two individuals whose help and guidance leave me deeply in their debt. First, while doing graduate work at the University of Pennsylvania Moore School of Electrical Engineering I was impressed by the fact that after the initial hurdle of differential equations and Laplace transform derivations, the linear control theory presented to us was handled almost entirely by algebra. I therefore undertook a thesis to explore the teaching of control theory on a solid mathematical basis but on an algebraic level. I was particularly fortunate is having as my thesis adviser Dr. C. N. Weygandt, Professor of Electrical Engineering and Chairman, Graduate Group in Electrical Engineering. Dr. Weygandt's teaching expertise, high standards of thesis work, and genuine interest and helpfulness were an inspiration. Second, at about this same time I was made aware of a little red book entitled *Servo Engineer's Handbook* by Frank E. Hagen, an industrial servo designer who clearly understood the theory and practice of servo design and could explain in detail the reasons for all his procedures. He was interested enough and patient enough to answer my endless questions on the application of theory to industrial design of servomechanism components and systems.

---

* I did not avoid the calculus; it just was not needed in most of the book. Calculus is used in only two places: in Section 3.1 an integral is derived from a Laplace transform, and in Section 6.2 a maximum is found by differentiation. But the student who has never had calculus can understand the point of these sections. Calculus is never used in an example problem or in the problems for the student.

I used the completed thesis twice as class notes to teach the subject to evening technical institute students in a one-semester course entitled "Servomechanisms and Automatic Control." The enthusiasm of these students was gratifying. They showed their Bode plots and Nichols charts and the accompanying calculations to senior engineering school students, who could not believe that technical institute students were capable of such advanced work.

All tables, examples, and answers given in this book are accurate to three figures (slide-rule accuracy). All the problems are paired, with answers provided for the first one of its type; the student can cover the course by doing only these problems. The second problem of each pair is usually more difficult than the preceding one and provides a challenge to the better student.

To explore the unorthodox approach of this book I have consulted many sources, but only the major ones will be listed here. One is Chestnut and Mayer, *Servomechanisms and Regulating System Design* (Wiley, 1955, 1959), which I came to respect even more than when using it as a text. I also used extensively Frank Hagen's *Servo Engineer's Handbook* (Weston Instruments Inc., Transicoil Division), from which the examples of Chapter 5 were taken. Mr. Hagen was kind enough to write the data for the problems in Chapter 5 (which are also used in Chapters 6 and 7), thus giving one more instance of his helpfulness. Figure 1.27 and certain definitions in the text followed by the notation (ASA C85.1-1963) have been taken from American Standard *Terminology for Automatic Control, ASA C85.1-1963* with permission of the publishers, The American Society of Mechanical Engineers, United Engineering Center, 345 East 47th Street, New York, N.Y. 10017. Thanks for permission to reproduce photographs of servo components are due Bowmar Instrument Corporation; Cedar Engineering, a division of Control Data Corporation; Technology Instrument Corporation of California; and Weston Instruments, Inc., Transicoil Division. Addresses of these companies are given in Appendix D. Thanks for kind help are also due to William F. Melchior, Jr., Coordinator, Temple University Technical Institute Evening School. Finally for understanding, assistance, and encouragement during the gestation period of this book I thank my patient wife, Rachel.

B. E. DeRoy

Philadelphia, Pa.
July 1966

Contents

1 Introduction to Control Theory   1

1.1 Linear Systems 1
1.2 Amplifier Frequency Response 2
1.3 Feedback (or Closed-Loop) Amplifier Frequency
     Response. 7
1.4 Feedback Amplifier as Oscillator 10
1.5 One-Line Block Diagrams 13
1.6 Analysis of a Control System 15
1.7 Frequency Response of an Automobile Open-Loop
     Steering System 17
1.8 Frequency Response of an Automobile Closed-
     Loop Steering System 20
Summary 24

2 Laplace Transforms   25

2.1 From Logarithms to Laplace Transform . . . 25
2.2 A Circuit Problem Solved by the Laplace Transform 27
2.3 Laplace Transform Procedures 31
2.4 Laplace Transfer Function of Control Systems and
     Components. 34
Summary 41

3 Bode Diagrams   42

3.1 Graph of a Time Function 42
3.2 Introduction to Bode Diagrams 44
3.3 Bode Diagram Construction and Analysis . . . 50
3.4 Bode Diagram Building Blocks 55
3.5 Plotting of More Complex Transfer Functions . . 60
3.6 Stability Information from Bode Diagrams . . . 68
Summary 70

x   Contents

4   Control System Components   72

    4.1   Instrument Servomechanisms   72
    4.2   Impedance of Control Components   74
    4.3   Transmitting and Error-Detecting Components . .   75
    4.4   Amplifiers, Modulators, and Demodulators . . .   84
    4.5   Servomotors   86
    4.6   Gear Trains   106
    4.7   Compensators   107
    4.8   System Transfer Functions and Bode Diagrams .   117
    Summary   120

5   Design of a Control System   121

    5.1   Choice of Components and Analysis of System
         Performance   121
    5.2   System Specifications   123
    5.3   Control System Analysis by Closed-Loop Frequency
         Response.   126
    5.4   Control System Analysis by Open-Loop Frequency
         Response.   135
    5.5   Control System Compensation by a Rate Generator   140
    5.6   Control System Compensation by Networks . . .   145
    5.7   Compensation by Use of an Inertially Damped
         Servomotor (IDSM)   152
    5.8   Effects of Load Inertia and Viscous Friction . .   155
    5.9   Summary of System Compensation Results . .   158
    5.10   Drawing Closed-Loop Diagrams from Open-Loop
         Data   159
    Summary   167

6   Transient Analysis   168

    6.1   Control System Response to a Step Input . . .   169
    6.2   Plotting the Transient-Response Curve of the
         Uncompensated Course Recorder System . .   173
    6.3   Analysis of Transient Response Curve and its
         Constants   177
    6.4   Complex S-Plane Analysis   187
    Summary   193

7 Root Locus   195

7.1   Introduction   195
7.2   Root Locus Derivation   200
7.3   Third-Order System Transient Response Versus
       Second-Order System Transient Response . .   217
7.4   Rules for Construction of the Root Locus . . .   220
7.5   Root Locus of Course Recorder Compensated . .   230
Summary   242

APPENDIX A   Servomechanism Conversion Factors . . .   243
APPENDIX B   Decibel Table and Calculations   247
APPENDIX C   Vector Conversion Table   251
APPENDIX D   Partial List of Servomechanism Component
              Manufacturers   257
APPENDIX E   Selected Bibliography   259

Answers to Selected Problems   261
Index of Symbols and Abbreviations   265
Subject Index   269

1.

Introduction to control theory

Finding power to do his work has been man's big problem since time began. To solve his power problem he has used his own muscles, domestic animals, falling water, coal, oil, the atom, and the sun. Today we are still searching for new power sources and more efficient engines, but are spending much more effort to *control* the machines we have. We want to automatically control the direction and speed of automobiles, ships at sea, and satellites. We want to design automatic controls for the making of soup, soap, and gasoline, as well as for the manufacture of engine blocks, sheet steel, and paper. Modern weapons must also be controlled—nuclear submarines, supersonic airplanes, missiles, and rockets. The development of all these sophisticated systems has brought about the *theory of automatic control*. To treat this subject in all its aspects, we would have to cover in detail the controls of all the systems just mentioned—from oil refineries to guided missiles. In a sense we do cover all of them, because *the control theory developed in this book is applicable to all control systems.*

1.1 LINEAR SYSTEMS

From our study of a few simple systems we develop the general theory of control of *linear* systems. A linear system is one whose output is proportional to its input; if we double the input, the output is doubled. Resistors, inductors, and capacitors are usually linear, that is, they have the same value of resistance, inductance, and capacitance regardless of applied current or voltage, as long as current and voltage ratings are not exceeded. Doubling the current in a resistor doubles the voltage. If this relationship is graphed, a straight *line*

1

results, and the relationship is *linear*. The same is true of linear mechanical systems and the elements of such systems. If one end of a spring is fixed, the displacement of the other end is proportional to the force applied. Linear systems are made up of these and other linear elements.

Nonlinear elements are transistors, diodes, and coils with magnetic cores. Many nonlinear systems and elements can be treated as linear in a restricted area; we use this principle in obtaining almost linear amplification from transistors and vacuum tubes.

1.2 AMPLIFIER FREQUENCY RESPONSE

Let us begin our discussion with a system that most people are familiar with: a high-fidelity audio system for record, tape, or FM radio sound reproduction, and let us concern ourselves, in particular, with the amplifier in such a system. Such an amplifier is a system by itself—a system of electronic parts that receives an electrical input signal and produces electrical power output, which hopefully is an undistorted amplification of the input signal.

To analyze the quality of an audio amplifier we test it for frequency response. We can put a test record on the turntable and listen to the low, middle, and high frequencies (bass, middle, and high or treble notes) as reproduced by a speaker that has excellent frequency response. We compare the loudness of the different frequencies to see if any are suppressed or "lost" by the amplifier. A more scientific test method is to use a good audio (sine-wave) signal generator and an ac electronic voltmeter connected in the fashion shown in Fig. 1.1. We use a sine wave because it is the only input waveform that gives an output wave of the same form (sine wave) and of the same frequency as the input. The signal generator is varied in short steps from very low to very high frequencies; at each frequency the ac electronic

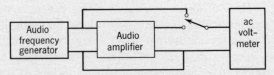

Fig. 1.1 Test setup for sine-wave frequency-response test of an audio amplifier.

voltmeter is used to read the input and output voltages. The output/-input voltage ratio is the gain of the amplifier, and a plot of gains or voltage ratios versus frequencies is the *frequency response* of the amplifier. Much time can be saved and more information obtained if a high-speed, two-channel oscillograph is used to record input and output voltage waves simultaneously (Fig. 1.2). Note that at the midfrequency shown input and output amplitudes are made equal by the use of the attenuator, and input and output waves are almost exactly in phase, as shown coming out of the oscillograph. Note also that if the amplifier creates no distortion, an input sine

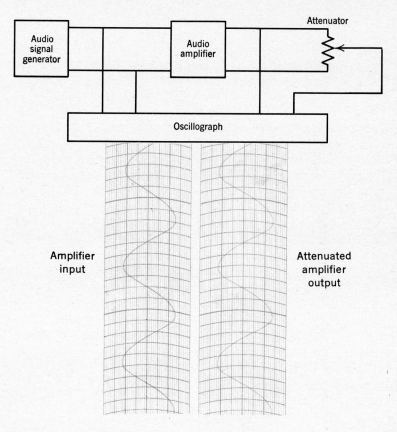

FIG. 1.2 Test setup for recording amplifier input and attenuated output voltages at midfrequency.

wave of fixed frequency always gives an undistorted output sine wave
of the same frequency.

As we raise the frequency of the signal generator, we notice that
the output begins to diminish in amplitude and shift in phase, as
shown in Fig. 1.3. Note that the peaks of the output sine waves are
displaced one full division to the right of the input peaks, giving a
negative phase shift or *phase lag*. At low frequencies we also find the
output signal magnitude decreasing and the phase shifting, giving us
positive phase shift or *phase lead*, as shown in Fig. 1.4a. At very high
frequencies amplifier output is so small that we cannot hear it, as
every hi-fi fan knows (Fig. 1.4b).

To describe all these situations, we make certain sine-wave measurements (shown in Fig. 1.5a) from which we can measure and
compute two basically important values—*gain* and *phase shift* of the
output wave with respect to the input wave.

$$\text{Gain} = \frac{\text{output amplitude}}{\text{input amplitude}} = \frac{E_{\text{out}}}{E_{\text{in}}} = A \qquad (1.1)$$

$$\text{Phase shift} = \theta \text{ (in degrees)} \qquad (1.2)$$

We can make these measurements at every frequency and plot curves
for each of these series of measurements, as is illustrated in Fig. 1.5.
The data for this figure were taken from a two-stage *R-C* coupled
amplifier. We see in this figure that at midrange or midfrequency (for

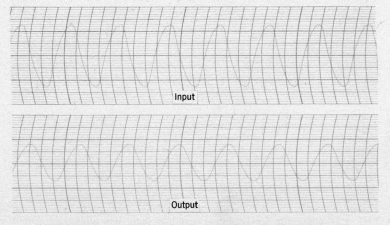

Fig. 1.3 Phase shift and loss of amplitude at higher frequency.

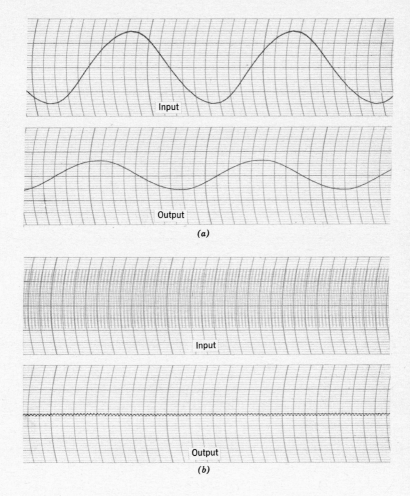

Fig. 1.4(*a*)   Phase shift and loss of amplitude at lower frequency. (*b*) Loss of amplitude at very high frequency.

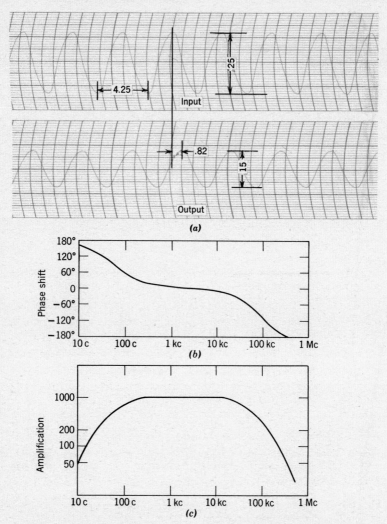

Fig. 1.5 Voltage gain and phase shift values of an audio amplifier. (*a*) Measurements of amplitude ratio and phase shift: Amplitude ratio =

$$\frac{\text{output amplitude}}{\text{input amplitude}} = \frac{15}{25} - 0.60; \text{ Phase shift} = \frac{0.82}{4.25} \times 360° = 67.5°.$$ Ver-

tical measurements are in small vertical graph paper divisions; horizontal measurements are in horizontal graph paper divisions. (*b*) Gain versus frequency. (*c*) Phase shift versus frequency.

example, 1 kilocycle, kc) we have a certain amplification and practically zero phase shift. In Fig. 1.5*b* we see that the amplification is "flat" from 110 c to 10 kc. In Fig. 1.5*c* on each side of 1 kc there is some phase shift, resulting in phase distortion.

1.3 FEEDBACK (OR CLOSED-LOOP) AMPLIFIER FREQUENCY RESPONSE

The amplifier whose frequency response is shown in Fig. 1.5 is good enough for most of us. The *bandwidth* of an amplifier is the difference between the high and low frequencies at the points where the gain is down to 0.707 times the maximum. These points are the 3-decibel (dB) down points, since a voltage loss of 0.707 is −3 dB. In Fig. 1.5*a* the maximum gain is 1000, and the frequencies at which the gain is down to 0.707 times the maximum are a little higher than 100 c at the low end, and about 12 kc at the high end. The bandwidth is thus 12,000 − 100 = 11,900 cycles.

The hi-fi fan wants to hear higher frequencies and to hear and feel lower frequencies. To satisfy him by improving the response of our audio amplifier, we introduce negative voltage feedback, as shown in Fig. 1.6*b*. β is the ratio of E_{out} fed back to the input; if $\beta = 1$, we have 100% feedback, and if $\beta = 0.5$, we have 50% feedback.

As may be seen from Fig. 1.6, systems without feedback are called *open-loop*. Systems with feedback are called *closed-loop*, and introducing feedback is called *closing the loop*. The original open-loop part is now called the *forward* part of the closed loop; the return path at the bottom is the *feedback* part of the closed loop. Note that our output E_{out} is an amplification of the input E_{in} and is in phase with it, since the two-stage *R-C* amplifier gives two 180° phase shifts, or a total of 360°. The wiring of the feedback circuit reverses the phase of the output, and in Fig. 1.7 we see the result at the input of the amplifier.

Note that since the two sine waves illustrated in Fig. 1.7, E_{in} and E_{out}, are 180° out of phase they subtract and give a smaller resultant sine wave E applied to the amplifier input terminals. This is *negative feedback*.

We now connect our two-channel oscillograph to the input and output of our feedback amplifier, make a series of gain and phase

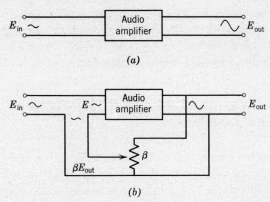

Fig. 1.6 Open-loop and closed-loop amplifier circuits. (a) Open-loop two-stage amplifier. (b) Closed-loop negative feedback two-stage amplifier.

shift measurements as before, plot the results on the same sheet as our open-loop amplifier curves, and find the results shown in Fig. 1.8.

Obviously we have lost some amplification, but we can turn up the volume control to compensate for this. The result is an amplifier that is flat from 10 c/s to 140 kc, with very much less phase distortion at all frequencies. Bandwidth is up from about 12 kc to 140 kc.

All of these advantages are predicated on the fact that the feedback voltage is 180° out of phase with the signal voltage. This is true over most of the frequency range of our amplifier. But by looking at the high- and low-frequency ends of the feedback amplifier phase shift curve in Fig. 1.8, we see that the output voltage is not in phase with the input. This results in a phase shift of the feedback voltage and causes, as we shall see presently, the bumps at the ends of the feedback amplitude curves. A $\pm 180°$ phase shift of the output voltage gives a phase difference between feedback voltage and signal voltage of $180° \pm 180° = 0°$ or $360°$. This means that feedback voltage is in phase with the signal voltage, and *adds* to it as shown in Fig. 1.9. Under these conditions, if feed-

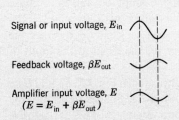

Signal or input voltage, E_{in}

Feedback voltage, βE_{out}

Amplifier input voltage, E
$(E = E_{in} + \beta E_{out})$

Fig. 1.7 Voltages of negative feedback amplifier shown in Fig. 1.6b.

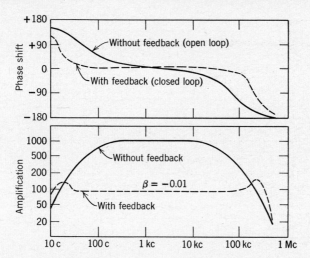

Fig. 1.8 Gain and phase curves of amplifier with and without negative feedback (closed-loop and open-loop).

back voltage is equal to amplifier input voltage, that is if $A\beta = 1$, we can introduce a signal, short circuit the signal input terminals, and theoretically the signal will continue around the loop indefinitely. We have almost achieved a *feedback oscillator;* we need only some frequency controlling element in the loop. (An oscillator is any non-rotating device for generating alternating current of various frequencies; rotating devices such as generators are excluded.)

If we have a total amplification-feedback product $A\beta$ of 2, our feedback is $2\times$ the input the first time around the loop, $4\times$ the second time, $8\times$ the third time, etc., until the amplifier saturates and thus limits the amplitude of the oscillations. Our two-channel oscillograph shows the results illustrated in Fig. 1.10. This response is *positive feedback,* similar to audio feedback of a public address

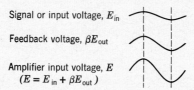

Fig. 1.9 Voltages of positive feedback amplifier.

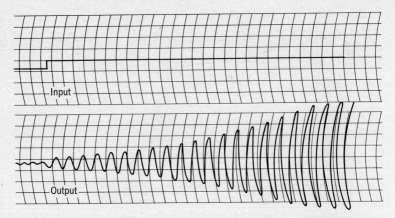

Fig. 1.10   Response of an unstable feedback amplifier to a step input.

system when some of the speaker output feeds back into the micro-
phone. Any value of $A\beta > 1$ would give the same result: *instability*
of the amplifier.

1.4   FEEDBACK AMPLIFIER AS OSCILLATOR

Most common types of electronic oscillators—tuned plate, tuned
grid, Hartley, Colpitts—are basically feedback oscillators and can be
thought of as specially designed feedback amplifiers with short
circuited input leads, such as those shown in Figs. 1.11 and 1.12. An
extended analysis of these circuits is not attempted here, but the basic
feedback conditions necessary to develop and maintain oscillations
will be explored. We will find that a very thin line separates feedback
amplifiers and oscillators, and that keeping feedback amplifiers and
control systems from oscillating is one of our biggest problems. To
help solve this problem we develop a criterion for stable feedback
amplifiers and control systems.

By looking at Fig. 1.6, which shows a feedback amplifier, we see
that overall amplifier gain is calculated as follows:

$$E = E_{\text{in}} + \beta E_{\text{out}} \tag{1.3}$$

$$E_{\text{out}} = AE \tag{1.4}$$

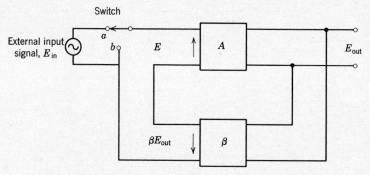

Fig. 1.11 Feedback amplifier. It becomes an oscillator when, with voltage and phase of E_{in} and βE_{out} both equal, the switch is thrown from a to b.

Substituting for E in equation (1.4) yields

$$E_{out} = A(E_{in} + \beta E_{out}) = AE_{in} + A\beta E_{out} \qquad (1.5)$$

$$E_{out} - A\beta E_{out} = AE_{in} \qquad (1.6)$$

$$E_{out}(1 - A\beta) = AE_{in} \qquad (1.7)$$

$$\frac{E_{out}}{E_{in}} = \frac{A}{1 - A\beta} \qquad (1.8)$$

If in equation (1.8) and in Fig. 1.6 amplifier gain times feedback is exactly one and the phase shift is 180°, or mathematically $A\beta = 1$, we have an oscillator. Let us see why. In Fig. 1.11 we have a feedback amplifier with a switch which enables us to disconnect E_{in} and to short circuit the input to the amplifier. If we adjust the gain of our amplifier so that the feedback signal is the same amplitude as E_{in} (the input to the amplifier) and both voltages are in phase, we can throw the switch from a to b, and theoretically a signal will travel forever from feedback to output to feedback, from βE_{out} to E to E_{out} to βE_{out} . . . with the same amplitude. This circuit with no input is now an oscillator (Fig. 1.12). We can see this mathematically in equation (1.3); if $\beta E_{out} = E$, then E_{in} must equal 0 (a short circuit).

In actual practice the conditions described in the preceding paragraph are difficult to maintain for any length of time, and oscillations do not remain with constant amplitude. They either build up until the amplifier saturates (Fig. 1.10), or they die down. Much of feedback control system theory and practice is devoted to insuring that

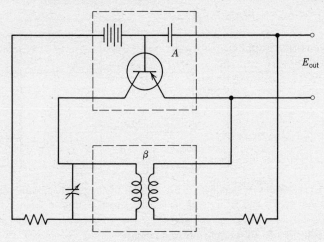

Fig. 1.12 Tickler feedback oscillator.

oscillations will die away rapidly and not be sustained or build up with increasing amplitude. The cardinal rule for *stability* is:

At the frequency which results in an output amplitude/input amplitude ratio of 1 be sure the phase shift is less than 180°.

Figure 1.8 is the type of graph on which we read frequency, amplitude, and phase shift values. In actual practice, *nearness* to the 180° point causes persistent oscillations, even though they eventually die out. We therefore stay at a respectable distance below the 180° point, as shown in Fig. 1.8. Even here we see humps at the ends of the curves caused by phase shifts much less than 180°. For control systems these humps are usually kept to less than 1.5 times the amplitude of the flat portion of the curve. One way to do this is to reduce gain so that near the 180° point amplification is very low. By reducing amplification we could damp out oscillations altogether in amplifiers and control systems, but such systems would be very sluggish. We can think for a moment of the movement of the pointer of a voltmeter, an ammeter, or a VTVM. In reading these instruments we dislike large and repeated swings back and forth past the value of voltage or current we are measuring, but we also dislike to wait for a sluggish overdamped pointer to move slowly to its final reading. We compromise on a lively pointer and one or two fast swings before it settles down to the value we read.

1.5 ONE-LINE BLOCK DIAGRAMS

To analyze amplifiers and other systems we use block diagrams; these diagrams can be combined mathematically using simple algebra. An open-loop amplifier is shown in Fig. 1.13. We know that the equation linking the three variables, E_{in}, A, and E_{out}, is

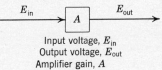

Input voltage, E_{in}
Output voltage, E_{out}
Amplifier gain, A

E_{in} = input voltage

E_{out} = output voltage

A = amplifier gain

Fig. 1.13   Block diagram of open-loop amplifier.

$$E_{out} = AE_{in} \qquad (1.9)$$

We generally make use of the input-output relation called a *transfer function* and restate equation (1.9)

$$\text{Transfer function} = \frac{\text{output}}{\text{input}} = \frac{E_{out}}{E_{in}} = A \qquad (1.10)$$

An open-loop, two-stage amplifier with gains of A_1 and A_2 for stages 1 and 2, respectively, is shown in Fig. 1.14. We know that the output of the two stages is A_1 times A_2 times the input, or

$$E_{out} = A_1 A_2 E_{in} \qquad (1.11)$$

Thus our first block-diagram mathematics rule is: *If two blocks are in series, multiply them together.* The transfer function of our two-stage amplifier is then

$$\frac{E_{out}}{E_{in}} = A_1 A_2 \qquad (1.12)$$

$A_1 A_2$ is the overall gain of the amplifier. It is natural for us to think of amplifier gain. The gain is "what happens to the input signal in the amplifier." Or, given the amplifier input signal, gain tells us what the amplifier output signal will be. Gain is the *transfer function* of the

Fig. 1.14   Block diagram of two-stage amplifier.

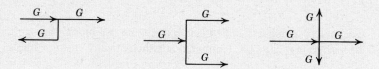

Fig. 1.15 Nodes or branch points.

amplifier, and every electrical and electronic network has a transfer function. This transfer function is the *effect* of the network on a signal.

In order to make a block diagram of an amplifier with feedback, we need two more symbols. One is the node or branch point or junction point, shown in Fig. 1.15. The node has no effect other than to connect points. It is like a wire connector or a terminal on a connector block.

The last symbol is a *summing point*. This symbol is used when the algebraic sum of inputs is desired, as shown in Fig. 1.16. Every input is shown as an arrow touching the circle, and it must have a plus or minus sign next to it to indicate whether the input is to be added or subtracted.

We can now diagram the feedback amplifier shown in Fig. 1.6*b*; the resulting block diagram is Fig. 1.17. β is negative for negative feedback and positive for positive feedback. From Fig. 1.17 we develop our transfer function as follows:

$$E_{\text{out}} = (E_{\text{in}} + \beta E_{\text{out}})A = AE_{\text{in}} + A\beta E_{\text{out}} \tag{1.13}$$

$$E_{\text{out}}(1 - A\beta) = AE_{\text{in}} \tag{1.14}$$

$$\frac{E_{\text{out}}}{E_{\text{in}}} = \frac{A}{1 - A\beta} \tag{1.15}$$

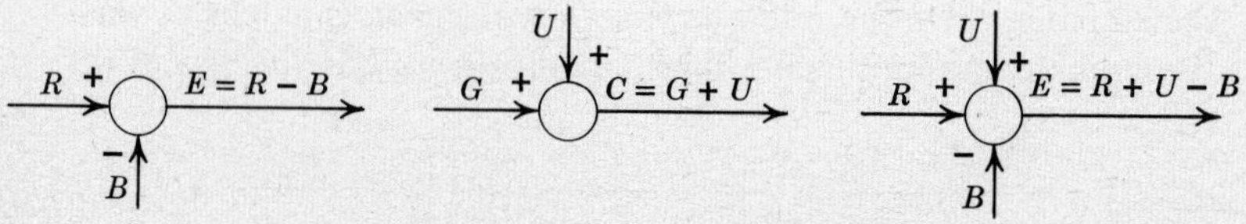

$R \xrightarrow{+} \bigcirc \xrightarrow{E = R - B}$
B

$G \xrightarrow{+} \bigcirc \xrightarrow{C = G + U}$ $U \downarrow +$

$R \xrightarrow{+} \bigcirc \xrightarrow{E = R + U - B}$ $U \downarrow +$
B

Fig. 1.16 Summing points.

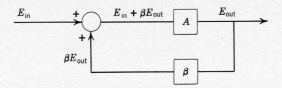

Fig. 1.17   Feedback amplifier block diagram.

Thus the transfer function of the system is

$$\frac{A}{1 - A\beta}$$

as we previously found in equation (1.8).

1.6   ANALYSIS OF A CONTROL SYSTEM

Amplifiers have been used to introduce the subject of frequency response; now let us apply frequency response to control systems. You and your automobile, an automated steel rolling mill, and an automatically controlled oil refinery are all control systems. For an exact definition of the term *control system* we turn to the American Standard publication entitled "Terminology for Automatic Control," hereafter referred to as ASA C85.1 (1963). In this Standard we find the definition, "*control system:* A system in which deliberate guidance or manipulation is used to achieve a prescribed value of a *variable.*"

No doubt, automatically steered automobiles on expressways and freeways are soon to become a reality because this will allow roadways to carry many more cars. Given a "white-line follower" on a car and a white line down the middle of each lane of a highway, we could have an automatically steered car today. A more permanent and dependable system might use a buried wire running along the center of the lane with ac current flowing in it. The car would be equipped with two magnetic pick-up coils which would sense the magnetic field surrounding the wire (Fig. 1.18).

Design of a steering system for an automobile is complicated by certain basic problems. Anyone who has steered a small sports car, a heavy car, and a truck does not need a course in physics to know that the mass or weight of a steered body makes a big difference in

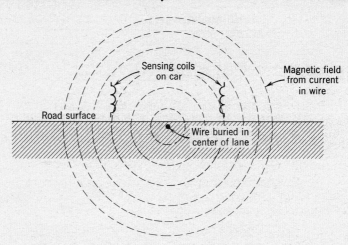

Fig. 1.18   Diagram of buried-wire system of car control.

performance. Before we design we want to know values of mass, speed, acceleration, friction, and other items that affect steering. We want equations composed of measurable quantities, and techniques of analysis which give answers in terms of controllability. We have to be sure the rear seat occupants do not slide to one side as we round a corner. We also need techniques of improving controllability. The luxury automobile is a heavy car, but we want to improve its handling so that it will drive better than a small truck of comparable weight.

There are many approaches to the analysis of control systems, but the two most common ones are *frequency response* and *time* or *transient response*. Time response is discussed in Chapters 6 and 7. Frequency response we began to talk about in Section 1.2, where we saw that an amplifier's characteristics can be found by applying a sine wave of a very low frequency, by noting the amplitude and phase of the amplifier output, and by repeating this operation using higher and higher input frequencies. We can carry out the same type of procedure with light-weight, medium-weight, and heavy automobiles and can find the quantitative differences between the controllability of each car and how to design the best steering system for each. Let us see how this is done. First let us analyze the open-loop steering system and then return to the automatically steered car with the buried wire and sensors closing the loop (feedback).

1.7 FREQUENCY RESPONSE OF AN AUTOMOBILE OPEN-LOOP STEERING SYSTEM

Let us use as an example a car with power steering, as is shown in the block diagram of Fig. 1.19. If such a system were perfect, the front wheels and the body of the car would turn immediately in response to every move of the steering wheel. If, as the car moves steadily forward, we turn the steering wheel very slowly and evenly until it reaches 10° left, then turn it at the same speed past zero to 10° right, then again at the same speed to 10° left, and so on, the front wheels would describe a sine-wave path on the ground. If the steering wheel is thus *oscillated* at a low frequency, then a slightly higher one, and so on to higher and higher frequencies until the steering wheel is jerked back and forth as fast as possible, there comes a time when the front wheels lag appreciably behind the movements of the steering wheel and the movement of the car body lags even more. It takes time to accelerate the mass of the wheels and steering mechanism, and much more time to accelerate the body. The inertia of the wheels and the body causes a loss of amplitude and a phase shift at higher frequencies, just like reactance in an electrical circuit. Friction in the steering mechanism causes a reduced amplitude, much the same as electrical resistance. This fall off of amplitude and increase of phase shift are most valuable in telling us the characteristics of our system, as we have seen in the case of the audio amplifier.

Let us diagram the sine-wave motion of the steering wheel and the motion of the automobile, assuming a steady forward speed. With very slow oscillations of the steering wheel the car "follows" exactly, as shown in Fig. 1.20. With faster movement of the steering wheel the car reacts late and is out of phase with the steering wheel motion. In addition the amount of car motion (amplitude) is less (Fig. 1.21). A pattern similar to that shown in Fig. 1.22 might result if it were physically possible to turn the steering wheel fast enough. Plotting gain and phase shift from many curves such as those in Figs. 1.20,

Fig. 1.19 Open-loop automobile steering system.

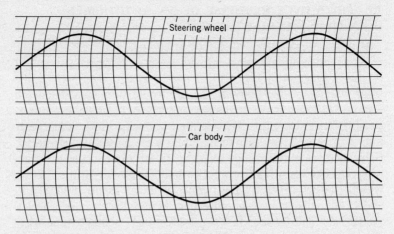

Fig. 1.20 Automobile frequency response at low and middle frequencies; note same amplitude and phase of both curves.

1.21, and 1.22 would give the graph shown in Fig. 1.23. We see that the car reacts dynamically like an amplifier, as comparison of Figs. 1.23 and 1.5 shows. One important difference between the amplifier and the car output/input relationships: the amplifier response is "down" at low frequencies and there is a phase shift, whereas the car

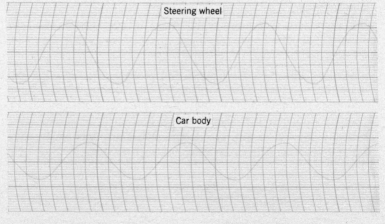

Fig. 1.21 Phase shift and loss of amplitude at higher frequency.

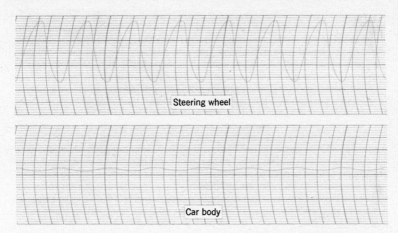

Steering wheel

Car body

Fig. 1.22 Loss of amplitude and 180° phase shift at very high frequency.

and most electromechanical systems are "flat" from zero to middle frequencies. Another difference is that the *R-C* coupled amplifier response is much faster than mechanical systems. Useful frequencies for amplifier and electrical systems usually run from megacycles per second to cycles per second; electromechanical systems operate from

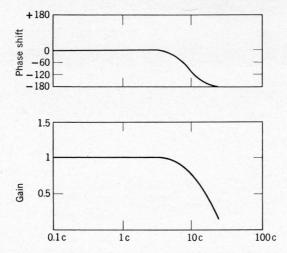

Fig. 1.23 Gain and phase-shift curves of open-loop automobile steering system.

cycles per second to cycles per minute, and the highest electromechanical system frequency usually slightly overlaps that of the
lowest electrical system frequency.

1.8 FREQUENCY RESPONSE OF AN AUTOMOBILE CLOSED-LOOP STEERING SYSTEM

We might suspect that a closed-loop electromechanical system
reacts in a manner similar to the closed-loop amplifier, and in this
we would be correct. Let us return to the system of a buried wire in
the roadway and magnetic sensing coils on the car (Fig. 1.18) to close
the loop. The two coils are mounted one on either side of the middle
of the front bumper (Fig. 1.24a). Electrically the coils are connected

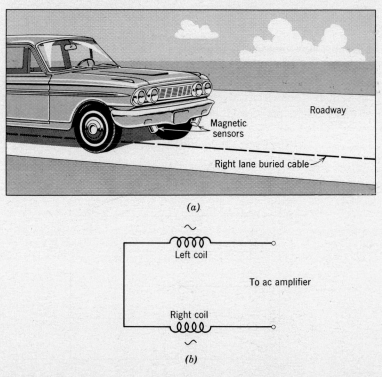

(a)

(b)

Fig. 1.24(a)   Automatic steering mechanism for automobile. (b) Magnetic
coil circuit. The coils are connected so that the output of one is 180° out of
phase with the other.

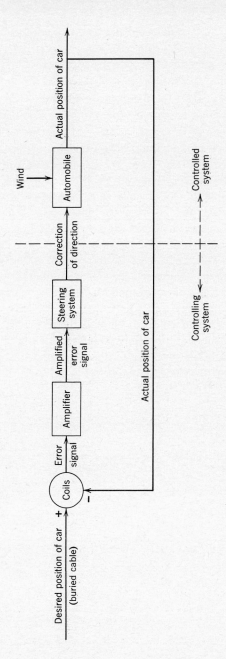

Fig. 1.25   Block diagram of automatic steering system.

21

differentially as shown in Fig. 1.24*b*. Since they are in phase opposition, equal-strength signals cancel each other out. If one signal becomes stronger, the difference of the two signals appears at the input to the ac amplifier. A one-line block diagram of our system is shown in Fig. 1.25. To conduct a frequency-response test of our car, we could lay out a wire in a sine-wave pattern on the ground and tape it down. We could then drive the car at different speeds over the wire. The gain-phase plot summarizing a typical series of frequency-response tests is shown in Fig. 1.26. We have a curve with a peak similar to the high-frequency resonant peak of our feedback amplifier curve shown in Fig. 1.8. Such a peak is desirable, because it denotes a lively system with fast response. Increasing the gain of our system increases the peak. If we set the steering system gain control too low, our car would slowly wander away from the wire before any steering correction was made, because the control action would be sluggish. Increasing the gain would reduce the amount of wandering by making the steering control respond to a smaller error (that is, a "livelier" control system).

Too much gain would cause a "jittery" performance; the car would tend to overshoot and possibly go into continuous oscillation to the left and right of the wire. Our feedback system with too high a gain can become completely unstable, as in Fig. 1.10.

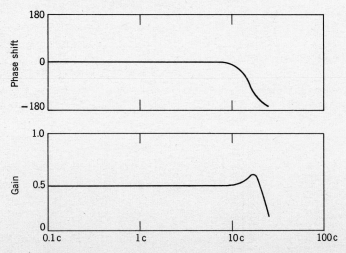

Fig. 1.26   Gain-phase plot of closed-loop automobile steering system.

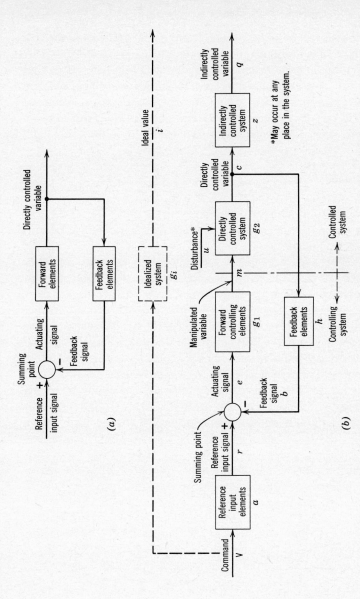

Fig. 1.27 Block diagram of automatic control system. (*a*) Essential elements. (*b*) A more complex system. Reproduced from ASA C85.1 (1963) with permission.

We ought to know the standard terminology of control systems, and Fig. 1.27 is the standard control loop diagram taken from ASA C85.1 (1963). If we compare this diagram with Fig. 1.15, we see that the pair of magnetic coils is our *error detector* or *summing point;* the amplifier and the steering system are our *forward control elements;* the car is our *directly controlled system*, and the wind, stones in the road, or an oil slick might be our *disturbances.*

SUMMARY

In this chapter we have shown that:

1. Frequency response is as useful for analysis of control systems as it is for amplifiers.

2. Control system frequencies are lower than electrical and electronic circuit frequencies because physical systems cannot respond as quickly as electrical systems.

3. Like negative feedback amplifiers, feedback control systems become unstable and oscillate if the gain of the system reaches a value of 1 when the output is 180° out of phase with the input.

4. Frequency-response diagrams or plots are very helpful in analyzing and in designing feedback control systems.

Thus far we have used frequency response data found by testing amplifiers and automobiles in the "laboratory." But physically testing an amplifier, an automobile, or any other controlled system, making design changes, then retesting and repeating this process until the system is satisfactory is a very slow and expensive procedure. It is much cheaper to construct a *mathematical model*, test it mathematically, make changes, and retest it until desired performance is achieved. We can then use the mathematical information to build a physical model that is quite close to the ideal. We need only our final testing to make a few changes to the physical model if our mathematical model is a good one. To construct mathematical models of control systems we use the Laplace transform, which is introduced in Chapter 2.

2.

*Laplace transforms**

In Chapter 1 we analyzed amplifiers and control systems by the use of laboratory or field-trial frequency-response methods. The results are neatly summarized in the graphs (Figs. 1.8, 1.23, and 1.26). Although frequency-response testing is extremely valuable, it is expensive and time consuming. In addition, it has so far provided us with no algebraic or numerical results in any concise form; we have collected data, plotted points, and drawn graphs.

Contrast this procedure with the accepted method of solving an electric circuit problem—say the current in an *R-C* circuit. We do not take our resistors and capacitors into the laboratory, wire up the circuit, vary the applied voltage, plot current values, and draw a graph. Instead, by the use of electrical laws and theorems we analyze the circuit *mathematically* and get figures quite close to those we would obtain if we tested the physical circuit in the laboratory.

Our problem in control system analysis is to find the "Ohm's law of control systems." The technique most widely and successfully used is the Laplace (pronounced Lah-plah's) transform, which we study in this chapter and use throughout the book. In the next few chapters we will find that the graphs of the Laplace transforms of control systems, such as those we studied in Chapter 1, will be very similar to Figs. 1.23 and 1.26. We call the open-loop graphs *Bode diagrams*, and we can base our control system designs on these diagrams.

2.1   FROM LOGARITHMS TO LAPLACE TRANSFORM

The Laplace transform has aided enormously in the development of technological mathematics. By its use we reduce most calculus operations (some of them extremely difficult) to fairly simple algebra.

* Read Appendix D and write for literature now.

The process is not unlike the use of logarithms. If we want to multiply 1234 by 4321, we first *transform* these ordinary numbers into logarithms, which are 3.09132 and 3.63558. We *add* these two *transformed* numbers

$$
\begin{array}{r}
3.09132 \\
3.63558 \\
\hline
6.72690
\end{array}
$$

and get another *transformed* number. We then look in the body of a table of logarithms and find that the *transformed* number 6.72690 is the antilogarithm (inverse transform) of the real number 5,332,000. Instead of performing a long involved multiplication we have—with the use of a table of logarithms—solved our problem with one very simple addition. We can diagram the logarithmic operation as shown in Fig. 2.1.

An important point to note is that we do not always return to the domain of ordinary numbers; sometimes we use logarithmic values as our answer. A good example is seen in the use of decibels. Gain, a real number value, does not convey the same information as decibels, a logarithmic value, so we use decibels often. Sound level increases logarithmically, and we use a logarithmic rule to measure it—similar to the way in which we use the slide of a slide rule instead of a twelve-inch ruler in laying out the vertical scale of a graph of amplifier dB gain versus frequency. We must always use the abbreviation dB after a number in decibels to indicate that it is a *logarithmic* ratio. For

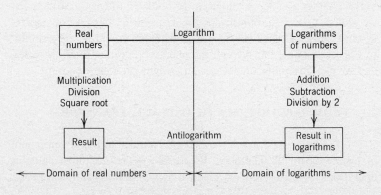

Fig. 2.1 Operations in using logarithms.

example, a voltage gain of 10 is a gain of 20 dB. The *numbers* 10 and 20 are certainly different, although a gain of $10 = 20$ dB. Ordinary numbers do not need identification; *transformed* or *logarithmic* numbers do.

The Laplace transform also transports us to another world or domain, from the world where time is the variable dimension to *s-land* where s is the variable instead of t (time). This s is a complex algebraic variable, like $a + jb$, but we call it $\sigma + j\omega$, σ (sigma) and ω (omega) being real numbers. Occasionally we use the variable f with the dimension of cycles per second. If there is no real part, making $\sigma = 0$, then $s = 0 + j\omega$, or $s = j\omega$. Our dimension is then frequency, and our variable ω has the dimensions of radians per second (rad/sec).

We know that frequency is the reciprocal of time, that is $\omega = 1/T$, T being the time of one cycle. Therefore the dimensions of s-land are *frequency* or *reciprocal time*. Note that we are talking about three different *functions* of the same network, with three different variables: the *time* function, $f(t)$; the *frequency* function, $G(j\omega)$; and the *Laplace* function or transform, $F(s)$ (also a function of frequency). Note also that we follow the mathematical format in which the symbol in parentheses represents the function variable.

2.2 A CIRCUIT PROBLEM SOLVED BY THE LAPLACE TRANSFORM

To see what the Laplace transform is and how it is used, let us solve an important electrical circuit problem that usually requires the use of calculus. The problem is to derive the formula for the charging current in an initially uncharged capacitor. The circuit is shown in Fig. 2.2. The formula is

$$i = \frac{E}{R} e^{-t/RC} \tag{2.1}$$

We know that the reactance of a capacitor is

$$X_c = \frac{1}{2\pi fC} = \frac{1}{j\omega C} \tag{2.2}$$

We also know that the complex impedance Z of the series resistor and capacitor shown in Fig. 2.2 is

$$Z = R - jX_c = R - \frac{j}{j}jX_c = R - \frac{j^2 X_c}{j} = R + \frac{X_c}{j} = R + \frac{1}{j\omega C} \quad (2.3)$$

For $j\omega$ in equation (2.4) we substitute s, making the transformed impedance

$$Z = R + \frac{1}{sC} \quad (2.4)$$

We assume that the capacitor has no initial charge (voltage before the switch is closed). Then the applied voltage is 0 until the switch is closed at time $t = 0$, when it becomes E. Thus a voltage step is applied suddenly at $t = 0$, as shown in Fig. 2.3. Most transform functions used in control systems have the value 0 before time $t = 0$; that is, they have no "initial conditions."

Table 2.1 *Laplace Transform Pairs*

Time Functions		Laplace Transforms
$f(t)$ starting at time $t = 0$		$F(s)$
Pair 1	1 (unit step)	$\dfrac{1}{s}$
Pair 2	E (voltage step)	$\dfrac{E}{s}$
Pair 3	$\dfrac{1}{T}e^{-t/T}$	$\dfrac{1}{sT + 1}$
Pair 4	$1 - e^{-t/T}$	$\dfrac{1}{s(sT + 1)}$
Pair 5	i or $i(t)$	I or $I(s)$
Pair 6	e or $e(t)$	E or $E(s)$

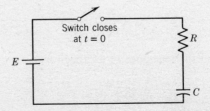

Fig. 2.2 Circuit for charging a capacitor.

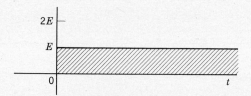

Fig. 2.3   Voltage step. Laplace transform is E/S.

In looking at the Laplace transforms of Table 2.1 we find pair 2, which tells us that the time function of Fig. 2.3 transforms into E/s. We know that $E = IZ$ is the general expression relating voltage, current, and impedance. (If we use admittance Y, $I = EY$.) It is therefore logical to write the Laplace transform equation $E(s) = I(s)Z(s)$, or rearranged we have

$$I(s) = \frac{E(s)}{Z(s)} \tag{2.5}$$

with s indicating that the quantity preceding it is in terms of s. Our $E(s)$ is E/s and our $Z(s)$ is $R + 1/sC$. Operations with the Laplace transform are algebraic; thus we can write

$$I(s) = \frac{E(s)}{Z(s)} = \frac{E/s}{R + \dfrac{1}{sC}} = \frac{E/s}{R + \dfrac{R}{sRC}} = \frac{E\,\dfrac{1}{s}}{R\left(1 + \dfrac{1}{sRC}\right)} = \frac{E}{R}\,\frac{1/s}{1 + \dfrac{1}{sRC}}$$

$$= \frac{E}{R}\,\frac{1/s}{\dfrac{sRC + 1}{sRC}} = \frac{E}{R}\,\frac{RC}{sRC + 1} \tag{2.6}$$

If we substitute T for RC in the last expression in equation (2.6), this yields

$$I(s) = \frac{E}{R}\,\frac{T}{sT + 1} = \frac{ET}{R}\,\frac{1}{sT + 1} \tag{2.7}$$

To determine the time equivalent of equation (2.7) we find portions of it in Table 2.1. Thus going from right to left and using Pair 3 we find that the inverse Laplace transform of $\dfrac{1}{sT + 1}$ is $\dfrac{1}{T}e^{-t/T}$. Similarly, using Pair 5 we find that the inverse transform of $I(s)$ is $i(t)$. Finally E, a step voltage = a constant; T = a time constant; R, a resistance value = a constant; therefore ET/R is a constant. Now a constant when a *multiplied* factor is unaffected by transformation or inverse transformation (see the first item of Table 2.3). Therefore ET/R as a multiplier of the Laplace transform becomes a multiplier of the time function. Thus equation (2.7) inverse transforms to the time-domain equation

$$i(t) = \frac{E}{R} T \frac{1}{T} e^{-t/T} = \frac{E}{R} e^{-t/T} = \frac{E}{R} e^{-t/RC}; \qquad T = RC \quad (2.8)$$

which is the same as equation (2.1), which we set out to prove.

Similarly we can calculate the formula for the current in an inductor after the switch is closed at time $t = 0$ (Fig. 2.4). The time constant of an R-L circuit is L/R. We again apply a voltage step E/s. The circuit impedance Z is $R + j\omega L$; thus with $s = j\omega$

$$Z(s) = R + sL \qquad\qquad\qquad (2.9)$$

Then
$$I(s) = \frac{E(s)}{Z(s)} = \frac{E/s}{R + sL} = E \frac{1/s}{R + sL} = \frac{E}{R} \frac{1/s}{1 + \dfrac{sL}{R}}$$

$$= \frac{E}{R} \frac{1}{s\left(1 + s\dfrac{L}{R}\right)} = \frac{E}{R} \frac{1}{s(1 + sT)}; \qquad T = \frac{L}{R} \quad (2.10)$$

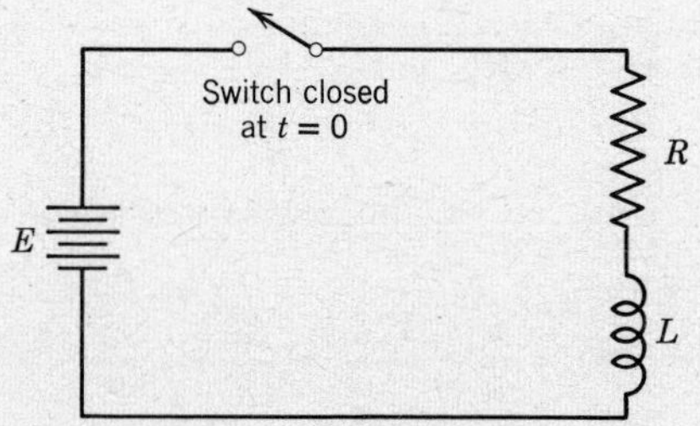

Fig. 2.4   After switch is closed current is

$$i(t) = \frac{E}{R}(1 - e^{-Rt/L})$$

Pair 4 in Table 2.1 tells us that corresponding to Laplace transform $\dfrac{1}{s(1 + sT)}$ is the time function $1 - e^{-t/T}$, which if $T = L/R$, becomes $1 - e^{-t/L/R}$ or $1 - e^{-Rt/L}$. By use of pair 5, $I(s)$ transforms back to $i(t)$. Therefore equation (2.10) has the corresponding time function

$$i(t) = \frac{E}{R}(1 - e^{-Rt/L}) \tag{2.11}$$

which we recognize as the formula for the current in an inductor.

2.3 LAPLACE TRANSFORM PROCEDURES

Let us now review what we have done, because the process is so successful that we will use it throughout this book. First we said that $s = j\omega$; therefore $1/j\omega C = 1/sC$, and $j\omega L = sL$. All our circuit computations can be carried out in terms of $j\omega$, and then as a last step we replace all $j\omega$ by s and all $(j\omega)^2$ or $-\omega^2$ by s^2. However, engineers and technicians who use Laplace transforms usually think of impedance or admittance of circuit elements in terms of s; thus we can start with our circuit impedance expressed in terms of s. Table 2.2 gives some circuit combinations.

Finally we need a few operational rules for Laplace transforms, and these are given in Table 2.3. We must add to this table the fact that Laplace transformed functions obey the same electrical circuit laws and theorems as time functions. We can therefore use Ohm's and Kirchhoff's laws and Thevenin's and Norton's theorems.

Our Laplace transform procedure rules are now complete. They seem a little involved, as did logarithms and exponents when we first learned them. Actually we have followed a few simple steps to find the time function of a circuit from its Laplace transform, which we derived from the circuit's complex impedance. The steps we followed are:

1. Find the circuit or network impedance or admittance transform, using Table 2.2.

2. Multiply the impedance transform $Z(s)$ by the Laplace transform of the current excitation function $I(s)$ to get the voltage function

Table 2.2 Network Impedance and Admittance Functions

Circuit Elements	Symbol	Complex Impedance	Impedance Transform	Admittance Transform
Resistor	—⌇—	R	R	$\dfrac{1}{R}$
Inductor	—⌇—	$j\omega L$	sL	$\dfrac{1}{sL}$
Capacitor	—‖—	$\dfrac{1}{j\omega C}$	$\dfrac{1}{sC}$	sC
Series R and C	—⌇‖—	$R + \dfrac{1}{j\omega C}$	$R + \dfrac{1}{sC} = \dfrac{sRC+1}{sC}$	$\dfrac{sC}{sRC+1}$
Series R and L	—⌇⌇—	$R + j\omega L$	$R + sL$	$\dfrac{1}{R+sL}$
Series L and C	—⌇‖—	$j\omega L + \dfrac{1}{j\omega C}$	$sL + \dfrac{1}{sC} = \dfrac{s^2LC+1}{sC}$	$\dfrac{sC}{s^2LC+1}$
Parallel R and C		$\dfrac{R/j\omega C}{R + 1/j\omega C}$	$\dfrac{R}{1+sRC}$	$\dfrac{1}{R} + sC$
Parallel R and L		$\dfrac{Rj\omega L}{R + j\omega L}$	$\dfrac{sRL}{R+sL}$	$\dfrac{1}{R} + \dfrac{1}{sL}$
Parallel L and C		$\dfrac{j\omega L/j\omega C}{j\omega L + 1/j\omega C}$	$\dfrac{sL/sC}{sL + 1/sC} = \dfrac{sL}{s^2LC+1}$	$\dfrac{1}{sL} + sC$

Table 2.3 *Laplace Transform Operations*

Operation	Time Function $f(t)$	Laplace Transform $F(s)$
Multiplication by a constant K	$Kf(t)$	$KF(s)$
Addition	$f_1(t) + f_2(t)$	$F_1(s) + F_2(s)$
Subtraction	$f_1(t) - f_2(t)$	$F_1(s) - F_2(s)$
Differentiation (no initial conditions)	$\dfrac{df(t)}{dt}$	$sF(s)$
Integration (no initial conditions)	$\displaystyle\int_0^t f(t)\,dt$	$\dfrac{F(s)}{s}$

$E(s)$, or multiply the admittance transform $Y(s)$ by the Laplace transform of the voltage excitation function $E(s)$ to get the current function $I(s)$.

$$E(s) = I(s)Z(s) \qquad (2.12)$$

$$I(s) = E(s)Y(s) \qquad (2.13)$$

Usually we use a step excitation function (E/s or I/s).

3. By algebraic manipulation simplify the product found in step 2, and put it into a form found in a table of Laplace transforms.

4. From the table of Laplace transforms find a pair whose transform contains the same terms in s as the result found in step 3 (possibly times a constant). The time function half of this pair, multiplied by the constant, if any, is the desired result.

From this point on we omit the t and s we have just used for time functions and Laplace functions. Ordinary time-function equations will be indicated by lower case letters, as shown in the Ohm's law equation

$$e = ir \qquad (2.14)$$

and Laplace function equations will be indicated by capital letters, as shown in the transform of equation (2.14)

$$E = IR \qquad (2.15)$$

2.4   LAPLACE TRANSFER FUNCTION OF CONTROL SYSTEMS AND COMPONENTS

We use the Laplace transform extensively to provide a mathematical description of control systems and components. When we described amplifiers in Chapter 1, we used the gain E_{out}/E_{in} (both E_{out} and E_{in} being sine waves). This output/input relationship gives what is known as the *transfer function;* and there is a transfer function for every system component, as well as a transfer function for the system itself. Most of these components have four terminals or connections, as does the R-C filter network shown in Fig. 2.5. Let us find the Laplace transfer function of this network, E_{out}/E_{in}. Let us assume that terminals 3 and 4 are open-circuited, as is essentially true of such networks when a high impedance is connected between terminals 3 and 4. Then the impedance Z_{in} of the input loop is the impedance of R and C in series, or

$$R + \frac{1}{sC} = \frac{sRC + 1}{sC}$$

(see Table 2.2). Then if I is the current through R and C,

$$I = \frac{E_{in}}{Z_{in}} = \frac{E_{in}}{\dfrac{sRC + 1}{sC}} = E_{in} \frac{sC}{sRC + 1} \qquad (2.16)$$

If E_c is the voltage across the capacitor, and Z_c the impedance of the capacitor, which is $1/sC$ in Table 2.2, then

$$E_c = IZ_c = I\frac{1}{sC} \qquad (2.17)$$

and by combining equations (2.16) and (2.17) we have

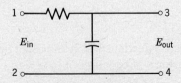

Fig. 2.5   R-C network.

$$E_c = E_{in} \frac{sC}{sRC + 1} \frac{1}{sC} = E_{in} \frac{1}{sRC + 1} \qquad (2.18)$$

Now E_c is the same as E_{out}, thus

$$E_{out} = E_{in} \frac{1}{sRC + 1} \qquad (2.19)$$

and our network transfer function is

$$\frac{E_{out}}{E_{in}} = \frac{1}{sRC + 1} = \frac{1}{sT + 1} ; \quad T = RC \qquad (2.20)$$

It is easier to find the transfer function if we consider our circuit to be a voltage divider. Let us derive the transfer function of a resistance voltage divider.

Figure 2.6a is a voltage divider network and is shown rearranged for ease of calculation in Fig. 2.6b. We know that if there is a negligibly small current flowing through the load (terminals 3-4), essentially the same current that flows through R_1 also flows through R_2. If this is so, we have

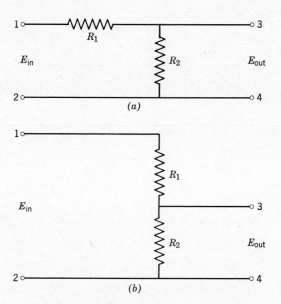

Fig. 2.6   Resistance voltage divider network.

$$\frac{E_{34}}{E_{12}} = \frac{IZ_{34}}{IZ_{12}} = \frac{Z_{34}}{Z_{12}} = \frac{R_2}{R_1 + R_2} \qquad (2.21)$$

and the transfer function of the network is

$$\frac{E_{\text{out}}}{E_{\text{in}}} = \frac{R_2}{R_1 + R_2} \qquad (2.22)$$

We can use this voltage divider technique on the network shown in Fig. 2.5 if we rearrange it as shown in Fig. 2.7. Table 2.2 of circuit element transforms tells us that

$$Z_{34} = \frac{1}{sC} \qquad (2.23)$$

$$Z_{12} = R + \frac{1}{sC} \qquad (2.24)$$

from which it follows that the transfer function is

$$\frac{E_{\text{out}}}{E_{\text{in}}} = \frac{IZ_{34}}{IZ_{12}} = \frac{Z_{34}}{Z_{12}} = \frac{1/sC}{\dfrac{sRC + 1}{sC}} = \frac{1}{sRC + 1} = \frac{1}{sT + 1} \; ; \quad T = RC \qquad (2.25)$$

which is identical with the result in equation (2.20).

As another example of the voltage divider technique let us find the transfer function of the $R\text{-}L$ network shown in Fig. 2.8a. In Fig. 2.8b we have, using Table 2.2,

$$\frac{E_{\text{out}}}{E_{\text{in}}} = \frac{Z_{\text{out}}}{Z_{\text{in}}} = \frac{sL}{R + sL} \qquad (2.26)$$

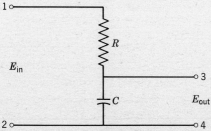

Fig. 2.7 $R\text{-}C$ network of Fig. 2.5 rearranged as a voltage divider.

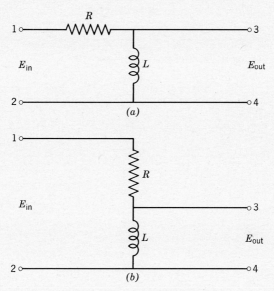

Fig. 2.8(*a*)   *R-L* network. (*b*) Rearrangement of (*a*) as a voltage divider.

The *R-L* circuit time constant is L/R; thus both numerator and denominator of equation (2.26) must be divided by R, giving

$$\frac{E_{\text{out}}}{E_{\text{in}}} = \frac{sL}{R + sL} = \frac{sL/R}{R/R + sL/R} = \frac{sT}{1 + sT} \; ; \quad T = \frac{L}{R} \qquad (2.27)$$

and we have our answer in time-constant form. We can handle many network calculations very easily if we use the voltage divider method. It is suggested that the problems at the end of this chapter be tried using this method.

By means of Table 2.1 we could transform some of our answers back to time functions, but it is preferable to leave our transfer functions in terms of *s*. We will find that as functions of *frequency* (since $s = j\omega$), they tell us a great deal about our network. Similarly, our *frequency-response* methods of Chapter 1 revealed much about amplifiers and control systems. With Laplace transfer functions we are again using a frequency ruler instead of a time ruler. Instead of measuring what happens in the next second, we measure what happens at the next higher frequency.

PROBLEMS

2.1. Find the transfer function of the *R-C* network shown in Fig. P2.1. Express your answer in time-constant form.

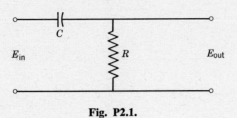

Fig. P2.1.

2.2. Find the transfer function of the *R-L* network shown in Fig. P2.2. Express your answer in time-constant form.

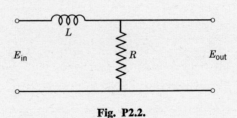

Fig. P2.2.

2.3. Find the transfer function of the *R-C* network shown in Fig. P2.3. Express your answer in time-constant form, letting $T_1 = R_2C$ and $T_2 = (R_1 + R_2)C$. (This is a phase-lag network, and is very important in servomechanism compensation.)

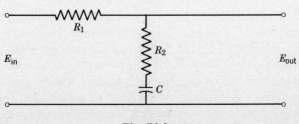

Fig. P2.3.

2.4. Find the transfer function of the R-L network shown in Fig. P2.4.

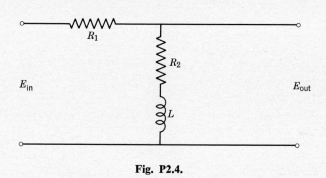

Fig. P2.4.

2.5. Find the transfer function of the R-L network shown in Fig. P2.5.

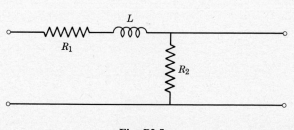

Fig. P2.5.

2.6. Find the transfer function of the R-C network shown in Fig. P2.6. Express your answer in time-constant form, letting $T_1 = R_2C$ and $T_2 = (R_1 + R_2)C$.

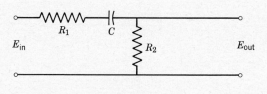

Fig. P2.6.

2.7. Find the transfer function of the *R-L* network shown in Fig. P2.7. Express your answer in time-constant form, letting $T_1 = L/R_1$ and $T_2 = L/R_2$.

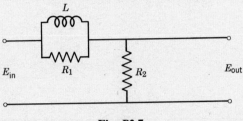

Fig. P2.7.

2.8. Find the transfer function of the *R-L* network shown in Fig. P2.8. Express your answer in time-constant form, letting $T_1 = L/R_1$ and $T_2 = L/R_2$.

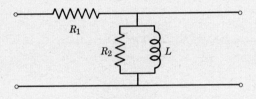

Fig. P2.8.

2.9. Find the transfer function of the *R-C* network shown in Fig. P2.9. Express your answer in time-constant form, letting $T_1 = R_1 C$ and $T_2 = \dfrac{R_1 R_2 C}{R_1 + R_2}$. (This is a phase-lead network, and is very important in servo-mechanism compensation.)

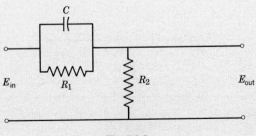

Fig P2.9.

2.10. Find the transfer function of the *R-C* network shown in Fig. P2.10.

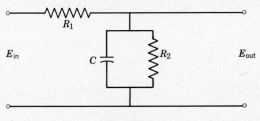

Fig. P2.10.

2.11. Find the transfer function of the compensated attenuator network shown in Fig. P2.11. Show that if $R_1C_1 = R_2C_2$, even though $R_1 \neq R_2$ and $C_1 \neq C_2$ the transfer function is independent of frequency and is a function of R_1 and R_2 only.

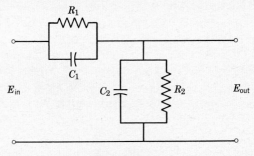

Fig. P2.11.

SUMMARY

In this chapter we developed a basic tool for use throughout the rest of the book: the Laplace transform. We found it an excellent algebraic means for relating time and frequency. We also found that it is the basis for network and control system transfer functions; we will use these transfer functions extensively in the next three chapters.

A graphic method of interpreting the Laplace transfer function aids us in seeing its meaning, and the Bode diagram is an excellent graph for this purpose. In Chapter 3 we will find that some Bode diagrams look almost exactly like the graphs we drew from experimental data in Chapter 1 (Figs. 1.23 and 1.26), indicating that the experimental (frequency-response) and mathematical (Laplace and Bode) techniques are equivalent.

3.

Bode diagrams

3.1   GRAPH OF A TIME FUNCTION

In Section 2.4 we derived the Laplace transfer function of the four-terminal R-C network (Fig. 2.5), shown again in Fig. 3.1a. We will graph this Laplace function as a Bode (pronounced Bō′-dē) diagram, but first let us graph the time function of this network.

As was previously stated, the load connected to terminals 3 and 4 has a very high resistance and therefore a negligible current; thus we can treat terminals 3 and 4 as essentially open-circuited. For the time function of our network we connect it as shown in Fig. 3.1b. If this circuit has a long time constant, that is, if $R \gg X_c$, this net-

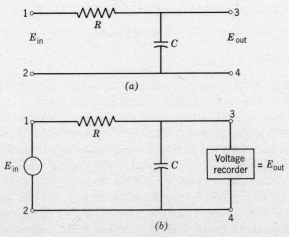

(a)

(b)

Fig. 3.1 R-C network transient analysis experiment. E_{in} is *any* voltage.

work is an integrating circuit, and we prove this statement by the mathematical procedure that follows.

E_{in} is the sum of the voltage drops across R and C. We use the Laplace impedance expressions for R and C given in Table 2.2 and find that

$$E_{in} = V_R + V_C = IR + I\left(\frac{1}{sC}\right) = IR + \frac{I}{sC} \qquad (3.1)$$

But given

$$R \gg X_c \qquad (3.2)$$

$$V_R \gg V_c \qquad (3.3)$$

$$\therefore E_{in} \approx IR \quad ; \quad I \approx \frac{E_{in}}{R} \qquad (3.4)$$

$$E_{out} = \frac{I}{sC} \qquad (3.5)$$

Combining (3.4) and (3.5) gives

$$E_{out} = \frac{E_{in}/R}{sC} = \frac{E_{in}}{sRC} = \frac{1}{RC}\frac{E_{in}}{s} \qquad (3.6)$$

In Table 2.3 of *Laplace Transform Operations* we find that if $F(s) = E_{in}$ the Laplace transform E_{in}/s corresponds to an *integration* in the time domain and therefore gives us the time function $\int_0^t e_{in}\,dt$. Therefore the time function equivalent of equation (3.6) is

$$e_{out} = \frac{1}{RC}\int_0^t e_{in}\,dt \qquad (3.7)$$

showing that the output voltage of this circuit is a constant times the integral of the input voltage.

In Fig. 3.2 we see how this circuit integrates pulses. With a circuit time constant much longer than the pulse width, one input pulse and the ideal output of this circuit are shown in Fig. 3.2a and b. In Fig. 3.2c and d are shown a train of pulses at the input and the resulting ideal output. This circuit of Fig. 3.1a cascaded is used in TV receivers to separate the vertical sync signal from total sync.

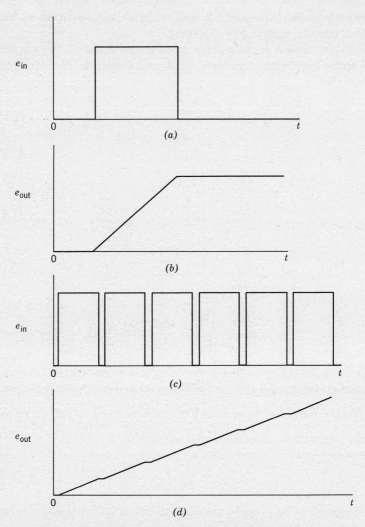

Fig. 3.2 Idealized input and output waveshapes of Fig. 3.1*b*.

3.2   INTRODUCTION TO BODE DIAGRAMS

The *time* or *transient* picture of a network is very valuable to us, and we explore this subject further in Chapters 6 and 7. But in the next three chapters we are not interested in the circuit of Fig. 3.1*a*

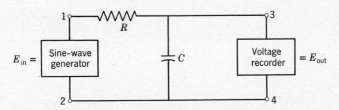

Fig. 3.3   *R-C* network connected for frequency-response test.

as an *integrator* or as a function of *time;* we explore it as a filter—a function of *frequency*. Therefore we change our input to that shown in Fig. 3.3, and in testing this circuit we vary the frequency of the sine-wave input signal, keeping its magnitude constant. This is the same *frequency-response* test we used in Chapter 1, in which we derived our graphs experimentally. This experimental procedure is the same as finding the values of I and E_R by reading the ammeter and voltmeter, connected as shown in Fig. 3.4, and plotting the readings on a graph. If R were a fixed linear resistor, we would find the graph to be a straight line through the origin, as shown in Fig. 3.5. The mathematical equation of this straight line is

$$E_R = IR \qquad (3.8)$$

or Ohm's law. To graph the *equation* is certainly easier than setting up a laboratory experiment and plotting the readings of an ammeter and a voltmeter as the battery voltage is varied.

In Chapter 2 we explored a fairly simple group of mathematical expressions for linear circuits and control systems—Laplace transfer

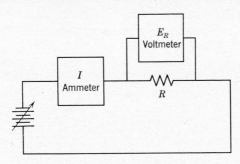

Fig. 3.4   Ohm's law experiment.

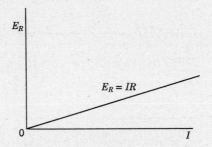

Fig. 3.5   Graph of Fig. 3.4 data.

functions. These frequency functions are graphed in this chapter as
Bode diagrams, which are very similar to those found experimentally
in Chapter 1. H. W. Bode of the Bell Telephone Laboratories simplified the work of plotting frequency transfer functions, enabling us to
approximate these functions by asymptotic straight lines. He did this
by using logarithms of magnitude or gain A, and logarithms of
frequency ω.

Amplifier gain values are usually given as logarithmic or decibel
values (see Fig. 3.6).

$$\text{Magnitude} = \text{voltage gain} = A = \frac{E_{\text{out}}}{E_{\text{in}}} \qquad (3.9)$$

$$\text{Log magnitude} = \text{gain in decibels} = \text{dB } A = 20 \log \frac{E_{\text{out}}}{E_{\text{in}}} \quad (3.10)$$

Logarithmic values are very convenient, as shown by the two cascaded
amplifiers in the Fig. 3.6b. The overall gain is A_1A_2, but in decibels the
gain is dB A_1 + dB A_2. This is true of all transfer functions in series;
the overall transfer function is the product of all the individual transfer functions. This procedure holds for most control systems as well
as cascaded amplifiers.

The Bode diagram shown in Fig. 3.7 is really two graphs: one of
gain versus frequency or dB A versus ω (lower half of Fig. 3.7), and

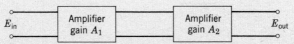

Fig. 3.6   Two-stage amplifier; Gain$_{\text{db}}$ = dB A_1 + dB A_2.

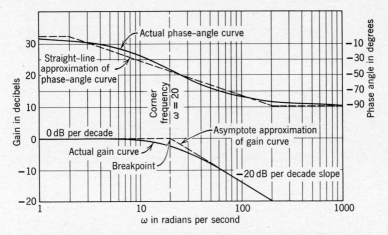

Fig. 3.7 Bode diagram of $\dfrac{1}{1 + j0.05\omega} = \dfrac{1}{1 + j\omega/20}$.

one of phase shift versus frequency or $\underline{/\theta}$ versus ω (upper half of Fig. 3.7). Note that:

1. Straight lines are used to approximate all magnitude curves and the simpler phase curves. These straight-line approximations are then corrected according to values given later in this chapter. Both straight-line approximations (dashed lines) and the corrected curves (solid lines) are shown in Fig. 3.7.

2. The graph paper used is "semilog," that is, the horizontal divisions are logarithmic, and the vertical divisions are even.

3. Values of ω are plotted on the horizontal scale, but the graph is of log ω due to the logarithmic divisions. The units of ω are rad/sec. Individuals concerned with mechanical control often use f in c/s (cycles per second), and those working with chemical process control usually use f in c/s or c/min.

4. The vertical scale log magnitude or gain, dB A, is also a logarithmic value. Therefore the gain-frequency curve is a log–log plot.

5. Because the gain plot is logarithmic, magnitude values A that are *multiplied* can be *added* on the graph and in computation because they are converted to dB A.

6. The phase-angle or phase-shift curve has the same horizontal axis divisions as the gain curve; thus its values always correspond to the gain values at any frequency (ω) vertical division.

7. When two functions of $j\omega$ are multiplied, their angles are added. Since the phase-angle vertical scale is evenly divided and angle values are plotted directly, angle values of two functions *multiplied* together can be *added* on the graph and in computation.

The logarithm of the frequency ω presents a slight mathematical problem. The dimensions of ω are rad/sec, or sec^{-1}, since radians are dimensionless. But all logarithms *must* be of dimensionless numbers. We can see that 10 feet = 120 inches, but that log 10 feet = log 120 inches has no meaning. As a way out of this dilemma some books let $\omega_0 = 1$ rad/sec and use ω/ω_0 as the horizontal axis divisions. We could also use ωT (rad/sec $\times$ sec), but the values would be different from ω/ω_0. In this book we compromise by using ω to represent *a dimensionless number having the numerical value of frequency in radians/second*.

For our first Bode diagram we will plot *all* values instead of drawing the straight-line approximations. We do this because we need to calculate exact gain and phase values to: (1) find at least one check point on plotted gain and phase curves to make sure we have made no errors; (2) plot the more complex phase curves, which cannot be approximated by straight lines; (3) satisfy ourselves that the approximate curves are correct, and (4) be able to find the value of gain and phase at any one frequency without plotting the whole Bode diagram.

Note: Henceforth in this book fractions such as

$$\frac{1}{sT+1} \quad \text{and} \quad \frac{1}{1+j20\omega}$$

may be written as $1/(sT+1)$ and $1/(1+j20\omega)$. *Please study this method of presentation carefully to avoid misunderstanding.*

Let us graph the four-terminal *R-C* network solved in Section 2.4, which was shown again in Fig. 3.1a. In Section 2.4 we found the Laplace transfer function of this network to be $1/(sT+1)$ or $1/(1+sT)$, where $T = RC$. To graph this function we reverse the process of Chapter 2 by substituting $j\omega$ for s, which gives

$$\frac{1}{1+sT} = \frac{1}{1+j\omega T} \tag{3.11}$$

Review of complex numbers takes us back to the complex quantity
$a + jb$, which is shown graphically in Fig. 3.8. We see in Fig. 3.8a
that

$$A = |a + jb| = \sqrt{a^2 + b^2} \qquad (3.12)$$

$$\tan \theta = \frac{b}{a} \ ; \quad \arctan \frac{b}{a} = \underline{/\theta} \qquad (3.13)$$

$$a + jb = A\underline{/\theta} \qquad (3.14)$$

Using numbers given in Fig. 3.8b, we find

$$A = \sqrt{3^2 + 4^2} = 5 \qquad (3.15)$$

$$\tan \theta = \frac{3}{4} \ ; \quad \underline{/\theta} = \arctan 0.75 = 36.9° \qquad (3.16)$$

$$\therefore \ 4 + j3 = 5\underline{/36.9°} \qquad (3.17)$$

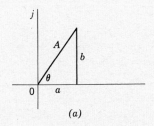
(a)

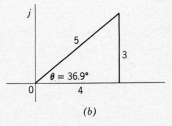
(b)

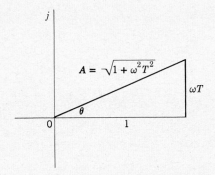

Fig. 3.8 Complex quantities.

Then, given $a + jb = 1 + j\omega T$ (see Fig. 3.8c) we have

$$A = \sqrt{1^2 + \omega^2 T^2} = \sqrt{1 + \omega^2 T^2} \qquad (3.18)$$

$$\tan \theta = \frac{\omega T}{1} = \omega T; \quad \arctan \omega T = \theta \qquad (3.19)$$

$$1 + j\omega T = A\underline{/\theta} \qquad (3.20)$$

To make the foregoing conversions from rectangular to polar coordinates, or from a complex number to a vector, the slide rule may be used. If this method is not familiar, the vector conversion table given in Appendix C should be used. Some key values of decibel conversions are given in Table 3.1.

Table 3.1 *Some Key Values of Approximate Gain in* dB: dB $A = 20 \log A$

	dB A	
A	Actual	Approximate
1	0.00	0
1.4	2.92	3
2	6.02	6
3	9.54	9.5
4	12.04	12
6	15.56	15.5
8	18.06	18
10	20.00	20

3.3 BODE DIAGRAM CONSTRUCTION AND ANALYSIS

The Bode diagram in Fig. 3.7 is of the *R-C* network shown in Fig. 3.1a. Let us give C the value 0.05 microfarads (μF) and R the value 1 MΩ. Then $RC = T = 0.05$ sec $= 1/20$ sec. Our function then becomes

$$\frac{1}{1 + j\omega T} = \frac{1}{1 + j0.05\omega} = \frac{1}{1 + j\omega/20} \qquad (3.21)$$

Now
$$\frac{1}{1 + j\omega T} = \frac{1}{A\underline{/\theta}} = \frac{1}{A}\underline{/-\theta} \qquad (3.22)$$

We therefore have as our amplitude $1/A$, and $\underline{/-\theta}$ as our angle. For the Bode diagram we need

$$\text{dB} \frac{1}{A} = 20 \log \frac{1}{A} = 20(\log 1 - \log A) = 20(0 - \log A) =$$

$$-20 \log A = -\text{dB} \, A \qquad (3.23)$$

For our function $1/(1 + j0.05\omega)$ given in equation (3.21) we consider first the function $1 + j0.05\omega$, let ω vary, and find A and $\underline{/\theta}$. We do this by using the vector conversion table in Appendix C. We choose values of ω, multiply these values by 0.05 to obtain 0.05ω, which is our ωT, and then find our 0.05ω values in the ωT column of the vector conversion table. Table 3.2 is given to show the process; in actual practice such a table is unnecessary because as soon as we calculate the values of $-\text{dB} \, A$ and $\underline{/-\theta}$ we plot them directly on the graph.

Table 3.2 *Values for Plotting* $1/(1 + j0.05\omega)$

ω	ωT	$1 + j0.05\omega$			$1/(1 + j0.05\omega)$	
rad/sec	0.05ω	A	dB A	$\theta°$	$-$ dB A	$-\theta°$
1	0.05	1.001	0.01	2.9	-0.01	-2.9
2	0.10	1.005	0.04	5.7	-0.04	-5.7
4	0.20	1.020	0.17	11.3	-0.17	-11.3
6	0.30	1.044	0.38	16.7	-0.38	-16.7
8	0.40	1.077	0.65	21.8	-0.65	-21.8
10	0.50	1.118	0.98	26.6	-0.98	-26.6
15	0.75	1.250	1.94	36.9	-1.94	-36.9
20	1.00	1.414	3.01	45.0	-3.01	-45.0
30	1.50	1.802	5.12	56.3	-5.12	-56.3
40	2.00	2.235	6.99	63.5	-6.99	-63.4
60	3.00	3.167	10.01	71.6	-10.01	-71.6
80	4.00	4.12	12.30	76.0	-12.30	-76.0
100	5.00	5.10	14.15	78.7	-14.15	-78.7
200	10.00	10.05	20.05	84.3	-20.05	-84.3
400	20.00	20.02	26.07	87.2	-26.07	-87.2
600	30.00	30.02	29.57	88.1	-29.57	-88.1

Note: Values obtained from vector conversion table in Appendix C (see Fig. 3.7 for graph of values plotted).

The Bode diagram shown in Fig. 3.7 shows that the decibel gain (in this case a loss) is 0 at very low values of ω and decreases at a rate of 20 dB per decade at very high values of ω. (A *decade* is any group of ten consecutive major divisions on the graph; for example from $\omega = 50$ to $\omega = 500$ is a decade.) Note on the graph and in the table that at $\omega = 60$ there is a loss of 10 dB, and that one decade higher at $\omega = 600$ there is a loss of 29.55 dB. In this decade there is a loss of 29.55 − 10.00, or 19.55 dB. There is thus a loss of almost 20 dB/decade, and if we were to go to a higher frequency, the loss per decade would be much closer to 20 dB. Besides the exact gain curve drawn through plotted points, the asymptotes of the curve (dashed lines) are drawn in and extended until they meet. These asymptotes, which can be drawn quickly with a straight-edge, tell us almost as much as the laboriously plotted exact curve. The maximum error in the asymptotic curve is 3.01 dB, usually a negligible amount. The point where the two asymptotic lines meet is called the *breakpoint*, and ω at this point is called the *corner frequency*. When we use the transfer function form

$$\frac{1}{1 + j\omega/20}$$

the breakpoint and corner frequency at $\omega = 20$ are obvious.

The Bode diagram phase-shift curve was plotted using the values in the last column of Table 3.2. It approaches $0°$ at very low frequencies, is exactly $-45°$ at the corner frequency, and approaches $-90°$ at very high frequencies.

A dashed line shows the straight-line approximation of the phase curve. This line starts out at the left margin at $0°$; beginning at one decade less than the corner frequency the line slopes at $45°$ per decade through two decades (a total of $90°$) to one decade beyond the corner frequency; then the line continues at $90°$ to $\omega = \infty$. The corrections that must be applied to the phase-shift curve are indicated in Fig. 3.9 and in Table 3.3 in terms of ω_c, the corner frequency.

Wherever possible, phase-shift or phase-angle curves in this book are constructed using corrected straight-line approximations, as shown in Fig. 3.9.

By considering the R-C network of Fig. 3.1a, whose Bode diagram is Fig. 3.7, we know that this network indeed has no voltage loss if E_{in} is dc or very low in frequency, and that the network has an increasing loss at higher frequencies due to the shunting effect of the capacitor. There is no phase shift at very low frequencies, and almost $90°$ phase shift at high frequencies, due to the capacitor. Thus the

Table 3.3 *Corrections to*
Approximate Phase-Shift or Phase-Angle Curve

ω	Corrections
$0.05\omega_c$	$-3°$
$0.1\omega_c$	$-6°$
$0.3\omega_c$	$+5°$
$0.5\omega_c$	$+5°$
$1.0\omega_c$	$0°$
$2.0\omega_c$	$-5°$
$3.0\omega_c$	$-5°$
$10.0\omega_c$	$+6°$
$20.0\omega_c$	$+3°$

gain and phase curves of the Bode diagram agree with our experience.

Another way of looking at the Bode diagram of our *R-C* network is to consider the time-delay aspect. If we replaced the capacitor of Fig. 3.1*a* with a resistor, our gain and phase-shift plots would look like Fig. 3.11—zero phase shift and a constant loss, regardless of frequency (for example, $K = 0.1$). The capacitor causes a delay between input and output—a *time* constant, due to its *storage* qualities. It takes time for electrons to fill and empty the capacitor through the resistor. In the Bode diagram of $1/(1 + j0.05\omega)$ the key

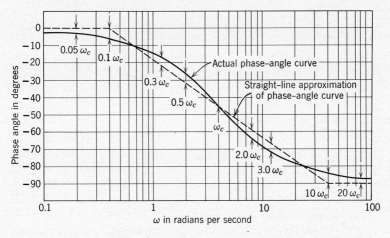

Fig. 3.9 Errors of approximate Bode phase-angle plot (see Table 3.3).

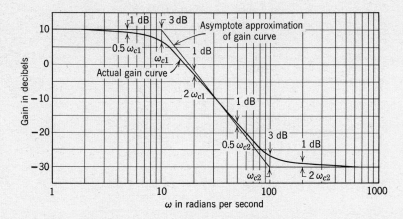

Fig. 3.10 Bode diagram of K (any constant).

value is the *time constant*, 0.05 sec, which is the result of the resistor-capacitor combination in the network.

Looking at Fig. 3.7 we see that below 2 rad/sec (0.32 c/s) there is time to charge and discharge the capacitor, and almost no phase shift occurs between E_{in} and E_{out}. In addition, no signal amplitude is lost in passing through the network. But at 200 rad/sec (32 c/s) there is an 84° phase shift and a loss of 20 dB in the signal passing through the network.

The key word in this concept is *storage*. Devices that store energy—capacitors, inductors, springs, flywheels—cannot *immediately* lose or gain energy. When there is a change of energy in one of these devices a time delay ensues. How much delay occurs depends on the size of the storage element and the amount of resistance in electrical networks or the amount of friction or damping in mechanical or electromechanical networks.

Most Bode diagram gain plots consist of horizontal or sloping lines that are easy to plot. For example, the sloping straight asymptotic line in Fig. 3.7 is easily drawn from the break point, 0 dB at $\omega = 20$, to the next decade, $\omega = 200$, where it will be 20 dB down from the value at $\omega = 20$. More complicated gain plots are almost this simple, as we will see later in this chapter.

In the unusual case that we want to draw the exact gain curve, an easy way to do this is to first sketch in the straight-line approximation. Then by plotting a few points to compensate for the errors in the straight-line plot, we can draw through these corrected points the exact curve. Figure 3.10 shows a straight-line approximation, the exact curve, and the corrections that need to be made to the straight-line plot at six points. As can be seen in Fig. 3.10, the correction values are 3 dB at the corner frequency, and 1 dB at half the corner frequency and twice the corner frequency. At one-fourth the corner frequency and four times the corner frequency the correction is one-fourth decibel, but this correction is not shown and is usually unnecessary. As has been stated, the straight-line approximation is usually sufficient. *Henceforward in this book all Bode gain plots will be uncorrected straight-line approximations unless otherwise noted.*

3.4 BODE DIAGRAM BUILDING BLOCKS

The function used in plotting a Bode diagram may contain any of the following four items:

(1) K (a constant)
(2) $j\omega$ or any power of $j\omega$, such as $(j\omega)^3$
(3) $1 + j\omega T$ or any power of $1 + j\omega T$, such as $(1 + j\omega T)^2$
(4) $1 + j\omega K_1 + (j\omega)^2 K_2$. This quadratic factor with complex roots occurs infrequently, and is not treated in this text.

Samples of complete transfer functions, the general term followed by a specific one, are given below.

$$\frac{1}{1 + j\omega T} : \frac{1}{1 + j0.05\omega} \qquad \text{with } T = 0.05 = \frac{1}{20}$$

$$\frac{1 + j\omega T_1}{1 + j\omega T_2} : \frac{1 + j2\omega}{1 + j20\omega} \qquad \text{with } T_1 = 2 \text{ and } T_2 = 20$$

$$\frac{K}{j(1 + j\omega T)} : \frac{25}{j(1 + j0.2\omega)} \qquad \text{with } K = 25, T = 0.2 = \frac{1}{5}$$

$$\frac{K(1 + j\omega T_2)}{(1 + j\omega T_1)(1 + j\omega T_3)} : \frac{72(1 + j0.4\omega)}{(1 + j2\omega)(1 + j0.1\omega)}$$

with $\qquad K = 72, T_1 = 2 \quad ; \quad T_2 = 0.4, T_3 = 0.1$

Let us examine items 1, 2, and 3 in order, first considering K. Any constant plots as a straight horizontal line; since K is a constant, $20 \log K$ or K dB is also a constant. If $K = 1$, $\log 1 = 0$, and we have a straight line at 0 dB. Various values of $20 \log K$ are plotted in Fig. 3.11. Note that K causes no phase shift; therefore the phase angle is 0°.

The second factor, $j\omega$, has both magnitude and phase angle. As shown in Fig. 3.12, the angle of j is 90°, of j^2 is 180°, of $1/j$ is $-90°$, $1/j^2$ is $-180°$. Since ω, ω^2, and ω^3 are all constants, they do not affect the angle of $j\omega$ or any power of $j\omega$. There is amplitude to $j\omega$; it is the distance ω up or down the j or 90° axis. The log magnitude or gain we plot in decibels, and it is $20 \log j\omega$. For $(j\omega)^2$ we have log magnitude or gain $20 \log |(j\omega)^2| = 20 \times 2 \log |j\omega| = 40 \log |j\omega|$; $20 \log |(j\omega)^3| = 20 \times 3 \log |j\omega| = 60 \log |j\omega|$. We can see this if we consider the value of $20 \log |j\omega|$ when $\omega = 10$, 100, and 1000. Then $\log |j\omega| = \log 10$, $\log 100$, and $\log 1000 = 1$, 2, and 3; and $20 \log |j\omega| = 20 \times 1$, 20×2, and 20×3. These points, 20, 40, and 60 dB, lie on an upward-sloping straight line, 20 dB higher each decade ($\omega = 10$, 100, 1000). The log magnitudes of $(j\omega)^2$ and $(j\omega)^3$ can be similarly shown to have slopes of 40 dB/decade and 60 dB/decade. The reciprocal of $j\omega$ is $1/j\omega$; if $\omega = 10$, 100, and 1000; then $20 \log |1/j\omega| = 20 \log 10^{-1}$, $20 \log 10^{-2}$, and $20 \log 10^{-3}$, giving us $20(-1)$, $20(-2)$, and $20(-3)$. This gives us a downward-sloping straight line, 20 dB less each decade. Table 3.4 summarizes the foregoing information.

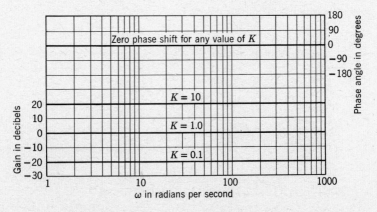

Fig. 3.11 Errors of approximate Bode gain plot.

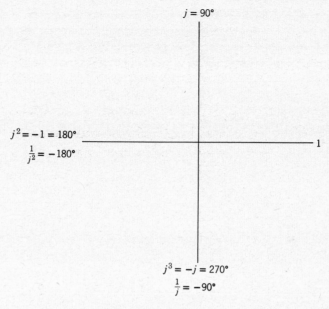

Fig. 3.12 Angles of j^n.

Table 3.4 *Gain and phase of* $(j\omega)^n$

Transfer Function	Slope of Log Gain Line in Decibels per Decade	Phase Angle $\underline{/\theta}$
$j\omega$	$+20$	$90°$
$(j\omega)^2$	$+40$	$180°$
$(j\omega)^3$	$+60$	$270°$
$\dfrac{1}{j\omega}$	-20	$-90°$
$\dfrac{1}{(j\omega)^2}$	-40	$180°$
$\dfrac{1}{(j\omega)^3}$	-60	$-270°$
$(j\omega)^n$	$20n$	$n \times 90°$

Bode diagrams of all these functions are shown in Figs. 3.13 and 3.14.

Having covered K and $j\omega$ we come to the third factor, $1 + j\omega T$. As we have seen, T is a constant (the time constant); ω is the fre-

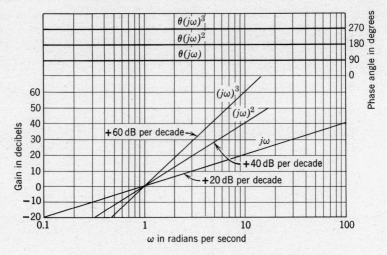

Fig. 3.13 Phase and amplitude of $j\omega$, $(j\omega)^2$, and $(j\omega)^3$.

quency variable. If ω is much less than $1/T$, then $j\omega T$ becomes negligibly small, and $1 + j\omega T$ becomes almost 1. At low frequencies then, our Bode diagram of this function is $K = 1$, and we see in Fig. 3.15 that this is a straight horizontal line at 0 dB, and the phase angle is $0°$. If ω is much greater than $1/T$, $j\omega T$ is very much larger than 1, and $1 + j\omega T$ becomes almost equal to $j\omega T$. In Fig. 3.13 we

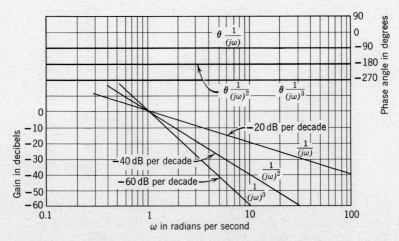

Fig. 3.14 Phase and amplitude of $\dfrac{1}{j\omega}$, $\dfrac{1}{(j\omega)^2}$, $\dfrac{1}{(j\omega)^3}$.

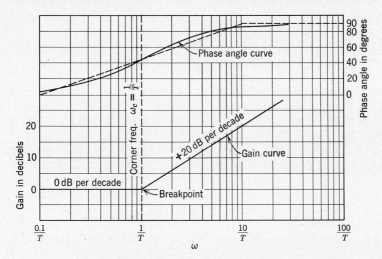

Fig. 3.15   Bode diagram of $1 + j\omega T$.

saw that $j\omega$ is a line of slope 20 dB/decade and a phase angle of 90°. (On a Bode diagram $j\omega$ and $j\omega T$ plot the same, except for a parallel shift of the log magnitude or gain line.) In Fig. 3.15 we see the logical result of the preceding analysis in the two straight lines meeting at the breakpoint, $\omega = 1/T$ and 0 dB. The phase-angle curve begins at 0°, is 45° at the corner frequency, and ends at 90°. For the phase curve we note that the corner frequency is $1/T$. Therefore as our phase-shift curve approximation we draw a $+45°$/decade line from 0° at $\frac{1}{10}$ of the corner frequency ($1/10T$) to 90° at 10 times the corner frequency ($10/T$). We continue with a straight line at 90° from $10/T$ to infinity. The corrections given in Table 3.3 are then applied to this line.

The Bode diagram of the function $1/(1 + j0.05\omega)$ has been extensively analyzed in Section 3.3 and is shown in Fig. 3.7.

PROBLEMS

General instructions for all Bode diagram problems: Use 3-cycle (or 4-cycle) semilogarithmic paper (similar to the paper used in the illustrations in this chapter.) Note that you have to plan your scales so that all breakpoints of the gain curve are shown as well as all the corresponding phase-shift curve. *All Bode diagram gain curves are to be uncorrected straight-line approximations unless otherwise noted. The phase curves should be corrected straight-line approximations.*

3.1. Draw the Bode diagram of $K = 2.5$ and $K = 15$.

3.2. Draw the Bode diagram of $K = 1.5$ and $K = 12.5$.

3.3. Draw the Bode diagram of $(j\omega)^4$.

3.4. Draw the Bode diagram of $1/(j\omega)^4$.

3.5. Draw the Bode diagram of the function $1 + j0.1\omega = 1 + j\omega/10$ by plotting gain and phase points for $\omega = 0.5, 2, 5, 8, 10, 12, 15, 20, 25, 40, 100$.

3.6. Draw the Bode diagram of the function $1 + j0.02\omega = 1 + j\omega/50$ by plotting gain and phase points for $\omega = 1, 10, 15, 25, 40, 50, 60, 100, 200, 500, 1000$.

3.7. Draw the Bode diagram of the function given in Prob. 3.5 using straight-line gain and phase approximations. Then apply to both curves the necessary corrections as shown in Figs. 3.9 and 3.11. Sketch in the corrected curves, and compare them to your Bode diagram constructed in Prob. 3.5.

3.8. Draw the Bode diagram of the function given in Prob. 3.6 using straight-line gain and phase approximations. Then apply to both curves the necessary corrections as shown in Figs. 3.9 and 3.11. Sketch in the corrected curves, and compare them to your Bode diagram constructed in Prob. 3.6.

3.9. Draw the Bode diagram of the function

$$\frac{1}{1 + j0.01\omega} = \frac{1}{1 + j\omega/100}$$

The circuit shown in Fig. 3.1a would result in the type of Bode diagram drawn for the function given in this problem. If in Fig. 3.1a $R = 1$ MΩ, what value of capacitor would give the preceding function? What value of attenuation and what value of phase shift would this network present to a signal whose frequency is 500 rad/sec? How many cycles per second is this?

3.10. Same instructions as Prob. 3.9 for the function

$$\frac{1}{1 + j0.001\omega} = \frac{1}{1 + j\omega/1000}$$

3.5 PLOTTING OF MORE COMPLEX TRANSFER FUNCTIONS

As we have stated, all transfer functions contain, in various combinations, the items thus far discussed. It is possible to plot factors of a transfer function and then add them graphically. For example, in equation (3.24) we can make a Bode diagram by plotting on one sheet of graph paper separate gain and phase plots of 25, $1/j\omega$, and $1/(1 + j0.2\omega)$. Then using a ruler or dividers we can add at a large number of frequency points the gain curves and the phase curves of the three transfer function elements to find the Bode diagram of the complete transfer function $25/j\omega(1 + j0.2\omega)$. We shall not do this here because it is not practical for functions of any complexity, and because it does not lead to as much understanding of the behavior of the functions. But let us keep in mind this idea of "building blocks" as we graph our functions, and start with the function

$$\frac{K}{j\omega(1 + j\omega T)} = \frac{25}{j\omega(1 + j0.2\omega)} = \frac{25}{j\omega(1 + j\omega/5)} \qquad (3.24)$$

whose Bode diagram is shown in Fig. 3.16. Here $K = 25$ and $T = 0.2$. There are three elements: 25, $1/j\omega$, and $1/(1 + j0.2\omega)$, which are multiplied together. To multiply we add logarithms. The decibel (logarithmic) values of the three function elements therefore are added together to yield the decibel values of the total function. We could use this fact to plot a table of values, but it is much easier and quicker to use a method of sketching in the plot, which we shall now develop. When we finish our plot we check our work by adding

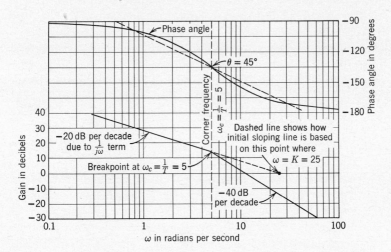

Fig. 3.16 Bode diagram of $\dfrac{25}{j\omega(1 + j0.2\omega)} = \dfrac{25}{j\omega(1 + j\omega/5)} = \dfrac{K}{j\omega(1 + j\omega T)}$.

decibels of function elements at a point on the curve near the right-hand edge of the paper to find out whether the calculated and plotted values agree.

For very small values of ω the element $1/(1 + j0.2\omega)$ becomes $1/1 = 1$, and the total function becomes $25/j\omega$. In Fig. 3.14 the function $1/j\omega$ is shown, but this must be multiplied by 25 in dB = 20 log 25; or as plotted we must add 20 log 25 to the plot. This means the line must be moved up parallel to itself by 20 log 25 or 27.96 dB. The line $25/j\omega$ or any function $K/j\omega$ has a slope of -20 dB/decade, but in order to place the line on the graph we must have one point on the line. Now

$$20 \log \left| \frac{K}{j\omega} \right| = 20 \log \frac{K}{\omega} \qquad (3.25)$$

When $\omega = K$ we have $\quad 20 \log \dfrac{K}{K} = 20 \log 1 = 0 \qquad (3.26)$

Therefore the initial slope either goes through the point $\omega = K$ at the 0-dB line, or would go through this point if the line were extended. This is the "anchor point" in all asymptotic or straight-line Bode diagram gain plots with $j\omega$ in the denominator. In the present case we draw from the point $\omega = 25$ on the 0 dB axis a line extending up and to the left at a slope of -20 dB/decade, as shown in Fig. 3.16.

The second line is derived from our function equation (3.24) with very large values of ω, which cause $|1 + j0.2\omega|$ to approach $|j0.2\omega| = 0.2\omega$. This may be seen if we let $\omega = 50$. Then $1 + j0.2\omega$ becomes $1 + j10$, the absolute value of which is $\sqrt{10^2 + 1^2} = \sqrt{101}$, which is almost $\sqrt{100} = 10$. Thus the 1 in $1 + j10$ is "swamped" by the high value of ω. At high values of ω, then, $1/(1 + j0.2\omega)$ approaches $1/j\omega$, and our function approaches

$$\frac{25}{j\omega} \frac{1}{j\omega} = \frac{25}{(j\omega)^2} \qquad (3.27)$$

This function has a slope of -40 dB/decade and starts at the breakpoint. The breakpoint is at $\omega = 1/T$, the value that makes the function in question become $1 + j1$. In our case, a value of $\omega = 5$ rad/sec makes $1 + j0.2\omega$ become $1 + j1$, and $\omega = 5$ is the corner frequency. Therefore, from the intersection of our -20 dB/decade initial line and the ordinate $\omega = 5$ we draw our final line at a slope of -40 dB/decade, as shown in Fig. 3.16. Note that the dashed line is not part of the Bode diagram, but is an extension of the initial slope to $\omega = 25$ at 0 dB. The dashed line merely shows how we started our initial line in the proper position. It is a good idea to check our plot at the right-hand end of the gain line, since we began at the left and are fairly sure of it there. Checking at $\omega = 100$ we should have in decibels

$$20 \log \left| \frac{25}{j\omega(1 + j0.2\omega)} \right| = 20 \log \left| \frac{25}{j100(1 + j20)} \right|$$

$$= 20 \, (\log 25 - \log 100 - \log |1 + j20|)$$

$$= (27.96 - 40 - 26.07) \, \text{dB}$$

$$= -38.11 \, \text{dB} \tag{3.28}$$

Our graph shows a value of -38 dB, which checks the correctness of our gain curve.

The phase-shift curve is sketched in approximately by three straight lines. The first line begins at $-90°$, because when $\omega = 0$ we have $25/j\omega$. The 25 does not affect the phase, so we have $1/j\omega = 1/90° = -90°$. (See Table 3.4 and Figs. 3.12 and 3.14.) At very high frequencies we have $25/j\omega(j\omega) = 25/(j\omega)^2$, because with very large ω the value of $j0.2\omega$ swamps the 1. We therefore plot $1/(j\omega)^2$, which is $1/180° = -180°$. In midfrequencies from $0.1\omega_c$ to $10\omega_c(\omega_c =$ the corner frequency), we draw a straight line starting at $0.1\omega_c$ which slopes down at a rate of $-45°$/decade. This line meets the $-180°$ line at $10\omega_c$. To these straight lines we apply the corrections given in Table 3.3.

Because we have to plot more complex phase curves point by point, for practice we plot a few phase angle values. In the function

$$\frac{25}{j\omega(1 + j0.2\omega)} = \frac{25}{j\omega(1 + j\omega/5)} \tag{3.29}$$

the 25 does not affect the phase. The term $1/j\omega = -90°$ at all values of ω (see Fig. 3.14). The term $1/(1 + j0.2\omega)$ has a phase curve similar to the one shown in Fig. 3.7. To calculate the phase angle θ of the total function, we let ω assume various values and find values of the phase angle of $1 + j0.2\omega$ in the vector conversion table in Appendix C. We add the negative of these angles to $-90°$ (for the term $1/j\omega$). A few values are given in Table 3.5.

Table 3.5 *Phase-Shift or Phase-Angle Values of Equation* (3.29)

ω	$1 + j0.2\omega$	θ	$-\theta -90°$
1	$1 + j0.2$	11.3°	$-101.3°$
2	$1 + j0.4$	21.8°	$-111.8°$
5	$1 + j1$	45.0	-135.0
10	$1 + j2$	63.4	-153.4

A case that sometimes occurs is a function with $(j\omega)^2$ in the denominator, for example, the equation,

$$\frac{0.25}{(j\omega)^2(1 + j0.5\omega)} = \frac{0.25}{(j\omega)^2(1 + j\omega/2)} \tag{3.30}$$

shown in Fig. 3.17. We know that the slope of $1/j\omega$ is -20 dB/decade
and its phase angle is $-90°$. From Table 3.4 we see that $1/(j\omega)^2$ has
a slope of -40 dB/decade and an angle of $-180°$. This line does *not*
intersect the 0 dB line at $\omega = K = 0.25$ in our function (3.30), but
at $\omega = \sqrt{K} = \sqrt{0.25} = 0.5$, as is shown in Fig. 3.17. (Note that
the decibel scale in Fig. 3.17 is different from the previous plots in
this chapter. The scale is chosen for the best placement of the plot
on the page.) The phase-angle calculation is simply $-180°$ minus

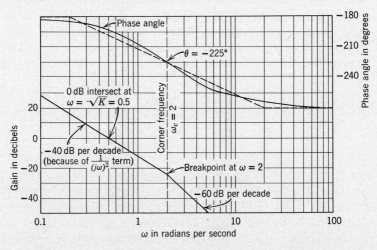

Fig. 3.17 Bode diagram of $\dfrac{0.25}{(j\omega)^2(1 + j0.5\omega)} = \dfrac{0.25}{(j\omega)^2(1 + j\omega/2)}$.

the angle due to $1 + j0.5\omega$ (since the latter is in the denominator). The corner frequency ω_c is 2. Therefore the straight-line approximation starts at $-180°$. At $0.1\omega_c = 0.2$ the line drops at a rate of $-45°$/decade to $10\omega_c$; at $10\omega_c$ it reaches $-270°$ and stays there to $\omega = \infty$.

PROBLEMS

3.11. Draw the Bode diagram of the function

$$\frac{20}{1 + j0.1\omega} = \frac{20}{1 + j\omega/10}$$

This function would result from the network shown in Fig. 3.1a plus an amplifier with a gain of 20. If $C = 1 \ \mu\mu f$, what value of R would give the preceding function? What attenuation or gain and what phase shift would the preceding system have for a signal of 100 rad/sec? For a signal of 10 c/s?

3.12. Draw the Bode diagram of the function

$$\frac{15}{1 + j0.125\omega} = \frac{15}{(1 + j\omega/8)}$$

This function would result from the network shown in Fig. 3.1a plus an amplifier with a gain of 15. If $C = 1 \ \mu\mu F$, what value of R would give the foregoing function? What attentuation or gain and what phase shift would this system have for a signal of 100 rad/sec? For a signal of 10 c/s?

3.13. Draw the Bode diagram of the function

$$\frac{15}{j\omega(1 + j1.2\omega)} = \frac{15}{j\omega(1 + j\omega/0.833)}$$

3.14. Draw the Bode diagram of the function

$$\frac{20}{j\omega(1 + j0.5\omega)} = \frac{20}{j\omega(1 + j\omega/2)}$$

3.15. Draw the Bode diagram of the function

$$\frac{0.09}{(j\omega)^2(1 + j0.2\omega)}$$

3.16. Draw the Bode diagram of the function

$$\frac{0.04}{(j\omega)^2(1 + j0.1\omega)}$$

3.17. Draw the Bode diagram of the function

$$\frac{1 + j\omega}{1 + j10\omega}$$

3.18. Draw the Bode diagram of the function

$$\frac{1 + j\omega}{1 + j0.1\omega}$$

One more Bode diagram illustration is given here (Fig. 3.18). We shall graph the function

$$\frac{2.5(1 + j0.5\omega)}{j\omega(1 + j5\omega)(1 + j0.1\omega)} = \frac{2.5(1 + j\omega/2)}{j\omega(1 + j\omega/0.2)(1 + j\omega/10)} \qquad (3.31)$$

For drawing the gain plot we note that:

$j\omega$ causes an initial slope of -20 dB/decade crossing the 0 dB axis at $\omega = 2.5 = K$

$1 + \dfrac{j\omega}{0.2}$ has a corner frequency at $\omega = 0.2 = \omega_{c1}$

$1 + \dfrac{j\omega}{2}$ has a corner frequency at $\omega = 2 = \omega_{c2}$

$1 + \dfrac{j\omega}{10}$ has a corner frequency at $\omega = 10 = \omega_{c3}$

Therefore the gain line has an initial slope of -20 dB/decade "aimed at" the point $\omega = K = 2.5$ and 0 dB. This line breaks at $\omega = 0.2$, and from the end of this line we start another with a -40 dB/decade slope, which continues to $\omega = 2$. Then the line slopes at -20 dB/decade until it reaches $\omega = 10$. From this point the final line slopes at -40 dB/decade to the end of the plot.

To check the foregoing procedure we choose a point on the final line, that is, with ω greater than 10. If we choose $\omega = 50$, our function becomes

$$\frac{2.5(1 + j25)}{j50(1 + j250)(1 + j5)}$$

and our decibel magnitudes are (adding decibels for each factor in the numerator and subtracting decibels for each factor in the denominator, as found in Appendix B and Appendix C): dB 2.5+

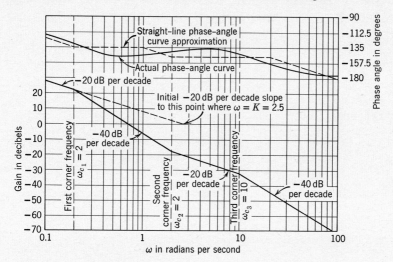

Fig. 3.18 Bode diagram of

$$\frac{2.5(1+j0.5\omega)}{j\omega(1+j5\omega)(1+j0.1\omega)} = \frac{2.5(1+j\omega/2)}{j\omega(1+j\omega/0.2)(1+j\omega/10)}.$$

dB $(1+j25)$ − dB 50 − dB $(1+j250)$ − dB $(1+j5)$ = $(7.96 +$ $28.00 − 33.98 − 47.96 − 14.15)$ dB = -60.13 dB. An alternate procedure is to work with numerical values first and then convert to decibels as a last step. Applying this approach to the preceding Bode diagram check and again using $\omega = 50$ yields

$$\left| \frac{2.5(1+j25)}{j(50)(1+j250)(1+j5)} \right| = \frac{2.5(25.02)}{50(250)(5.1)}$$

Since this fraction has a value of less than one and will therefore have a negative value when converted to decibels, we can invert the fraction and add a minus sign as shown in the following equation:

$$\frac{2.5(25.02)}{50(250)(5.1)} \text{ in dB} = -\left(\frac{50(250)(5.1)}{2.5(25.02)} \text{ in dB} \right)$$

$$= -(1020 \text{ in dB}) = -60.17 \text{ dB}$$

We started at the left, and we checked near the right end of our plot on the last slope; thus we are sure the entire magnitude plot is correct.

The phase-shift curve approximation, which is constructed by adding its elements, is not easy to draw and is not much help in constructing the exact curve. Errors are as high as 14°; therefore *we do not bother with the approximation*. The exact phase-shift curve is calculated with the numerator $(1 + j0.5\omega)$ angle positive and all the denominator factor angles negative. We use the vector conversion table in Appendix C for each factor. The $j\omega$ factor results in an initial phase shift of $-90°$; this phase shift continues for all values of ω. Examples of two calculations are

$$\text{at } \omega = 1: \quad 26.6 - 90° - 78.7° - 5.7° = -147.8°$$

$$\text{at } \omega = 50: \quad 87.7 - 90° - 89.8° - 78.7° = -170.8°$$

PROBLEMS

3.19. Draw the Bode diagram of the function

$$\frac{72(1 + 0.4\omega)}{(1 + j2\omega)(1 + j0.1\omega)} = \frac{72(1 + j\omega/2.5)}{(1 + j\omega/0.5)(1 + j\omega/10)}$$

3.20. Draw the Bode diagram of the function

$$\frac{72(1 + j0.2\omega)}{(1 + j0.1\omega)(1 + j0.4\omega)} = \frac{72(1 + j\omega/5)}{(1 + j\omega/10)(1 + j\omega/2.5)}$$

3.21. Draw the Bode diagram of the function

$$\frac{100(1 + j\omega)}{j\omega(1 + j0.0153\omega)(1 + j10\omega)} = \frac{100(1 + j\omega)}{j\omega(1 + j\omega/65.4)(1 + j\omega/0.1)}$$

3.22. Draw the Bode diagram of the function

$$\frac{100(1 + j0.002\omega)}{j\omega(1 + j0.0153\omega)(1 + j0.02\omega)} = \frac{100(1 + j\omega/500)}{j\omega(1 + j\omega/65.4)(1 + j\omega/50)}$$

3.6 STABILITY INFORMATION FROM BODE DIAGRAMS

Bode diagrams are useful in displaying Laplace transforms graphically and in giving control system characteristics. We discussed one such characteristic in Chapter 1—stability: that which keeps a feedback amplifier or control system from breaking into oscillations. We saw in Section 1.3 and 1.4, that when open-loop amplifier output is

180° out of phase with the input, the addition of feedback couples a positive output signal into the input of the amplifier, making the amplifier an oscillator. This change from negative to positive feedback is caused by the presence of *storage* elements (Section 3.3), which *delay* the *feedback* signal until at some frequency it is 180° out of phase with the input. If with 180° phase shift and a gain of one or greater we close the feedback loop, the signal would grow and uncontrollable oscillations would result. The Bode diagram shows *open-loop* amplifiers or control systems. We inspect the diagram and note the phase angle at the frequency at which the magnitude curve crosses the zero-decibel line; this frequency is called the *gain crossover frequency*. Zero decibels is a gain of 1 (since log 1 = 0 and 20 log 1 also equals zero). If when the gain curve crosses the zero-decibel line (gain = 1), the phase-angle curve indicates an angle of −180° or a higher negative value, the system is inherently unstable. To insure stability we keep the phase angle at the gain crossover frequency well under −180°; the amount under −180° is called *phase margin*. Thus for servomechanisms we keep the phase margin between 40° (phase angle: −180° + 40° = −140°) and 60° (phase angle: −180° + 60° = −120°). Table 3.6 shows the values of phase angle and phase margin for some of the Bode diagrams illustrated in this chapter. The first and third cases in Table 3.5 are too lively or "jittery," and might possibly break into oscillations for short periods since the phase margin in both cases is less than the 40° minimum. The second case is completely unstable at all times. On the other hand if we had a case with a 100° phase margin, the system would be too stable with a wide dead band, and therefore a sizable error would occur. In designing control systems we steer a precarious course between too much dead band (and error), and too fast a speed of response (and oscillations). There are ways of stabilizing or *compensating* control systems to meet

Table 3.6   *Phase Margins of Three Systems*

Figure	Phase Angle at Gain Crossover Frequency	Phase Margin
Fig. 3.16	−155°	25°
Fig. 3.17	−194°	−14°
Fig. 3.18	−148°	32°

the phase-margin requirements, and ways of making "dead" systems lively, as we shall see in Chapter 5. Raising the gain almost always makes the system livelier.

Figure 3.19 shows a typical Bode diagram which illustrates and reviews some of the terms used. Note the following: breakpoint, gain crossover, phase margin, corner frequencies, and gain crossover frequency. Note that the left-hand vertical scale is given both as *magnitude ratio* and as *gain in decibels;* the right-hand vertical scale is given as *phase angle* and as *phase margin*; and the horizontal frequency scale at the bottom is given in *cycles per second* and in *radians per second.*

SUMMARY

We are now prepared, using the concepts and mathematics of the previous chapters, to analyze any linear control system (see Section 1.1 for an explanation of linearity). We could discuss mechanical control systems, such as link-and-lever systems; electrical control systems, such as voltage regulators and power systems; electro-acoustic control systems for high-fidelity audio systems; hydraulic control systems, such as automobile steering and power-brake systems; pneumatic (compressed air) control systems, and many others. Each of these systems is basically similar to every other system, particularly if it is essentially a linear system. The same underlying principles are exhibited by all linear control systems, and if we study one system thoroughly we grasp the basic principles of all such systems.

Similarly, if we derive the transfer functions of the basic components of one type of control system, we find similar transfer functions apply to all such systems. Because the number of types of components is so vast, here we will discuss components used in instrument servomechanisms. In later chapters we use the transfer functions of these components to build and analyze typical instrument servomechanism models.

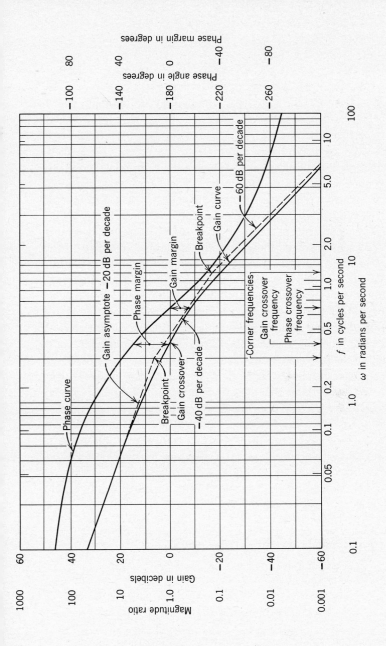

Fig. 3.19 Typical Bode diagram; function plotted is

$$\frac{\theta_{\text{out}}}{E} = \frac{4}{j\omega(1 + j0.125\omega)(1 + j0.5\omega)} = \frac{4}{j\omega(1 + j\omega/8)(1 + j\omega/2)}.$$

71

4.

*Control system components**

The concepts and mathematics we have so far developed cover all linear control systems (see Section 1.1). These control systems may range in size from a miniature package in an instrument or computer to a system operating the largest radar antenna. There are electrical control systems, such as large power systems; there are hydraulic control systems, such as those used for automobile brakes and for controlling steel mills; there are pneumatic (compressed air) control systems, such as those used in large oil refineries; and there are mechanical control systems, such as those used in automobile assembly lines. Most control systems are hybrid; the electronic amplifier drives an electromechanical servomotor in response to an electrical signal received from a mechanical-electrical transducer. The components of such systems may include transmitting elements, error detectors, transducers, amplifiers, power actuators, feedback elements, mechanical and electrical transformers, and others. In each group there are many types. For example, power actuators include hydraulic and pneumatic pistons, electrical motors, and hydraulic and air turbines. Were we to explore the hardware of all systems, we would find it an enormous job. Therefore we limit ourselves in the next four chapters to one class of control systems, and develop one specific system in detail. However, our work will be applicable to all linear control systems.

4.1 INSTRUMENT SERVOMECHANISMS

The class of systems we shall discuss is *instrument servomechanisms.* Servomechanisms are systems which control *position, speed,* or *accel-*

* It is a good idea to keep catalogs of one or two servo component manufacturers at hand to see how the component values of the next two chapters are derived from the manufacturer's specifications (see Appendix D).

72

eration. The automobile control system discussed in Chapter 1 kept the automobile in the proper position in the middle of the lane; we would therefore call this control system a servomechanism. We would also develop a speed control system and possibly an acceleration control system for a completely automatic automobile; each of these variables—position, speed, and acceleration—requires a servomechanism. Instrument servomechanisms are small servomechanisms—power output is usually less than 25 watts used to control, indicate, record, and compute. They are found in aircraft, missiles, satellites, machine tool controls, computers, and in industrial indicating, recording, and controlling instruments. Instrument servomechanisms may be operated pneumatically, hydraulically, or electrically; by far the largest percentage are electrical, or rather electromechanical. In this chapter we discuss the components of one particular type of electromechanical instrument servomechanism. In the following three chapters we will analyze this system and modifications of it in great detail to illustrate the general principles of control system analysis and design.

The instrument we shall "build" is a course recorder in an airplane (Fig. 4.1). The compass, which indicates the position of the plane, positions the pen of a course recorder by means of a servosystem which we shall design. The direction of the plane is recorded on paper which moves slowly underneath the recording pen. The paper has time divisions so that the course heading at any time can be determined from the record. The recorder is some distance away from the compass; therefore a flexible cable will not do the job. In addition, transmission of the signal by synchros only is inaccurate, since a load would be put on the receiving synchro. (Synchros are discussed later in this chapter.)

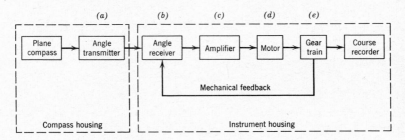

Fig. 4.1 Servo-operated course recorder.

Let us assume that the recorder span can be enlarged so that when the plane is on course the full scale of the instrument will be only a few degrees; one-tenth of a degree sensitivity is therefore desired. As shown in Fig. 4.1, to do this job we use (a) a small electrical component (transducer) to receive mechanical position (angle) information from the compass and to transmit a proportional electrical signal to the receiver, (b) a small electrical device in the recorder to receive the electrical angle information from (a) and convert it into a signal input to the amplifier (c), at the same time allowing for mechanical position feedback from the servomotor (d); (c) an amplifier to receive the signal from (b) and raise its power level so that the amplifier output can operate a servomotor as directed by the signal; (d) the servomotor and (e) the gear train which together position the recorder pen and reposition the angle receiver rotor (feedback path). The gear train reduces the fast-speed motor shaft down to the slower-speed output shaft, at the same time multiplying motor torque. In addition to these components, stability improvement devices such as a rate generator and servo-networks will be used. We discuss the components in order as we proceed from left to right across the block diagram in Fig. 4.1.

4.2 IMPEDANCE OF CONTROL COMPONENTS

The transfer function of the R-C network shown in Fig. 4.2 was calculated in Section 2.4:

$$\frac{E_{\text{out}}}{E_{\text{in}}} = \frac{1}{sT + 1} \tag{4.1}$$

This calculation was based on the assumption that the *same current* flowed through R and C. If there were a significant load resistance

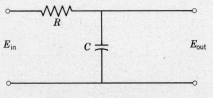

Fig. 4.2 *R-C* network.

across the E_{out} terminals, current would flow through this resistance, and the assumption on which our transfer function was based would be invalid, as would equation (4.1). This transfer function is correct only if there is infinite output impedance (an open circuit). Reasonable departures from this condition can be tolerated, and if E_{out} is the grid input to a vacuum tube, we can safely use our transfer function. But if a transistor amplifier were used, the input resistance would be a problem unless special precautions were taken in the design of the amplifier; for example, heavy feedback might be introduced in the first stage to raise the input impedance.

The transfer functions of all components in a system assume certain input and output impedances. The impedance relationship between adjacent items in the loop, such as the servoamplifier output and the motor it supplies, are also critical. This subject is discussed in Section 4.5 under ac servomotors. In general, the designer of a servo often has to make adjustments in his calculations because of nonideal impedances. This subject is covered very thoroughly in books on servocomponents, where extensive computations of normal and abnormal component impedances are made. These calculations are mostly straightforward circuit calculations and do not invalidate the control theory presented here. Therefore we proceed on the assumption that circuits and components have been adjusted for impedance so that transfer functions and manufacturers' catalog information may be used without any adjustments due to impedance mismatch.

4.3   TRANSMITTING AND ERROR-DETECTING COMPONENTS

Potentiometers

The potentiometers used in conjunction with servomechanisms are precision single- and multiturn devices of high accuracy (see Fig. 4.3). They can be used as transducers and as error detectors. A transducer "receives information in the form of one physical quantity and transmits this information in the form of another physical quantity." (ASA C85.1, 1963.) A precision potentiometer receives information in the form of mechanical angle, θ_{in}, of its wiper contact arm and transmits a proportional electrical signal, V_{out}, as shown in Fig. 4.4.

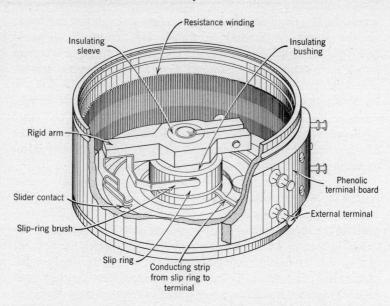

Resistance winding

Insulating
sleeve

Insulating
bushing

Rigid arm

Phenolic
terminal board

Slider contact

Slip–ring brush

External terminal

Slip ring

Conducting strip
from slip ring to
terminal

Fig. 4.3 Slider and slip-ring assembly forming typical electrical take-off
for potentiometer output. (Courtesy of Technology Instrument Corporation
of California, Subsidiary of Bowmar Instrument Corporation.)

Two potentiometers can be used in a bridge circuit which acts as
a transmitting-receiving and error-detecting component and is shown
in Fig. 4.5. The inputs to the bridge are the angular position of the
plane compass θ and the angular position of the servomotor ϕ. *Note
the dashed lines, which always represent mechanical connections.* These
inputs position the wiper arms and determine the voltages V_θ and

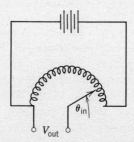

θ_{in}

V_{out}

Fig. 4.4 Potentiometer angle transmitter.

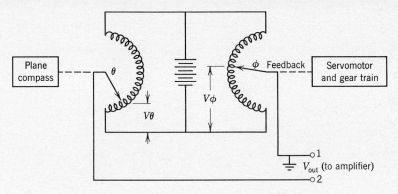

Fig. 4.5 Potentiometer transmitter-receiver bridge.

V_ϕ. The bridge output is a voltage $V_{out} = V_\theta - V_\phi$. The voltage V_{out} varies in amplitude and polarity. With the bridge as shown in Fig. 4.5, V_{out} terminal 2 is negative (terminal 1 is ground). If we leave the ϕ wiper arm where it is and turn the θ wiper arm up (counterclockwise) to the end of its travel, the voltage at the θ contact will be maximum positive, and V_{out} terminal 2 will likewise be positive. If both contacts are directly opposite each other, for example, both at the top or both in the center, then the output is zero. We therefore have the voltage possibilities shown in Fig. 4.6. If we set the ϕ wiper arm exactly in the middle of its travel and then move the θ wiper arm from bottom to top, the voltage output will be that shown in Fig. 4.7. (For clarity of explanation Fig. 4.5 shows only 180° total rotation, but a circular potentiometer may have 360° rotation.) Thus the *magnitude* of the V_{out} signal is a measure of the *angular difference* $\theta - \phi$ between the two potentiometer shafts. The *polarity* of the V_{out} signal is an indication of *direction*—clockwise or counterclock-

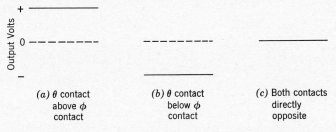

(a) θ contact above ϕ contact

(b) θ contact below ϕ contact

(c) Both contacts directly opposite

Fig. 4.6 V_{out} voltages of potentiometer bridge shown in Fig. 4.5.

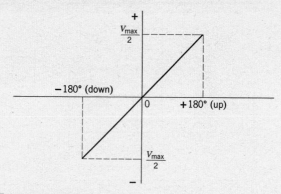

Fig. 4.7 Potentiometer bridge output voltage V_{out} with ϕ contact held at midpoint and θ contact moved as indicated.

wise. In a servomechanism we might have an amplifier feeding a dc motor field. By sensing the signal polarity, the amplifier causes the motor to turn in the proper direction; and sensing the signal amplitude, the amplifier causes the motor to turn at the proper speed. The direction is always toward reducing the error to zero, and when null is reached the signal becomes zero. If the system is stable, the motor stops the first time zero is reached or after a few overshoots.

In Fig. 4.8 we see the same situation as we did in Fig. 4.5, except that the battery has been replaced by a source of ac voltage. In Fig. 4.9*b* and *c* we see a phase reversal of 180°. V_{out} ac amplitude is a

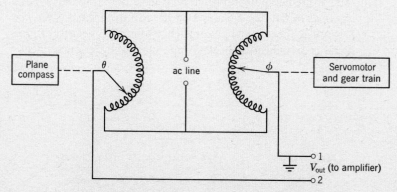

Fig. 4.8 Potentiometer bridge with ac excitation.

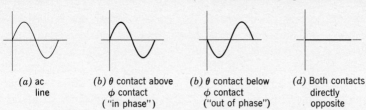

| (a) ac line | (b) θ contact above φ contact ("in phase") | (b) θ contact below φ contact ("out of phase") | (d) Both contacts directly opposite |

Fig. 4.9 V_{out} voltages of potentiometer bridge shown in Fig. 4.8.

measure of distance between wiper arms θ and ϕ, and V_{out} phase is a measure of direction. With the potentiometer bridge shown in Fig. 4.8, if the ϕ contact is at midpoint and θ contact is moved, we get the results shown in Fig. 4.10, which can be compared to Fig. 4.7. No longer is polarity the indicator of direction; instead phase reversal occurs as the θ contact is moved past the ϕ contact. With a phase-sensitive detector in the amplifier, the output of the amplifier can turn a servomotor clockwise for a signal in phase with the ac line Fig. 4.9b and counterclockwise for a signal 180° out of phase with the ac line Fig. 4.9c. As with dc excitation of the bridge, voltage amplitude determines speed of servomotor shaft turning. In Section 4.5 this action is explained.

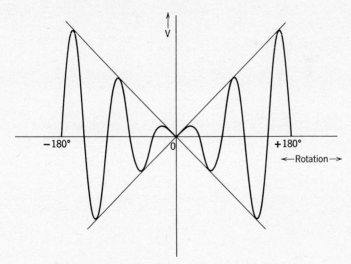

Fig. 4.10 Potentiometer bridge output voltage V_{out} with ϕ contact held at midpoint and θ contact moved as indicated.

We note that the ac system is a *carrier* system. An "envelope" contains the amplitude information, and the phase contains the direction information. This type of modulation is called *double-sideband suppressed-carrier*. It is worthwhile, as an experiment, to duplicate the hardware indicated in Fig. 4.8. As an ac low-voltage source, connect the secondary of a filament transformer to the ac line terminals. Two potentiometers, preferably of the same resistance, are connected as shown. An oscilloscope is tied to the V_{out} terminals. The waveshapes shown in Fig. 4.9 should be seen on the oscilloscope.

For the potentiometer-bridge block diagram we choose to include the entire bridge in one block (K_b) of the diagram, as shown in Fig. 4.11. The total bridge input is the angular error difference $\theta - \phi$ between the wiper arms of the two potentiometers. The bridge output is an error voltage V_{out} supplied to the next block, usually an amplifier. The potentiometer-bridge transfer function is therefore output/input = K_b V/deg or K_b V/rad, depending on whether $\theta - \phi$ is measured in degrees or radians.

Let us formalize a bit of control system algebra here. We have said that

$$\frac{\text{Output}}{\text{Input}} = \text{transfer function} \tag{4.2}$$

Algebraically this is the same as

$$\text{Input} \times \text{transfer function} = \text{output} \tag{4.3}$$

or more formally expressed,

$$\text{Excitation function} \times \text{transfer function} = \text{response function} \tag{4.4}$$

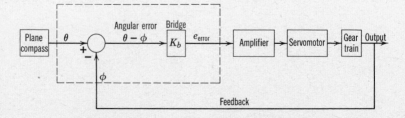

Fig. 4.11 Potentiometer bridge (inside dashed lines).

For our potentiometer bridge we have an *input* $(\theta - \phi)$, a *transfer function* K_b, and an *output* V_{out}. From equation (4.3) we have

$$(\theta - \phi) \deg \times K_b \frac{\text{volts}}{\deg} = V_{\text{out}} \qquad (4.5)$$

which shows that our dimensions combine to give the proper output—volts.

Synchros

There are two types of synchros: *torque* and *control*. The torque synchros are used to turn a remote shaft in synchronism with a nearby shaft when the remote synchro has to do work in turning the remote shaft. Control synchros transmit not work but information, and the remote or receiver synchro does no work except to overcome its own ball-bearing and brush friction.

Two control synchros—a transmitter and a receiver, usually called CX and CR, respectively—can be used to transmit shaft position information remotely by means of an electrical transmission system. Figure 4.12 shows a cutaway view of a commercial synchro. Note

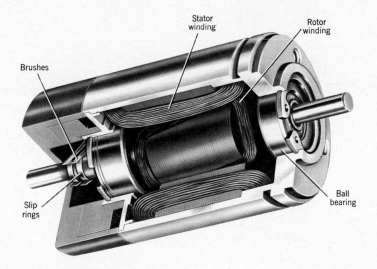

Fig. 4.12 Cutaway view of a typical synchro. (Courtesy Weston Instrument, Inc.; Transicoil Division.)

the stator windings: there are three of them 120° apart. There is
one rotor winding, as shown, and the ends of it are brought out
through the slip-rings and brushes shown at the left. Precision ball
bearings insure alignment of rotor in the housing and ease of turning. Wired as shown in Fig. 4.13, the synchros operate by means of
the currents circulating in the six stator windings and the magnetic
fields produced by these currents. The magnetic fields try to pull the
two rotors so that they point in the same direction. If one rotor is
held mechanically, the other rotor is pulled until it lines up with the
held rotor. For example, let us assume that in Fig. 4.13 the CX
rotor is turned 60° and held at that angle. The rotor thus held induces
circulating currents in the stator coils S_1, S_2, and S_3 of both CX
and CR. These currents produce a field pattern in the CR stator
which tends to pull the receiver rotor to the same position as the
transmitter rotor; note that the windings of both rotors are connected to the ac line. If unloaded, as control synchros always are, the
CR rotor will line up with the CX rotor with a very small error. If
there were a transfer function of such a synchro pair, it would be
only the losses, which are negligible for an unloaded receiver. Since
we start with shaft position and finish with the same shaft position,
there is no transfer function.

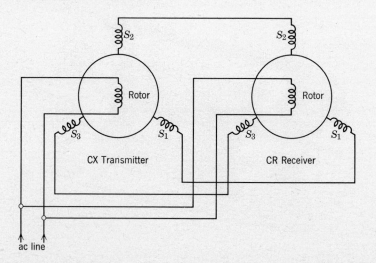

Fig. 4.13 Synchro pair schematic diagram. S_1, S_2, and S_3 stator windings.

The potentiometer bridge gives an output *voltage* proportional
to the difference in angle between the two potentiometer shafts. We
can accomplish the same thing with a control transmitter (CX) and
a *control transformer* (CT), as illustrated in Fig. 4.14. The CT rotor
is of different construction from the CX rotor and is not moved
by the magnetic fields. The CT rotor coil *senses* the fields, and its
rotor *voltage* is proportional to the *angular difference* between the
two synchro rotors. Using the CT rotor voltage as the output of the
CX–CT synchro pair, we can compare the potentiometer-bridge
output shown in Fig. 4.10 with the CX–CT pair output shown in
Fig. 4.15. The CX–CT pair output is a nonlinear function of angular
difference, but increases from null to plus or minus 90°. This output
is satisfactory because most position servos operate around a null
or zero voltage, and the servomotor moves full speed if the angular
difference voltage is more than a few per cent of full voltage. The
speed of the servomotor is proportional to small angular difference
voltages, but for any sizeable angular difference the motor reaches
full speed and the amplifier saturates.

The transfer function of the CX–CT synchro pair is a constant:

$$\frac{\text{Synchro-pair output}}{\text{Synchro-pair input}} = K_s \frac{\text{V}}{\text{deg}} \left(\text{or } \frac{\text{mV}}{\text{deg}} \text{ or } \frac{\text{V}}{\text{rad}}\right) \qquad (4.6)$$

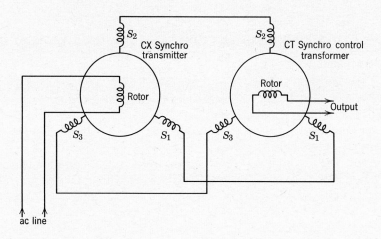

Fig. 4.14 Synchro transmitter—control transformer (CX–CT) pair schematic diagram.

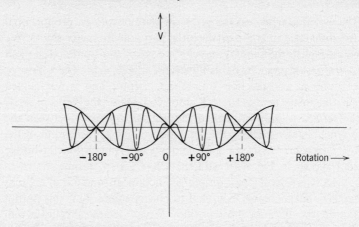

Fig. 4.15 Voltage output of CT rotor when CX rotor is held in a fixed position and CT is turned. If CT were held and CX turned, the CT output would be the same.

Oddly enough, this K_s is usually listed in manufacturers' catalogs as the sensitivity of the control transformer, not of the pair as it actually should be. The sensitivity of the CX when given is to be ignored when calculating the transfer function of a CX–CT synchro pair.

4.4 AMPLIFIERS, MODULATORS, AND DEMODULATORS

Servoamplifiers

Servoamplifiers are the heart of the servo loop. The amplifier is often the one "designable" element in the loop, and together with auxiliary circuits it may serve many functions such as phase shifting, compensating, and filtering. These functions are not inherent, however, in the amplifier's main function, which is to amplify the input signal. The bandwidth of a servoamplifier is usually far greater than that of the entire system, which often is a very low-frequency electromechanical device. Therefore the high-frequency cutoff point and phase shift of the servoamplifier need not be considered, because at the system frequencies the response of the amplifier is flat. Since the amplifier does only one thing—amplifies—its transfer function is a simple gain constant K_a (output volts/input volts).

The input impedance of a servoamplifier should be high so that it does not load the error detector. The amplifier output impedance should be very low to match the motor impedance. Dc servosystems would be used more often if good dc amplifiers were available, but dc amplifiers drift, that is, the output voltage is not stable. We therefore use ac amplifiers wherever possible, even when we wish to amplify dc signals.

Modulators and Demodulators

Many transducers—photoelectric cells measuring light, thermocouples measuring heat, and pH electrodes measuring acidity—produce dc voltages proportional to the quantity measured. To convert such a dc signal to ac so that we can use an ac amplifier, we use a *modulator*, shown in Fig. 4.16. Note the chopper (sometimes called a vibrator or converter) similar to the one in an automobile radio, but carefully made of precision parts. Inside the chopper a reed or contactor is vibrated at carrier or line frequency by the vibrating coil. The action of the modulator begins with dc applied to terminals 1 and 2. When the reed is in the "up" position, electron current flows up the upper half of the center-tapped input transformer primary winding. On the next half cycle the reed is in the "down" position, and current flows down the lower half of the winding. The input transformer's secondary winding first senses a flow of current up the primary winding, then a current down the primary winding. This action produces ac across the secondary winding.

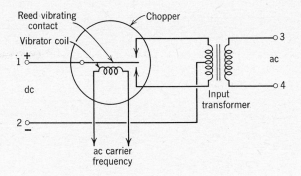

Fig. 4.16 Modulator (dc input, ac output). Demodulator (ac input, dc output).

The *demodulator* (Fig. 4.16) acts in the opposite manner, converting ac into dc. The vibrator coil must be in synchronism with the ac carrier or line frequency to produce a dc output; the coil is therefore fed from the same power source as the ac signal.

The transfer functions of the modulator and demodulator are simple constants and are, respectively,

$$K_m \frac{\text{ac V}}{\text{dc V}} \quad \text{and} \quad K_d \frac{\text{dc V}}{\text{ac V}}$$

4.5 SERVOMOTORS

DC Servomotors

Dc servomotors are used very little in low-power applications, such as instrument servomechanisms, because of dc amplifier drift problems mentioned in the preceding section, brush wear and replacement, commutator maintenance, radio-interference generation at the commutator, and their larger size and weight. In addition, ac servomotors are more rugged and less sensitive to shock and vibration.

AC Servomotors

We now develop the transfer function of an electromechanical device, the ac two-phase induction motor (or servomotor). As shown in Fig. 4.17, this motor is used extensively in control systems with one of its stator windings fed by the ac line, and the other by the output voltage of an ac amplifier. The input to the amplifier is a

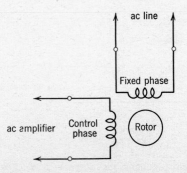

Fig. 4.17 Schematic diagram of ac servomotor.

control-signal voltage, often from a CX–CT synchro pair (see Section 4.3). When this control signal is applied to the amplifier, the servo-motor rotor revolves with a speed proportional to the signal voltage amplitude and in a direction determined by the signal voltage phase.

To increase the impedance of the control winding and decrease the current drain on the amplifier, a tuning capacitor is often added, as shown in Fig. 4.18. The addition of this capacitor results in a parallel resonant circuit, and the value of this capacitor is usually given in manufacturers' catalogs.

The ac servomotor is constructed as shown in Fig. 4.19. To reduce its moment of inertia, the squirrel-cage rotor is made longer and thinner than in the ordinary induction motor. Note that the rotor bars are skewed instead of being parallel to the shaft. This is common practice in all induction motors to avoid as much as possible the tendency of the motor to produce an uneven torque as the rotor bars move slowly through the magnetic field, causing slight bumpiness or "cogging." This unevenness also causes the servomotor to pull into a magnetically held position when with full voltage on the line winding, the voltage on the amplifier winding is slowly increased from zero volts. There is a minimum starting voltage called the *breakaway voltage* for every servomotor. We shall discuss the calculation of this voltage at length in Section 5.2 (see Fig. 5.2).

Let us analyze the stator and its production of a revolving magnetic field. Note that in Fig. 4.19 one of the four stator windings is cut away. The four windings are 90 mechanical degrees apart, and are connected as shown in Fig. 4.20. The relationship between the currents in the stator windings is shown in Figs. 4.21 and 4.22. Note that

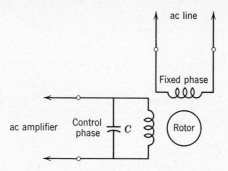

Fig. 4.18 AC servomotor with parallel tuning capacitor in control phase.

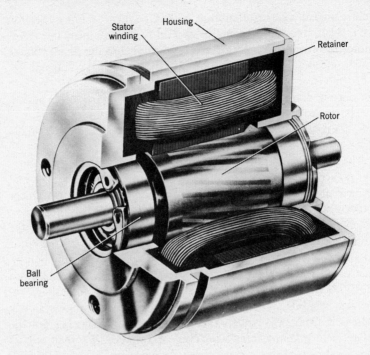

Fig. 4.19 Cutaway view of a typical servo control motor. (Courtesy Weston Instruments, Inc.; Transicoil Division.)

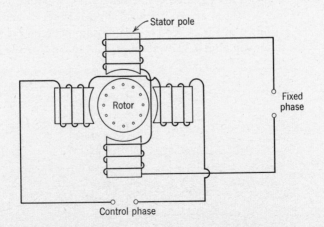

Fig. 4.20 Two-phase motor (connection diagram).

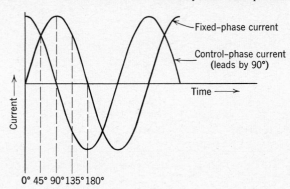

Fig. 4.21 Currents in stator windings of two-phase motor—phase displacement for counterclockwise rotation of rotor.

amplifier output current (control-phase current) always leads or lags by 90 electrical degrees the line or fixed-phase current. In Fig. 4.23 we see how a counterclockwise revolving magnetic field is set up by the stator windings fed by the currents shown in Fig. 4.21; the control-phase current *leads* the fixed-phase current by 90°. If we leave the fixed-phase current as is and at the same time supply the control-phase winding with a current 180° out from that shown in Fig. 4.21, this yields the currents shown in Fig. 4.22, with control-phase current *lagging* fixed-phase current by 90°. This reverses the control phase stator poles shown in Fig. 4.23 and causes a clockwise

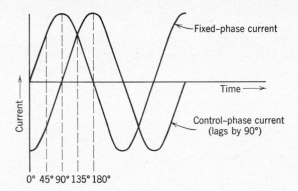

Fig. 4.22 Currents in stator windings of two-phase motor—phase displacement for clockwise rotation of rotor.

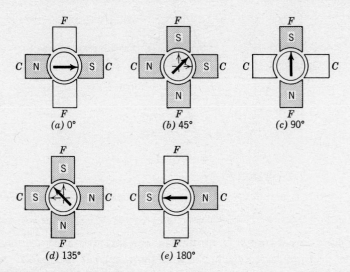

Fig. 4.23 Revolving field caused by changing stator currents when control-phase current leads by 90°, as shown in Fig. 4.21. (Key: N = North pole, S = South pole, C = control phase, F = fixed phase.)

revolving field, as the reader will find in Prob. 4.1. Most ac servomotors have a squirrel-cage rotor, which we know will have poles induced in it by the revolving field and will rotate somewhat more slowly than the revolving field because of the slip.

PROBLEM

4.1. Show by a series of sketches similar to Fig. 4.23 that the currents in Fig. 4.22 will result in a clockwise rotation of the magnetic field.

AC Servomotor Transfer Functions

We are now ready to develop our servomotor transfer function. A conventional induction motor with full voltage on the stator has a speed-torque curve R, shown in Fig. 4.24. R stands for rotor resistance of a typical power induction motor; $3R$ is a rotor resistance of $3 \times R$, and $8R$ is a rotor resistance of $8 \times R$. The resistance of a typical servomotor is $8R$, and this resistance results in the most linear speed-torque curve shown. An ordinary induction motor with rotor resistance R runs at almost full speed; this motor is designed to

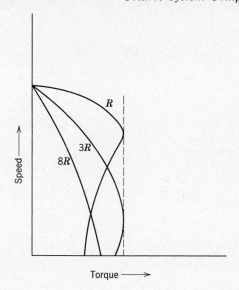

Fig. 4.24 Speed-torque characteristics of induction motors with various values of rotor resistance.

operate well above the *knee* of the curve, where the *pull-out torque* occurs. The typical servomotor, on the other hand, operates normally at nearly zero speed. The rotor turns only when an error occurs, and then, ideally, the motor quickly corrects the error. Servomotors therefore have speed-torque curves that are essentially linear, like the 8R curve in Fig. 4.24, with no "bulges" such as those in the R and 3R curves. In Fig. 4.25 we see the speed-torque curves of a typical servomotor with full voltage on the line or fixed-phase winding and four different voltages on the control-phase winding. Note the two zero points of the 100% control voltage curve. At the lower zero point of the curve we have zero speed and *stall torque L_s*; at the upper zero point, we have zero torque and *no-load speed* or *free speed ω_f*.

As we have discussed previously, the servomotor usually operates in both directions about a null, that is with a few volts (or even millivolts) plus or minus on the control-phase winding. If there is no error the motor remains at rest. When a slight but detectable error occurs, the motor goes to work at a low voltage and usually corrects the error before the voltage increases substantially. The

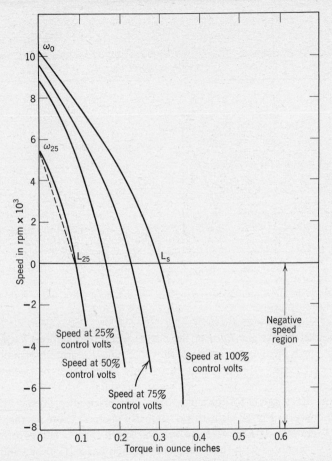

Fig. 4.25 Typical servomotor characteristics—full-line voltage on one winding.

ideal curve to represent these conditions would be the 0 volts curve, but this is very difficult to determine. And the 25% curve has almost the same slope as the 0 volts curve. For these reasons, most servomotor manufacturers include the 25% (or 20%) control volts curve in their catalogs. (If the 25% curve is not given, we will see later that we use $\frac{1}{2}$ the slope of the 100% control volts curve.)

The mathematical equation of the slightly bulging 25% control volts curve is difficult to calculate. We therefore simplify the mathematics by *linearizing* the curve, that is, we connect the two ends of the 25% curve by a straight line, the dashed line in Fig. 4.25.

The next step is to make all lines of Fig. 4.25 parallel to the 25% control voltage curve and evenly spaced. We note that the horizontal-axis intercept points (zero speed and stall torque) of the four curves in Fig. 4.25 are fairly evenly spaced, thus from these points we draw our lines parallel to the 25% line. The result is shown in Fig. 4.26.

Our linearization is now accomplished, and we can proceed to the problem of obtaining a transfer function for our motor. As we have seen, transfer functions are of the form output/input. What actuating or input signal do we put into our motor, that is, how do we *control* our motor? Usually the motor input is control-phase voltage that varies with the system error. (We do not consider the fixed-phase line voltage; it occupies a position similar to the power-

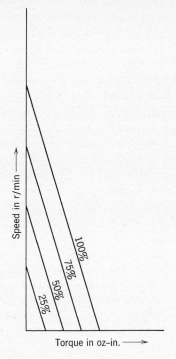

Fig. 4.26 Linearized servomotor speed-torque curves (based on the 25% curve of Fig. 4.25).

line connection to an electronic amplifier.) Our output could be of two sorts: speed or angular position. In most cases we use our servomotor to position a load—an antenna, a gun, an airplane flap, or a ship's rudder. Therefore we use the transfer function equation:

$$\frac{\text{Output}}{\text{Input}} = \frac{\text{angular displacement of motor rotor}}{\text{control-phase voltage}} = \frac{\text{radians}}{\text{volts}} = \frac{\theta}{E_c}$$

(4.7)

Let us look at Fig. 4.26 and consider motor torque, the turning force on the rotor and shaft. If we increase control-phase voltage from 25% to 75%, keeping speed constant, we increase torque. We can test this if we hold the rotor shaft between our fingers and slowly increase voltage; we can then feel the torque increasing. And if we hold control voltage constant, for example, along the 100% control volts line, we find a negative slope to our curve, that is, we get zero torque at full speed and maximum torque at zero speed. To test this, let us apply full-rated voltage to both windings with no-load on the motor. With the motor running at full speed, we can easily slow it down with our fingers, but we probably cannot stop the motor, because the torque increases as the speed decreases. Why does torque decrease with speed? Friction in the bearings is so slight as to be negligible, as are other mechanical losses. Since the loss is not mechanical, it must be electrical.

To test this theory we take a servomotor with no gear reduction or with the gears removed. We excite the stator fixed-phase winding with full-rated voltage, leave the control winding open circuited, and spin the rotor. We feel no opposition, no matter how fast we spin the rotor. But when we short the two ends of the control-phase winding, we get an entirely different result: the faster we turn the rotor, the more resistance we meet. There seems to be a viscous fluid like molasses between the rotor and the stator. The resistance we feel is due to the interaction between the magnetic fields of the rotor and the stator. The field in the rotor is caused by transformer action from the stator and by current produced by generator action as the rotor turns. This type of retarding force proportional to velocity is called *viscous friction*. In servomotors it is called *viscous damping*. Because it is electrical in nature, we use the symbol B_e for viscous damping. The torque due to viscous damping is: motor speed $\times$ damping $= \omega B_e$. This is a torque loss.

To gain familiarity with the procedure of calculating B_e, let us use Fig. 4.25. We find the values of ω_{25} and L_{25} at the two ends of the 25% curve; using an engineer's scale for measurement, we find

$$\omega_{25} = 5.3 \times 10^3 \text{ r/min (revolutions per minute)} \quad (4.8)$$

$$L_{25} = 0.084 \text{ oz-in.} \quad (4.9)$$

$$\therefore B_e = \frac{0.084 \text{ oz-in.}}{5.3 \times 10^3 \text{ r/min}} \times 6.74 \times 10^5 \frac{\text{dyn-cm/rad/sec}}{\text{oz-in./r/min}} \quad (4.10)$$

$$= 10.68 \text{ dyn-cm/rad/sec}$$

If the 20% or 25% voltage curve is not given, we can use the catalog values of ω_f and L_s, letting B_e equal $\frac{1}{2}$ of their quotient. For example, we have been given by the manufacturer for this motor

$$L_s = 0.25 \text{ oz-in. min} \quad \text{(min means minimum)} \quad (4.11)$$

$$\omega_f = 10{,}000 \text{ r/min} \quad (4.12)$$

$$B_e = \frac{1}{2} \frac{L_s}{\omega_f} \times 6.74 \times 10^5 = \frac{1}{2} \frac{0.25}{104} \times 6.74 \times 10^5$$

$$= 8.42 \text{ dyn-cm/rad/sec} \quad (4.13)$$

This value is somewhat smaller than 10.68. We would have been closer had we scaled the 100% line of Fig. 4.25 for our ω_f and L_s as follows:

$$B_e = \frac{1}{2} \frac{L_s}{\omega_f} = \frac{1}{2} \frac{0.3}{10.2} \times 6.74 \times 10^5 = 9.9 \text{ dyn-cm/rad/sec} \quad (4.14)$$

Sometimes the value of B_e is given in the catalog, where it is called damping or friction. For our motor the manufacturer gives for B_e a value of 16.8 dyn-cm/rad/sec; since this is double the actual value we halve it and get 8.4 dyn-cm/rad/sec. All values are not too far off, since our entire procedure is approximate. The most accurate method is to scale the graph using the 25% control volts line, which gave us a value of 10.68 dyn-cm/rad/sec.

We have not yet found how torque is produced in the motor, although it is logical to assume that it is produced by voltage applied to the control-phase winding. If we apply full-line voltage to the line winding and no voltage to the control-phase winding, the motor does not move. As we slowly increase the voltage on the control winding, the motor starts to move very slowly when we reach about 3% of rated control voltage. At this voltage we can easily keep the motor from turning by grasping the output shaft with our fingers, because the torque is very small. As we increase control winding voltage, it becomes more and more difficult to keep the motor from turning. From the original motor curves (Fig. 4.25) we see along the horizontal torque axis (zero speed) that between each per cent voltage intercept the stall torque increases the same amount. Assume we have the conditions shown in Fig. 4.27. If we look only at the horizontal axis, we can state that

$$\frac{\text{Stall torque}}{\text{Control voltage}} = \frac{20}{100} = \frac{15}{75} = \frac{10}{50} = \frac{5}{25} \qquad (4.15)$$

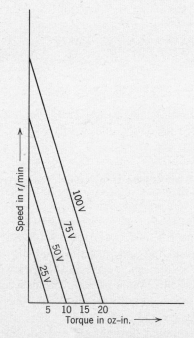

Fig. 4.27 Servomotor speed-torque curves.

showing that all values equal $\frac{1}{5}$ oz-in./V and giving us the right to say that some motor *torque constant*

$$K_{tm} = \frac{\text{stall torque at } 100\% \text{ control voltage}}{100\% \text{ control voltage}} = \frac{L_s}{e_c}$$

$$= \text{motor torque constant} \qquad (4.16)$$

Although equations (4.15) and (4.16) result in the equation

$$L_s = \text{motor } stall \text{ torque} = K_{tm} \times \text{control voltage} = K_{tm}e_c \quad (4.17)$$

the linearity of the curves in Fig. 4.26 enables us to state that equation (4.17) is true of *any* torque, not just stalled torque.

We now see that torque L *produced* by the motor is stall torque less motor viscous damping losses, or

$$L = K_{tm}e_c - B_e\omega = L_s - B_d\omega \qquad (4.18a)$$

The dimensions of equation (4.18a) are, using equations (4.16) and (4.13),

$$L = \frac{\text{torque}}{\text{voltage}} \times \text{voltage} - \frac{\text{dyn-cm}}{\text{rad/sec}} \times \text{rad/sec} = \text{torque} - \text{torque}$$

$$(4.18b)$$

since dyn-cm is a torque unit.

Torque is rotary force, and by Newton's third law ("to every action force there is an equal and opposite reaction force"), *produced* torque must equal torque *absorbed* by the motor and the load. Produced torque (a) accelerates the motor rotor and the load, and (b) is lost in overcoming the inertia and friction of the motor and the load. In instrument servomechanisms the motor is geared down and the load usually is insignificant; only inertia of the motor rotor and friction of the motor bearings constitute the countertorque. With this assumption of no appreciable load,

$$\text{Absorbed torque} = J\alpha + B_b \qquad (4.19)$$

where $\qquad J = $ moment of inertia of motor rotor

$\qquad\quad B_b = $ bearing friction

$\qquad\quad \alpha = $ angular acceleration

Now *produced* torque = *absorbed* torque; thus from equations (4.18) and (4.19) we have

$$K_{tm}e_c - B_e\omega = J\alpha + B_b\omega \qquad (4.20)$$

Equation (4.20) is in the time domain, and we must convert it to a Laplace transform equation. To do this we need more Laplace transform pairs, and these are given in Table 4.1.

Table 4.1 *Laplace Transforms of Rotational Quantities*

Time Function	Quantity	Units	Laplace Transform
e	Voltage	Volts	E
$\theta(t)$	Angular position	Radians	$\theta(s)$
ω	Angular velocity	Radians/second	$s\theta$
α	Angular acceleration	Radians/second^2	$s^2\theta$

If we use this table, equation (4.20) becomes

$$K_{tm}E_c - B_e s\theta = B_b s\theta + Js^2\theta \qquad (4.21)$$

K_{tm}, B, and J are constant factors and are unchanged by transformation from time functions to Laplace transform functions. B_b is negligible in a well-constructed motor with ball bearings. Letting $B_e + B_b = B$, a combined motor damping constant, equation (4.21) becomes

$$K_{tm}E_c = Bs\theta + Js^2\theta = \theta(Bs + Js^2) \qquad (4.22)$$

We said that our input to the motor was control-phase voltage E_c and that our output was angular displacement or position θ. Therefore our transfer function is

$$\frac{\text{Output}}{\text{Input}} = \frac{\theta}{E_c}$$

From equation (4.22) we find our transfer function

$$\frac{\theta}{E_c} = \frac{K_{tm}}{Bs + Js^2} \qquad (4.23)$$

This expression is fine, and is sometimes used, but generally we want our transfer functions in time-constant form. To accomplish this we divide both numerator and denominator of the right-hand side of equation (4.23) by B, which yields

$$\frac{\theta}{E_c} = \frac{K_{tm}/B}{s + Js^2/B} \tag{4.24}$$

This transfer function is now in time-constant form, because

$$\frac{J}{B} = T = \text{time constant in seconds} \tag{4.25}$$

We can prove that the dimensions or units of J/B are seconds, as follows:

$$\frac{J}{B} = \frac{\text{gm-cm}^2}{\dfrac{\text{dyn-cm}}{\text{rad/sec}}} = \frac{\text{gm-cm}}{\text{dyn-sec}} = \frac{\text{gm-cm}}{\dfrac{\text{gm-cm}}{\text{sec}^2} \times \text{sec}} = \text{sec} = T \tag{4.26}$$

(Radians are dimensionless and can be dropped.) Two very important servomotor constants are K_{tm}, the motor *torque* constant, and K_{vm}, the motor *velocity* constant. The dimensions of K_{tm} are torque/ volt, and of K_{vm} are speed/volt or velocity/volt, as can be shown.

$$K_{vm} = \frac{K_{tm}}{B} = \frac{\text{stall torque/rated control voltage}}{\text{stall torque/no-load speed}}$$

$$= \frac{\text{no-load speed}}{\text{rated control voltage}} \tag{4.27}$$

With $K_{tm}/B = K_{vm}$ and $J/B = T$, equation (4.24) becomes

$$\frac{\theta(s)}{E_c} = \frac{K_{vm}}{s + Ts^2} = \frac{K_{vm}}{s(1 + Ts)} \tag{4.28}$$

or

$$\frac{\theta(s)}{E_c K_{vm}} = \frac{1}{s(1 + Ts)} \tag{4.29}$$

with $\theta(s)$ spelled out in equations (4.28) and (4.29), because we want to be careful in inverse transforming it from a Laplace transform to a time function. By using Tables 2.1 and 4.1 we can transform equation (4.29) to

$$\frac{\theta(t)}{e_c K_{vm}} = 1 - e^{-t/T} \tag{4.30}$$

$$\frac{\theta(t)}{e_c K_{vm}} = \frac{\theta(t)}{e_c \dfrac{K_{tm}}{B}} = \frac{\theta(t)B}{e_c K_{tm}} = \frac{\theta(t)\dfrac{L_s}{\omega_f}}{e_c \dfrac{L_s}{e_c}} = \frac{\theta(t)}{\omega_f} \tag{4.31}$$

Combining equations (4.30) and (4.31) yields

$$\theta(t) = \omega_f(1 - e^{-t/T}), \quad T = J/B \tag{4.32}$$

with t the elapsed time in seconds, and ω_f the no-load speed.

Equation (4.32) describes an exponentially rising curve, with the time constant $T = J/B$, J being the inertia of the rotor mass and B the viscous friction. In one time constant the motor with no-load goes from rest to 63% of its full speed if full voltage is applied to both windings. The electrical analogy, the current in a series R-L circuit, is given in Section 2-3, as we can see by comparing equations (2.11) and (4.31). Inductance is very much like (analogous to) inertia, and resistance is analogous to friction. Therefore we would expect to find that the mathematics of the electrical and mechanical systems are similar. The Laplace transform enables us to handle the mathematics easily in both cases.

Three examples

When we look for the transfer function of a specific motor, we sometimes find it in the manufacturer's catalog along with other specifications. For example, one manufacturer gives the transfer function of a servomotor with full voltage (26 V) on the control phase

$$\frac{\theta}{E_c} = \frac{12.45}{s(1 + 0.0115s)} = \frac{K_{vm}'}{s(1 + T's)} \tag{4.33}$$

Thus their $K_{vm}' = 12.45$ rad/sec/V and their $T' = 0.0115$ sec. Note that K_{vm}, T, and B taken from the catalog have all had a prime added (K_{vm}', T', B'). We shall always use primes to indicate catalog incorrect values; unprimed values are correct or are values from the catalog that have been corrected. Thus we have

$$\text{Actual } B = \tfrac{1}{2} B' \quad \text{(catalog value)} \tag{4.34}$$

This is the slope error caused by the fact that a position servo operates around a null or very low control voltage, not around 100%

voltage on the control phase. Because of this error, we must change K_{vm}' and T' as follows:

$$K_{vm} = \frac{K_{tm}}{B} = \frac{K_{tm}}{B'/2} = 2\frac{K_{tm}}{B'} = 2K_{vm}' \qquad (4.35)$$

$$T = \frac{J}{B} = \frac{J}{B'/2} = 2\frac{J}{B'} = 2T' \qquad (4.36)$$

By using equations (4.35) and (4.36), we change the values of the transfer function in equation (4.33) to obtain a time constant $T = 2T' = 2 \times 0.0115 = 0.023$ sec and a motor velocity constant $K_{vm} = 2K_{vm}' = 2 \times 12.45 = 24.9$ rad/sec/V. We thus obtain a corrected transfer function

$$\frac{\theta}{E_c} = \frac{24.9}{s(1 + 0.023s)} = \frac{24.9}{s(1 + s/43.5)} \qquad (4.37)$$

(Most catalogs give transfer functions in terms of s. To draw Bode diagrams we substitute $j\omega$ for s.)

The Bode diagram of this transfer function, and therefore of the servomotor, is given in Fig. 4.28; the continuous lines show the phase and gain curves. This diagram tells us that the servomotor will "follow" slow commands in phase with the input, that the 3-dB down point is at $\omega = 3.5$ rad/sec or just over $\frac{1}{2}$ cycle per second. Therefore the motor has a bandwidth of 3.5 rad/sec, and at higher frequencies motor gain falls off rapidly and there is a large phase shift between input and output. We use the 3-dB down point for bandwidth as in electronic circuits and audio systems. The graphic Bode presentation similar to Fig. 4.28 shows us the frequency-response characteristics of the more complicated components. Furthermore, *a system transfer function is the product of the individual component transfer functions.* Because the Bode diagram gain curves are in decibels, we can *add* the curves of the components together. (The phase angle curves also add.) If we want to raise the bandwidth of the motor, we can lift the amplitude plot up parallel to itself by a K factor, usually supplied by an amplifier with a gain of K. The horizontal dashed line in Fig. 4.28 is the amplifier whose gain is 20 dB or 10. The motor with this amplifier added is raised by 20 dB and is also shown by a dashed line. (The amplifier response is "flat"—no attenuation—up to at least the right-hand edge of the

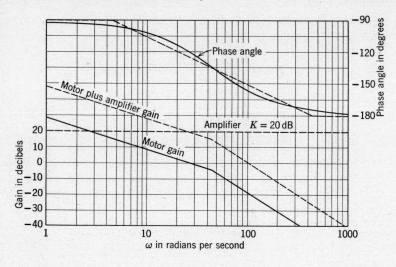

Fig. 4.28 Bode diagram of servomotor and amplifier. Motor transfer function:

$$\frac{\theta}{E_c} = \frac{24.9}{j\omega(1 + j0.023\omega)} = \frac{24.9}{j\omega(1 + j\omega/43.5)}$$

Motor + amplifier transfer function:

$$\frac{\theta}{E_c} = \frac{249}{j\omega(1 + j0.023\omega)} = \frac{249}{j\omega(1 + j\omega/43.5)}$$

Bode diagram—1000 rad/sec = 159 c/s—so we are correct in drawing its frequency-response curve as a straight line.) The new transfer function is increased by 20 dB or a gain of 10, thus equation (4.33) becomes

$$\frac{\theta}{E_c} = \frac{10 \times 24.9}{s(1 + 0.023s)} = \frac{249}{s(1 + 0.023s)} \tag{4.38}$$

The new bandwidth is 7 rad/sec, twice what it was before.

Not all manufacturers give the motor transfer function explicitly. Some give $K_{vm}{}'$ and T' in their specifications, and others do not. To get these constants for our motor transfer function we can take values from manufacturers' catalogs and use the equations

$$K_{tm}{}' = \frac{\text{stall torque in oz.-in.}}{\text{rated control voltage}} \times 72.01 \frac{\text{gm-cm}}{\text{oz.-in.}} = K_{tm}{}' \frac{\text{gm-cm}}{\text{V}} \tag{4.39}$$

$$T = 2T' = 2 \times \frac{\text{rotor inertia in gm-cm}^2}{\text{damping in dyn-cm/rad/sec}} = T \text{ sec} \quad (4.40)$$

$$K_{vm} = 2K_{vm'} = 2 \times \frac{\text{minimum no-load speed in r/min}}{\text{rated control-phase voltage}} \times \frac{2\pi}{60}$$

$$= K_{vm} \frac{\text{rad/sec}}{\text{V}} \quad (4.41)$$

$$B = \tfrac{1}{2}B' = \frac{1}{2} \frac{\text{stall torque in oz-in.}}{\text{no-load speed in r/min}} \times 6.74 \times 10^5 = B \frac{\text{dyn-cm}}{\text{rad/sec}}$$

$$(4.42)$$

Rotor inertia is also called *moment of inertia* and is usually given in gm-cm^2. If it is given in oz-in.^{2}, the value given must be multiplied by 1.829×10^2 gm-cm^2/oz-in.^{2}. Damping is also called *viscous damping, internal damping, friction coefficient,* and *damping coefficient.* Minimum no-load speed is sometimes called *minimum free speed.* If no-load speed is not given, it may be found from the graph of motor characteristics, and is our ω_f of Fig. 4.25. This value may be 10% higher than the minimum no-load speed, but we can tolerate this inaccuracy. After all, we have made too many assumptions along the way to worry about the third decimal point at this time.

Sometimes the transfer function is not given explicitly in the manufacturer's catalog, but the "raw material" is stated. This situation is covered in the following two examples based on actual constants given in two different catalogs.

Example 4.1. Given:

$$\text{Time constant} = T' = 0.0071 \text{ sec}$$

$$\text{No-load speed} = 6200 \text{ r/min}$$

$$\text{Control-phase voltage} = 26 \text{ V}$$

Then

$$T = 2T' = 0.0142 \text{ sec}$$

$$K_{vm} = 2 \times \frac{\text{no-load speed in r/min}}{\text{rated control voltage}} \times \frac{2\pi}{60}$$

$$= 2 \times \frac{6200}{26} \times \frac{2\pi}{60} = 49.9 \frac{\text{rad/sec}}{\text{V}}$$

$$\text{Transfer function} = \frac{\theta}{E_c} = \frac{K_{vm}}{s(1 + Ts)} = \frac{49.9}{s(1 + 0.0142s)}$$

Example 4.2. Given:

$$\text{No-load speed} = 10,000 \text{ r/min}$$

$$\text{Torque at stall} = 0.1 \text{ oz-in.}$$

$$\text{Rotor inertia} = 0.14 \text{ gm-cm}^2$$

$$\text{Control-phase volts} = 33 \text{ V}$$

Then:

$$B = \tfrac{1}{2} B' = \frac{1}{2} \frac{\text{stall torque in oz-in.}}{\text{no-load speed in r/min}} \times 6.74 \times 10^5$$

$$= \frac{1}{2} \frac{10^{-1}}{10^4} \times 6.74 \times 10^5$$

$$= 3.37 \frac{\text{dyn-cm}}{\text{rad/sec}}$$

$$T = \frac{J}{B} \frac{0.14}{3.37} = 0.042 \text{ sec}$$

$$K_{vm} = 2 \times \frac{10,000}{33} \times \frac{2\pi}{60} = 63.5 \frac{\text{rad/sec}}{\text{V}}$$

$$\text{Transfer function} = \frac{\theta}{E_c} = \frac{63.5}{s(1 + 0.042s)}$$

PROBLEMS

In the following problems it is assumed that the manufacturer has given viscous damping B' derived from the 100% control volts curve and that this value must be halved to obtain B. The transfer functions are based on the same curve, and must be corrected as indicated in Section 4.5, equations (4.33)–(4.42). *For drawing Bode diagrams of Laplace transforms (functions in s), substitute jω for s.*

4.2. Correct the following servomotor transfer function given by the manufacturer, and draw the complete Bode diagram (gain and phase curves.) In addition, give the bandwidth of the motor.

$$\frac{\theta}{E_c} = \frac{8.0}{s(1 + 0.038s)}$$

4.3. Correct the following servomotor transfer function given by the manufacturer, and draw the complete Bode diagram (gain and phase curves.) In addition give the bandwidth of the motor.

$$\frac{\theta}{E_c} = \frac{29.1}{s(1 + 0.050s)}$$

4.4. (*a*) With an amplifier whose gain is 10 dB added to the servomotor of Prob. 4.2, find the overall transfer function and draw the complete Bode diagram.

(*b*) Give the bandwidth of the motor and amplifier.

4.5. (*a*) With an amplifier whose gain is 15 dB added to the servomotor of Prob. 4.3, find the overall transfer function and draw the complete Bode diagram.

(*b*) Give the bandwidth of the motor and amplifier.

4.6. (*a*) Give the transfer function of the motor whose data is given by the manufacturer as:

$$\text{Time constant} = T' = 0.0156 \text{ sec}$$
$$\text{No-load speed} = 4800 \text{ r/min}$$
$$\text{Control voltage} = 36 \text{ V}$$

(*b*) Draw the complete Bode diagram of the motor.

4.7. (*a*) Give the transfer function of the motor whose data is given by the manufacturer as:

$$\text{Time constant} = T' = 0.026 \text{ sec}$$
$$\text{No-load speed} = 6500 \text{ r/min}$$
$$\text{Control voltage} = 26 \text{ V}$$

(*b*) Draw the complete Bode diagram of the motor.

4.8. (*a*) Give the transfer function of the motor whose data is given by the manufacturer as:

$$\text{Rotor inertia} = 0.50 \text{ gm-cm}^2$$
$$\text{No-load speed} = 6000 \text{ r/min}$$
$$\text{Stall torque} = 0.40 \text{ oz-in.}; \text{ control voltage} = 115 \text{ V}$$

(*b*) Draw the complete Bode diagram of the motor

4.9. (*a*) Give the transfer function of the motor whose data is given by the manufacturer as:

$$\text{Rotor inertia} = 1.4 \text{ gm-cm}^2$$
$$\text{Free speed} = 5900 \text{ r/min.}$$
$$\text{Stall torque} = 0.60 \text{ oz-in}$$
$$\text{Control-phase voltage} = 57.5 \text{ V}$$

(*b*) Draw the complete Bode diagram of the motor.

4.6 GEAR TRAINS

Servomotors are high-speed, low-torque devices. As shown in
Fig. 4.29, servomotor gear trains, between the motor output shaft
and the load shaft, are used to reduce speed and increase torque,
and in this process we often maximize power transfer from motor
to load. In Fig. 4.30 N_1 is the number of teeth on the input (primary)
gear, and N_2 the number of teeth on the output (secondary) gear.
Then for ratios of torque L, angular displacement θ, gear teeth N,
and speed ω,

$$\frac{L_1}{L_2} = \frac{\theta_2}{\theta_1} = \frac{N_1}{N_2} = \frac{\omega_2}{\omega_1} \qquad (4.43)$$

Gear trains are almost exactly analogous to electrical transformers.
In a transformer with turns ratio of primary to secondary N_1/N_2

$$\frac{E_1}{E_2} = \frac{I_2}{I_1} = \frac{N_1}{N_2} \qquad (4.44)$$

If we let $N_2/N_1 = N =$ turns ratio or gear ratio, the transfer function of a transformer would be

$$\frac{E_{\text{out}}}{E_{\text{in}}} = N \qquad (4.45)$$

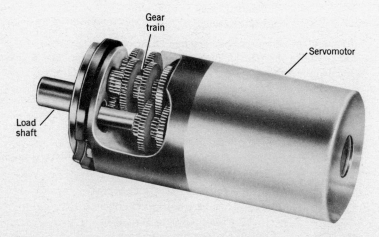

Fig. 4.29 Cutaway view of a typical servomotor and gear train unit.
(Courtesy Weston Instruments, Inc.; Transicoil Division.)

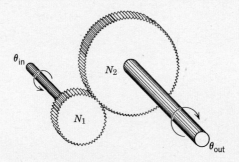

Fig. 4.30 Gear train.

and the transfer function of a gear train would be

$$\frac{\theta_{\text{out}}}{\theta_{\text{in}}} = \frac{1}{N} \tag{4.46}$$

which is the transfer function we shall use later.

4.7 COMPENSATORS

If a control system does not perform satisfactorily we can increase or decrease the gain of the amplifier. If by this technique we cannot achieve desired system performance without causing system instability, we use compensating devices to improve our system. These devices do not merely raise or lower the entire gain curve on the Bode diagram. They alter the *shape* of the gain and phase curves, and in so doing they usually enable us to stabilize our system.

Rate Generators or Tachometers

If we wish to measure the speed of a steam turbine, we can attach a generator with a linear output of $V/r/min$ to the output shaft of the turbine or of its gear reducer, and we read speed on a voltmeter whose dial is calibrated in revolutions per minute. In an instrument servomechanism we use a similar tachometer not to read motor speed but to produce a signal proportional to speed, and we feed this signal back to the amplifier input terminals to stabilize the servomechanism (see Fig. 5.5*a*). This tachometer or rate generator (Fig. 4.31) has a few special features. In order to reduce moment of

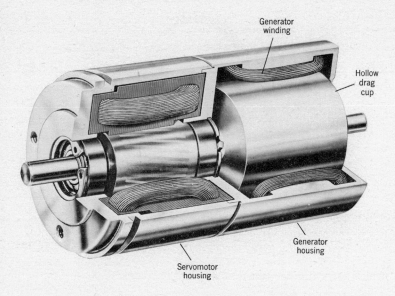

Generator
winding

Hollow
drag
cup

Generator
housing

Servomotor
housing

Fig. 4.31 Cutaway view of a typical servomotor and rate generator unit.
(Courtesy Weston Instruments, Inc.; Transicoil Division.)

inertia, the rotor is made in the form of a thin cup of aluminum or
other nonmagnetic material. When the cup is not rotating the stator
produces no output; as the cup rotates it magnetically couples one
pair of stator coils, which has line voltage applied to it, to another
pair of stator coils at an angle of 90° to the first pair. The output of
this second pair of coils is proportional to cup velocity. The cup shaft
is attached directly to the servomotor shaft in line with the motor
rotor. One integral housing is usually used for both motor and rate
generator.

The input to the rate generator is speed; the generator output is
a voltage (proportional to speed). Therefore we can say, letting
K_g = rate generator constant in V/1000 r/min

$$K_g \omega_{\text{in}} = e_{\text{out}} \tag{4.47}$$

and because ω transforms to $s\theta$ (see Table 4.1), the Laplace transform
of equation (4.47) is

$$K_g s \theta_{\text{in}} = E_{\text{out}} \tag{4.48}$$

Equation (4.48) gives us the transfer function

$$\frac{E_{\text{out}}}{\theta_{\text{in}}} = K_g s \tag{4.49}$$

In Chapter 5 we shall see how the rate generator is applied.

Servo networks

There are ac and dc servo networks. The dc networks are much simpler and easier to design; we have already developed an R-C network transfer function in Section 2.4. By the voltage divider method demonstrated there we develop transfer functions for more flexible networks used by servo designers. First let us discuss the phase-lag network, shown in Fig. 4.32. Assuming E_{in} to be a generator with negligible internal impedance, and assuming E_{out} to be into a load with almost infinite impedance, we have as our transfer function:

$$\frac{E_{\text{out}}}{E_{\text{in}}} = \frac{IZ_{\text{out}}}{IZ_{\text{in}}} = \frac{Z_{\text{out}}}{Z_{\text{in}}} = \frac{\dfrac{1}{sC} + R_2}{R_1 + \dfrac{1}{sC} + R_2} \tag{4.50}$$

$$= \frac{\dfrac{1 + sCR_2}{sC}}{\dfrac{sCR_1 + 1 + sCR_2}{sC}} = \frac{1 + sCR_2}{1 + sC(R_1 + R_2)} = \frac{1 + sT_1}{1 + sT_2} \tag{4.51}$$

where $T_1 = R_2 C$ and $T_2 = (R_1 + R_2)C$.

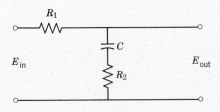

Fig. 4.32 Schematic drawing of phase-lag network.

The phase-lead network is shown in Fig. 4.33. The transfer function is

$$\frac{Z_{\text{out}}}{Z_{\text{in}}} = \frac{R_2}{\dfrac{R_1/sC}{R_1 + \dfrac{1}{sC}} + R_2} = \frac{R_2}{\dfrac{\dfrac{R_1}{sC} + \dfrac{R_2(sCR_1 + 1)}{sC}}{\dfrac{sCR_1 + 1}{sC}}}$$

$$= \frac{R_2}{\dfrac{R_1 + sR_2CR_1 + R_2}{sCR_1 + 1}} = \frac{R_2(sCR_1 + 1)}{R_1 + R_2 + R_1R_2sC}$$

$$= \frac{R_2(sCR_1 + 1)}{(R_1 + R_2)\left(\dfrac{R_1R_2}{R_1 + R_2} sC + 1\right)}$$

$$\frac{R_2}{R_1 + R_2}\frac{sT_1 + 1}{sT_2 + 1} \tag{4.52}$$

where $T_1 = R_1C$ and $T_2 = R_1R_2/(R_1 + R_2)C$. The factor $R_2/(R_1 + R_2)$ is a constant loss; the amplifier gain could be raised enough to cancel this loss, and the transfer function would not be affected.

When using these networks in an all ac system, a demodulator (Section 4.4) must be utilized before the network to convert the ac to dc; after the network, a modulator converts the dc back to ac. This is shown in Fig. 4.34.

There are also ac networks that are designed to operate only on the envelope of the ac suppressed-carrier signal, changing the amplitude and phase of both sidebands in equal amounts without affecting the carrier. For this purpose bridged T and twin T networks are used.

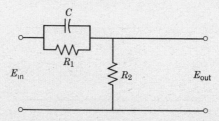

Fig. 4.33   Schematic drawing of phase-lead network.

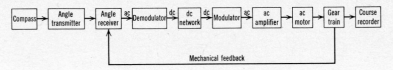

Fig. 4.34 A dc compensator network used in an ac system. (Compare with Fig. 4.1.)

PROBLEMS

Before solving the following problems, you may wish to refer to Fig. 5.7 in Section 5.6.

4.10. Given the phase-lag network transfer function

$$\frac{1 + j10\omega}{1 + j100\omega}$$

draw the Bode diagram of this network.

4.11. Given the phase-lag network transfer function

$$\frac{1 + j3\omega}{1 + j20\omega}$$

draw the Bode diagram of this network.

4.12. Given the phase-lead network transfer function

$$\frac{1 + j20\omega}{1 + j2\omega}$$

draw the Bode diagram of this network.

4.13. Given the phase-lead network transfer function

$$\frac{1 + j50\omega}{1 + j8\omega}$$

draw the Bode diagram of this network.

Viscous-Damped and Inertially Damped Motors

Instead of a winding on the stator of a rate generator we may install permanent magnets in place of the field coils. (See Fig. 4.31 with generator field coils replaced by permanent magnets.) Then as the motor rotor and the drag cup speed up, the viscous friction increases. At zero speed there is no friction, thus stall torque is unaffected, but we have now added another B term, changing the slope of our speed-torque curves. The motor time constant is decreased, bandwidth and corner frequency are raised. But we have added a load to the motor, thus decreasing efficiency, causing more heating, decreasing speed, and decreasing speed of correction of error. This is a viscous-damped servomotor, and because of its disadvantages its use is limited.

If we now allow the permanent-magnet assembly to rotate freely, we get an interesting improvement, the inertially damped servomotor (see Fig. 4.35). As the drag cup starts out, it pulls the magnet assembly with it, exerting an inertia force to slow down the motor change. However, at any steady speed the magnet rotates along with the rotor and has no effect. We can find the transfer function by first considering damping due to drag cup B_d, motor damping B, position of drag cup and motor θ, inertia of drag cup and motor J, and θ_m and J_m, position and inertia of magnet assembly, as shown in Fig. 4.36. Then $s\theta$ is the Laplace transform of the velocity of the motor and drag cup, and $s\theta_m$ is the Laplace transform of the velocity

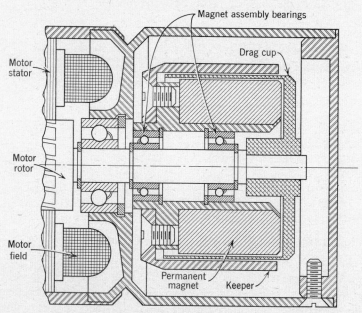

Fig. 4.35 Inertial damper added to servomotor. (Courtesy of Cedar Engineering Division, Control Data Corporation.)

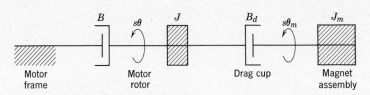

Fig. 4.36 Inertia-damped servomotor
B = Motor rotor viscous damping
J = Motor rotor inertia
B_d = Drag cup viscous damping
J_m = Magnet assembly inertia
$s\theta$ = Motor rotor velocity (Laplace transform)
$s\theta_m$ = Magnet assembly velocity (Laplace transform)

of the magnet assembly. Equation (4.22) of the uncompensated servomotor now has added to it the torque of the drag cup, which is proportional to the difference of velocity between the motor and the magnet assembly. The intertia-damped motor equation then is

$$K_{tm}E_c = Bs\theta + Js^2\theta + B_d(s\theta - s\theta_m) \qquad (4.53)$$

When the motor starts to turn there are two torques on the accelerating magnet assembly: the drag cup tends to accelerate it and the magnet inertia to decelerate it. Since these forces are equal (Newton's third law), we have

$$B_d(s\theta - s\theta_m) = J_m s^2\theta_m \qquad (4.54)$$

Substituting this in equation (4.53) we get

$$K_{tm}E_c = Bs\theta + Js^2\theta + J_m s^2\theta_m \qquad (4.55)$$

Comparing this equation with (4.22) we see that we indeed have added *damping* due to the *inertia* of the magnet assembly, but only as long as the magnet assembly is accelerating. When the assembly is fully accelerated, that is, traveling at the same speed as the drag cup and the motor rotor, $s^2\theta_m$ becomes zero, as does the term $J_m s^2\theta_m$.

We now solve equation (4.54) for θ_m and find

$$\theta_m = \frac{B_d\theta}{B_d + J_m s} \qquad (4.56)$$

Substituting this in equation (4.55) we obtain

$$K_{tm}E_c = Bs\theta + Js^2\theta + J_m s^2 \frac{B_d\theta}{B_d + J_m s}$$

$$= \frac{BB_d s\theta + BJ_m s^2\theta + JB_d s^2\theta + JJ_m s^3\theta + J_m B_d s^2\theta}{B_d + J_m s} \quad (4.57a)$$

Solving for θ/E_c, the transfer function becomes

$$\frac{\theta}{E_c} = \frac{K_{tm}(B_d + J_m s)}{s(BB_d + JB_d s + J_m B_d s + J_m B_s + JJ_m s^2)} \quad (4.57b)$$

If we divide numerator and denominator by BB_d we find

$$\frac{\theta}{E_c} = \frac{\dfrac{K_{tm}}{B}\left(1 + \dfrac{J_m}{B_d}s\right)}{s\left(1 + \dfrac{Js}{B} + \dfrac{J_m s}{B} + \dfrac{J_m s}{B_d} + \dfrac{JJ_m s^2}{B_d B}\right)} \quad (4.57c)$$

This transfer function can be factored into the form

$$\frac{\theta}{E_c} = \frac{K_{vm}(1 + sT_2)}{s(1 + sT_1)(1 + sT_3)} \quad (4.58)$$

where T_1, T_2, T_3, have approximately the following values:

$$T_1 = \frac{J_m}{B_d} + \frac{J_m}{B}, \quad T_2 = \frac{J_m}{B_d}, \quad T_3 = \frac{J}{B + B_d} \quad (4.59)$$

This motor simplifies the circuitry and provides a good way to stabilize a system. Unfortunately, the three time constants are fixed and cannot be adjusted in the field, as in a series network. Different motors of the same size but with different time constants are available. The response to a step function input is one enormous initial overshoot than can be tolerated in some systems, such as a dial-pointer position servo. This motor can be used on our course recorder since sudden (step) changes in course are not made in flight. After the initial overshoot the motor settles down very rapidly, as shown in Fig. 4.37. Note the three different *settling times* T_1, T_2, and T_3. Settling time is the time it takes after a step change for the output to enter and remain within a specified narrow band (indicated in Fig. 4.37 by the horizontal dashed lines). The inertia-damped

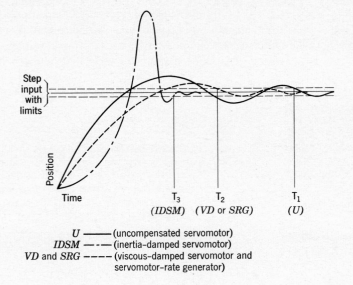

Fig. 4.37 Transient response of servomotors, including inertially damped (with large overshoot). (Courtesy of Beckman Instruments, Inc., Helipot Division.)

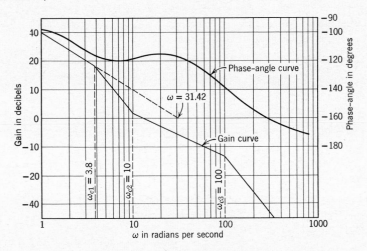

Fig. 4.38 Bode diagram of inertia-damped motor.

$$\frac{\theta}{E_c} = \frac{31.42(1 + j0.1\omega)}{j\omega(1 + j0.267\omega)(1 + j0.001\omega)} = \frac{31.42(1 + j\omega/10)}{j\omega(1 + j\omega/3.8)(1 + j\omega/100)}$$

motor settles out first (T_3), followed by the velocity-damped motor or servomotor-rate generator (T_2), and the servomotor settles out last (T_1). The use of inertia-damped servomotors, often abbreviated IDSM, is increasing. The Bode diagram of an IDSM is given in Fig. 4.38.

Table 4.2 summarizes the transfer functions we developed in this chapter.

Table 4.2 *Summary of Component Transfer Functions*

Component	Transfer Function	Dimensions
Potentiometer	$\dfrac{E_{\text{out}}}{\theta_{\text{in}}} = K_p$	V/deg or V/rad
Synchro pair (CX–CT)	$\dfrac{E_{\text{out}}}{\theta_{\text{in}}} = K_s$	V/deg or V/rad
Amplifier	$\dfrac{E_{\text{out}}}{E_{\text{in}}} = K_a$	
Modulator	$\dfrac{E_{\text{out}}}{E_{\text{in}}} = K_m$	acV/dcV
Demodulator	$\dfrac{E_{\text{out}}}{E_{\text{in}}} = K_d$	dcV/acV
AC servomotor	$\dfrac{\theta_{\text{out}}}{E_{\text{in}}} = \dfrac{K_{vm}}{s(1 + sT_m)}$	deg/V or rad/V
Gear train	$\dfrac{\theta_{\text{out}}}{\theta_{\text{in}}} = \dfrac{1}{N}$	
Rate generator	$\dfrac{E_{\text{out}}}{\theta_{\text{in}}} = K_g s$	V/1000 r/min or V/rad/sec
Servo networks Lag	$\dfrac{E_{\text{out}}}{E_{\text{in}}} = \dfrac{1 + T_1 s}{1 + T_2 s}$	
Lead	$\dfrac{E_{\text{out}}}{E_{\text{in}}} = \dfrac{1 + T_1 s}{1 + T_2 s}$	
Viscous-damped servomotor	$\dfrac{\theta_{\text{out}}}{E_{\text{in}}} = \dfrac{K_{vm}}{s(1 + sT_m)}$	deg/V or rad/V
Inertially damped servomotor	$\dfrac{\theta_{\text{out}}}{E_{\text{in}}} = \dfrac{K_{vm}(1 + sT_2)}{(1 + sT_1)(1 + sT_3)}$	deg/V or rad/V

PROBLEMS

4.14. The transfer function of an inertially damped servomotor is

$$\frac{K_{vm}(1 + j\omega T_2)}{j\omega(1 + j\omega T_1)(1 + j\omega T_3)}$$

Given that

$T_1 = 4.2$ sec
$T_2 = 10$ sec
$T_3 = 120$ sec
Minimum no-load speed = 6200 r/min
Rated control phase voltage = 26 V
(Use equation (4.41) to find K_{vm})

Find the servomotor transfer function and draw the Bode diagram.

4.15. The transfer function of an inertially damped servomotor is

$$\frac{K_{vm}(1 + j\omega T_2)}{j\omega(1 + j\omega T_1)(1 + j\omega T_3)}$$

Given that

$1/T_1 =$ Corner frequency $\omega_{c1} = 3.8$ rad/sec
$1/T_2 =$ Corner frequency $\omega_{c2} = 10$ rad/sec
$1/T_3 =$ Corner frequency $\omega_{c3} = 100$ rad/sec
Minimum no-load speed = 6000 r/min
Rated control phase voltage = 40 V
(Use equation (4.41) to find K_{vm})

Find the servomotor transfer function and draw the Bode diagram.

4.8 SYSTEM TRANSFER FUNCTIONS AND BODE DIAGRAMS

In Section 4.5 we stated that the system transfer function is the *product* of the individual component transfer functions. For the system shown in Fig. 5.1 (Chapter 5), we take the product of the component transfer functions given in Fig. 5.1c. We thus get the *system* open-loop transfer function

$$K_s \times K_a \times \frac{K_{vm}}{s(1 + T_m s)} \times \frac{1}{N} = \frac{K_s K_a K_{vm}}{s(1 + T_m s)N} \qquad (4.60)$$

Given the values

Synchro pair constant $K_s = 22.5$ V/rad
Amplifier constant $K_a = 150$

Motor velocity constant $K_{vm} = 5.64 \dfrac{\text{rad/sec}}{\text{V}}$ (corrected)

Motor time constant $T_m = 0.0153$ sec (corrected)
Gear ratio $N = 100$

we calculate the system transfer function as follows:

$$\frac{K_s K_a K_{vm}}{s(1 + T_m s)N} = \frac{22.5 \times 150 \times 5.64}{s(1 + 0.0153s)100}$$

$$= \frac{190}{s(1 + 0.0153s)} = \frac{190}{s(1 + s/65.4)} \qquad (4.61)$$

We substitute $j\omega$ for s in this transfer function and then draw the Bode diagram (shown as Case III in Fig. 5.4).

In Section 3.6 we learned that one criterion of stability is phase margin, which is 180° minus the phase angle at gain crossover frequency, the frequency at which the gain crosses the zero decibel line. We also learned that the phase margin should be between 40° and 60°, corresponding to phase angles between 140° and 120°, respectively. The phase margin of Case III in Fig. 5.4 is about 30°. Since this indicates an unstable system, we must use compensation. One way of doing this is to add a lead network.

Compensated by a network the system block diagram is given in Fig. 5.8. We assume no losses in the modulator and demodulator. Therefore the constants $K_m = K_d = 1$ have no effect on the system and are therefore omitted from the system transfer function, which is

$$\frac{K_s K_a K_m (1 + jT_1\omega)}{j\omega(1 + j\omega T_m)(1 + jT_2\omega)N} \qquad (4.62)$$

If the lead network shown in Fig. 4.33 is used with the values

$$\frac{1 + j0.02\omega}{1 + j0.002\omega} = \frac{1 + j\omega/50}{1 + j\omega/500} \qquad (4.63)$$

the system transfer function becomes

$$\frac{K_s K_a K_m (1 + jT_1\omega)}{j\omega(1 + j\omega T_m)(1 + jT_2\omega)} = \frac{190(1 + j0.02\omega)}{j\omega(1 + j0.0153\omega)(1 + j0.002\omega)} \qquad (4.64)$$

The Bode diagram of this compensated system transfer function is shown in Fig. 5.10. The phase margin of this Bode diagram is about 65°. If this system does not meet specifications, it is easy to raise the gain of the amplifier. By this means we can raise the gain curve up until the phase margin is about 50°, for example, and then the system will have a larger bandwidth and less error. In actual practice this usually means adjustment of the amplifier gain potentiometer by a small screwdriver until system performance is just right. By adding compensation we have made an unstable and unusable system meet all our specifications.

PROBLEMS

4.16. For the transfer function given in equation (4.60) and repeated below

$$\frac{K_s K_a K_{vm}}{s(1 + T_m s)N}$$

use the following values given by the manufacturer of the servomotor:

$K_s = 22.4$ V/rad
$K_{vm}' = 20\,(\text{rad/sec})/\text{V}$
$T_m' = 0.015$ sec
$N = 2000$

and let $\qquad\qquad\qquad K_a = 225$

Correct K_{vm}' and T_m' (equations (4.35) and (4.36)), and from the resulting transfer function draw the Bode diagram (gain and phase curves) of the system. What is the phase margin of the system? Is this a stable system?

4.17. For the transfer function given in equation (4.60) and repeated below

$$\frac{K_s K_a K_{vm}}{s(1 + T_m s)N}$$

use the following values given by the manufacturer of the servomotor:

$K_s = 22.4$ V/rad
$K_{vm}' = 20\,(\text{rad/sec})/\text{V}$
$T_m' = 0.045$ sec
$N = 1000$

and let $\qquad\qquad\qquad K_a = 300$

Correct K_{vm}' and T_m' (equations (4.35) and (4.36)), and from the resulting transfer function draw the Bode diagram (gain and phase curves) of the system. What is the phase margin of the system? Is this a stable system?

4.18. For the lead-network compensated system transfer function given in equation (4.62) and repeated below

$$\frac{K_s K_a K_{vm}(1 + jT_1\omega)}{j\omega(1 + jT_m\omega)(1 + jT_2\omega)N}$$

and given the same values as Prob. 4.16 plus

$T_1 = 0.03$ sec
$T_2 = 0.003$ sec

find the compensated system transfer function. Draw the Bode diagram (gain and phase curves) of the compensated system. What is the phase margin of this system? Can the gain of the system be raised 10 dB without causing system instability?

4.19. For the lead-network compensated system transfer function given in equation (4.62) and repeated below

$$\frac{K_s K_a K_{vm}(1 + jT_1\omega)}{j\omega(1 + jT_m\omega)(1 + jT_2\omega)N}$$

and given the same values as Prob. 4.17 plus

$T_1 = 0.03$ sec
$T_2 = 0.003$ sec

find the compensated system transfer function. Draw the Bode diagram (gain and phase curves) of the compensated system. What is the phase margin of this system? Can the gain of this system be raised 10 dB without causing system instability?

SUMMARY

In this chapter we developed transfer functions of instrument servomechanism components. In the preceding section we saw how these component transfer functions are combined to give system transfer functions. In Chapter 5 we will construct a mathematical model of a typical system and analyze it for error, speed of response, sensitivity, and stability. Since the system that we "build" proves to be unstable, we will compensate it so that it becomes stable and still meets our specifications.

5.

Design of a control system

Here we begin to design the system that was shown in Fig. 4.1 and was described in Section 4.1 (which should be reread at this time). We first choose components of the proper size and characteristics. The transfer functions of the components are then used to get the system transfer function, from which the system Bode diagram is drawn. Both closed-loop and open-loop diagrams are drawn. From an analysis of these diagrams we see the system's shortcomings, and by the use of compensation devices we improve the system. This is a typical procedure of the control system designer.

The instrument we are to design, the airplane course recorder, is shown in Fig. 5.1. In this instrument servomechanism the compass positions the control transmitter rotor to the plane's heading. The difference in mechanical angle between the control transmitter rotor and the control transformer rotor is converted to voltage, which appears across the control transformer rotor terminals and is the input to the amplifier. The amplifier raises the voltage and power of the input signal and delivers the proper output to the motor control phase. The motor converts voltage to torque, which results in mechanical motion of the motor rotor, the gears, and the course recorder pen, which is the load. At the same time the motor repositions the control transformer rotor to close the loop by mechanical feedback.

5.1   CHOICE OF COMPONENTS AND ANALYSIS OF SYSTEM PERFORMANCE

The components available to us are listed in the manufacturer's catalog. Small precision electromechanical components for military

121

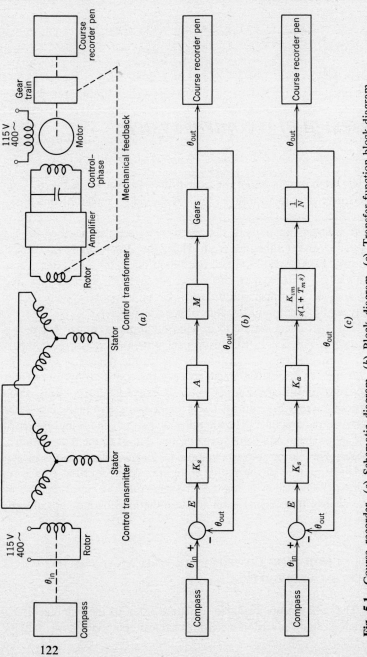

122

Fig. 5.1 Course recorder. (*a*) Schematic diagram. (*b*) Block diagram. (*c*) Transfer function block diagram.

and aircraft use are standardized by military and SAE (Society of Automotive Engineers) specifications. In these specifications the size of motor, synchro, gearhead, or other rotating component is the maximum outside diameter in tenths of an inch; size 8 means less than 0.800 in., actually 0.750 in.; size 11 units are 1.062 in. in outside diameter. For our instrument we choose a size 11 motor, because the output is adequate for the load. The recorder pen is very light and well balanced so that it rests lightly on the paper. The result is very little friction and inertia in our load—so little that when the load is driven by the motor through a step-down gear train with a large ratio such as 100 to 1, the pen load is negligible in inertia and viscous friction compared to the motor's own viscous friction and the inertia of the motor rotor. We will use the 400-cycle power supply of the plane for all our electrical components.

In choosing the error detector we have two alternatives. We might use the least expensive system, two potentiometers in a bridge circuit (shown in Fig. 4.5). A number of shortcomings soon appear when this choice compared to the more expensive control transmitter-control transformer (CX–CT) synchro pair alternative shown in Fig. 4.14. The potentiometers having higher torque requirements and possibly requiring a larger motor are not as accurate, do not produce an electrical signal for the full 360° of travel because of the gap between the ends of the resistance element, and have resolution problems due to the turn-to-turn movement of the wiper contact. Besides avoiding these disadvantages, synchros have longer life, require less maintenance, and have almost no noise problems. We choose a size 11 synchro transmitter and control transformer simply because the size is adequate. The transfer function K_s of this synchro pair (see Section 4.2 and equation (4.6)) is listed in the manufacturer's catalog as control transformer sensitivity, and its value is given as 0.393 V/deg.

5.2   SYSTEM SPECIFICATIONS

Dead Band

Naturally we desire a fairly accurate system, and we specify a *dead band* of 0.2 deg. Dead band is defined in ASA C85.1 (1963) as " . . . the range through which an *input* can be varied without initiating response." To understand what this means we note that with full voltage on the line or fixed phase winding of a servomotor and zero volts on the control phase, the rotor will not turn. If the control phase voltage is increased slowly, at some value of voltage the rotor will start to turn. If we reverse the polarity of the voltage the same thing will happen, but the rotor will turn in the reverse direction.

This is clearly shown in Fig. 5.2. If the motor were perfect, it would reverse with no dead band, and our graph would be a straight line through the origin. The motor starting voltages are V_1 and V_2 at either side of the dead band. The dead band is due to magnetic lock or "cogging" (see Section 4.5), and to gear train and load friction. For a precision servomotor with a well-designed gear train the value of starting voltage is about 5% of the rated voltage: $2\frac{1}{2}\%$ to overcome motor static friction and magnetic effects, and $2\frac{1}{2}\%$ to overcome gear-train friction. The rated control phase voltage is 115 V, so we will need $0.05 \times 115 = 5.75$ V to start the motor in either direction. We can therefore turn our synchro transmitter a certain very small angle both sides of zero degrees and create a voltage (in the control transformer rotor), which even when amplified will not exceed the 5.75 V necessary to start the motor turning. This very small angle

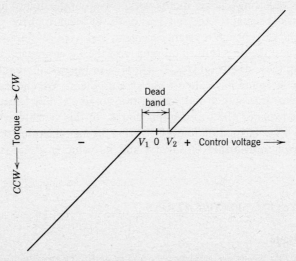

Fig. 5.2 Dead band of a servomotor. (Full voltage on the fixed or line winding; variable voltage on the control winding.) $V_2 = -V_1 =$ motor starting voltage.

is a function of the control transformer *sensitivity* in volts per degree, the amplifier gain, and the motor starting voltage. Twice the angle is the dead band.

2 × motor starting voltage
   = dead band × control transformer sensitivity × amplifier gain.

$$(5.1)$$

Since we have decided on all values except amplifier gain, we solve the rearranged equation.

$$\text{Amplifier gain} = \frac{2 \times \text{motor starting voltage}}{\text{dead band} \times \text{control transformer sensitivity}}$$

$$= \frac{2 \times 5.75 \text{ V}}{0.2 \text{ deg} \times 0.393 \text{ V/deg}} = 146 \approx 150 \qquad (5.2)$$

We shall use the approximate value of 150 for the gain of our amplifier.

Before deciding on a specific gear reduction let us analyze our system with three different gear trains. In so doing we keep in mind the objectives for our system: *accuracy*, *speed of response*, and *stability*. Our system accuracy will be 0.2 deg. dead band plus other inaccuracies. Any errors in the synchro transmitter–control transformer pair will not be erased by our feedback system. The catalog says that each of these synchros has an accuracy of 10 min. Assuming the worst, we will have a system dead band of 0.2 deg. or 12 min., plus a possible transmitter error of 10 min., plus a possible control transformer error of 10 min. giving us a total possible error of 32 min., about half a degree.

Response Time

Response time tells us how long it will take to correct any error that the system recognizes and tries to correct. Primarily this is a function of speed of the motor in correcting an error. The first speed of response factor we find is the *velocity error coefficient* or *velocity lag error*, whose dimensions are degrees per revolutions per minute; in other words, we find the size of the error in degrees necessary to turn the motor at a speed of one revolution per minute. The second speed of response factor is the *rise time*, or time of instrument while correcting error to travel from 10% to 90% of its final position.

The third factor in speed of response is *settling time*. Any sensitive instrument usually will overshoot the correct position and oscillate about the point before settling down. This effect may be so slight as to be hardly noticeable, but it may also be so pronounced as to slow up the process of indicating or recording the true value of the variable being measured. The velocity error coefficient, rise time, and settling time thus determine *response time*.

Stability

Stability has been the subject of most of our investigations thus far. In seeking high accuracy and fast response time, we often find instability: slight continuous hunting or oscillations (pen "jittery"), or too lively a pen or pointer when coming to the point of measurement resulting in many overshoots of the pen before it settles down. We may even find complete instability in the form of increasing and uncontrollable oscillations. We will find many stability criteria.

5.3 CONTROL SYSTEM ANALYSIS BY CLOSED-LOOP FREQUENCY RESPONSE

We have so far in our Bode diagrams analyzed open-loop transfer functions only. We did this because graphing open-loop functions is much simpler than graphing closed-loop functions. From these open-loop graphs or Bode diagrams we have been able to analyze control system performance. But our systems are almost always closed loop, and it is time we graphed them as they are. We will then see what we can learn from these closed-loop frequency-response gain and phase diagrams that we could not determine from the open-loop Bode diagrams.

We begin by finding our open-loop transfer function. In Fig. 5.1c the transfer functions of each of the components of our system are shown. Ignoring the feedback loop, the forward (open-loop) function is the product of the component transfer functions (Section 4.8).

$$\theta_{out} = EK_sK_a \frac{K_{vm}}{s(1 + T_ms)} \frac{1}{N} = \frac{EK_sK_aK_{vm}/N}{s(1 + T_ms)} \qquad (5.3)$$

$$\frac{\theta_{out}}{E} = \frac{K_sK_aK_{vm}/N}{s(1 + T_ms)} = \frac{K_v/N}{s(1 + T_ms)} \qquad \text{(letting } K_v = K_sK_aK_{vm}) \quad (5.4)$$

With the feedback loop included, we see from the first block that

$$E = \theta_{in} - \theta_{out} \tag{5.5}$$

Combining equations (5.4) and (5.5) gives

$$\frac{\theta_{out}}{\theta_{in} - \theta_{out}} = \frac{K_v/N}{s(1 + T_m s)} \tag{5.6}$$

We must solve for θ_{out}/θ_{in} to find the closed-loop transfer function.

$$\theta_{out} = \frac{K_v/N}{s(1 + T_m s)} \theta_{in} - \frac{K_v/N}{s(1 + T_m s)} \theta_{out} \tag{5.7}$$

$$\theta_{out}\left(1 + \frac{K_v/N}{s(1 + T_m s)}\right) = \theta_{in} \frac{K_v/N}{s(1 + T_m s)} \tag{5.8}$$

$$\frac{\theta_{out}}{\theta_{in}} = \frac{\dfrac{K_v/N}{s(1 + T_m s)}}{1 + \dfrac{K_v/N}{s(1 + T_m s)}} = \frac{\dfrac{K_v/N}{s(1 + T_m s)}}{\dfrac{s(1 + T_m s) + K_v/N}{s(1 + T_m s)}} = \frac{K_v/N}{s(1 + T_m s) + K_v/N} \tag{5.9}$$

We can also put equation (5.9) in torque constant form if we use the substitutions $K_t = K_s K_a K_{tm}$, $K_v = K_t/B$, and $T_m = J/B$, and then multiply by B/B.

$$\frac{\theta_{out}}{\theta_{in}} = \frac{K_v/N}{s(1 + T_m s) + K_v/N} = \frac{K_t/BN}{s(1 + Js/B) + K_t/BN} \times \frac{B}{B}$$

$$= \frac{K_t/N}{s(B + Js) + K_t/N} \tag{5.10}$$

(In Chapter 4, equations (4.16) through (4.28), we developed our motor transfer function in torque form and then converted it to velocity constant form.) Equation (5.9) can be derived easily from equation (5.4) by the general rule that if the open-loop function

$$\theta_0/E = KG \tag{5.11}$$

where K is a lumped constant and G is any function of s, then by the same method we used above we can readily determine that

$$\frac{\theta_{out}}{\theta_{in}} = \frac{KG}{1 + KGH} = \frac{KG}{1 + KG}; \qquad H = 1 \tag{5.12}$$

where H is the feedback function, which in our case is 1 (100% feedback).

To find the closed-loop equivalent of equation (5.4) using equation (5.11), we would note that $K = K_v/N$ and $G = 1/s(1 + T_m s)$. Then making these substitutions in equation (5.12) would yield equation (5.9) directly. We refer frequently to the open-loop equation (5.11) and its closed-loop equivalent (5.12), and it is well to commit them to memory.

To analyze our closed-loop system graphically we plot points on gain and phase curves, using equation (5.9), in which we use the substitution $s = j\omega$.

$$\frac{\theta_{\text{out}}}{\theta_{\text{in}}} = \frac{K_v/N}{s(1 + T_m s) + K_v/N} = \frac{K_v/N}{j\omega(1 + j\omega T_m) + K_v/N} \quad (5.13)$$

In plotting these curves let us test three different gear ratios to see the effect of each on our system. To achieve a wide variety we choose ratios of 10,000:1, 1000:1, and 100:1.

The values for substituting in equation (5.13) are found in the manufacturer's catalog and corrected as indicated in Section 4.5. K_s is listed in the specifications for a size 11 control transformer as "sensitivity," but it is really the constant of both synchros, that is, of the CX–CT synchro pair; $K_{vm}'(= \frac{1}{2}K_{vm})$ is listed in size 11 motor specifications or can be found by dividing free speed by control phase voltage; $T_m'(= \frac{1}{2}T_m)$ is usually listed, and if not, it can be found by dividing moment of inertia in gm-cm^2 by viscous damping in dyn-cm/rad/sec. The values found in the catalog are (see Section 4-5 for explanation of corrections to catalog data):

$$K_s = 0.393 \frac{\text{V}}{\text{deg}} \times \frac{57.3}{1} \frac{\text{deg}}{\text{rad}} = 22.5 \text{ V/rad} \quad (5.14)$$

$$K_a = 150 \frac{\text{V output}}{\text{V input}} = 150 \quad \text{(dimensionless)} \quad (5.15)$$

$$K_{vm}' = 2.82 \text{ rad/V-sec}; \qquad K_{vm} = 2K_{vm}' \quad (5.16)$$

$$T_m' = 0.00765 \text{ sec}; \qquad T_m = 2T_m' \quad (5.17)$$

$$B' = 130.8 \text{ dyn-cm/(rad/sec)}; \quad B = \frac{1}{2}B' \quad (5.18)$$

$$J = 1.0 \text{ gm-cm}^2 \quad (5.19)$$

$$N = 10,000 \text{ (Case I)}, 1000 \text{ (Case II)}, \text{ and } 100 \text{ (Case III)}$$

The corrected values are

$$K_{vm} = 2K_{vm}' = 5.64 \frac{\text{rad}}{\text{V-sec}} \tag{5.20}$$

$$T_m = 2T_m' = 0.0153 \text{ sec} \tag{5.21}$$

$$B = \tfrac{1}{2}B' = 65.4 \frac{\text{dyn-cm}}{\text{rad/sec}} = 65.4 \text{ dyn-cm-sec} \tag{5.22}$$

(The dimensions of B are sometimes given in dyn-cm-sec since radians are dimensionless and can therefore be omitted.)

Substituting the foregoing values in equations (5.4) and (5.13) yields

$$K_v = K_s K_a K_{vm} = 22.5 \frac{\text{V}}{\text{rad}} \times 150 \times 5.64 \frac{\text{rad}}{\text{V-sec}} = \frac{19,000}{\text{sec}} \tag{5.23}$$

and

Case I: N = 10,000

$$\frac{\theta_{\text{out}}}{\theta_{\text{in}}} = \frac{K_v/N}{j\omega(1 + j\omega T_m) + K_v/N} = \frac{1.9}{j\omega(1 + j0.0153\omega) + 1.9} \tag{5.24a}$$

For ease of later computation the form of equation (5.24a) is changed to torque constant form by multiplying by $T_m^{-1}/T_m^{-1} = 65.4/65.4$ as in equation (5.10), changing the form of equation (5.24a) to

$$\frac{\theta_{\text{out}}}{\theta_{\text{in}}} = \frac{1.9}{j\omega(1 + j0.0153\omega) + 1.9} = \frac{1.9}{j\omega(1 + j\omega/65.4) + 1.9} \times \frac{65.4}{65.4}$$

$$= \frac{124.2}{j\omega(65.4 + j\omega) + 124.2} = \frac{124.2}{(j\omega)^2 + j65.4\omega + 124.2}$$

$$= \frac{124.2}{124.2 - \omega^2 + j65.4\omega} \tag{5.24b}$$

Case II: N = 1000

$$\frac{\theta_{\text{out}}}{\theta_{\text{in}}} = \frac{19}{j\omega(1 + j0.0153\omega) + 19} \times \frac{65.4}{65.4} = \frac{1242}{1242 - \omega^2 + j65.4\omega} \tag{5.25}$$

Case III: N = 100

$$\frac{\theta_{\text{out}}}{\theta_{\text{in}}} = \frac{190}{j\omega(1 + j0.0153\omega) + 190} \times \frac{65.4}{65.4} = \frac{12420}{12420 - \omega^2 + j65.4\omega}$$

$$\tag{5.26}$$

To plot the closed-loop gain and phase curves we substitute values of ω in equations (5.24), (5.25), and (5.26) and find magnitude ratio or gain for one curve, and phase angle for the other curve. The slide rule can be used very effectively here, or the vector conversion table in Appendix C can be used. An example follows.

Example 5.1

Case I: $\omega = 2$

$$\frac{\theta_{\text{out}}}{\theta_{\text{in}}} = \frac{124.2}{124.2 - \omega^2 + j65.4\omega} = \frac{124.2}{124.2 - 4 + j130.8}$$

$$= \frac{124.2}{120.2 + j130.8} \tag{5.27}$$

By slide rule:

$$\frac{\theta_{\text{out}}}{\theta_{\text{in}}} = \frac{124.2}{177.5\underline{/47.4°}} = 0.70\underline{/-47.4°} = -3.1 \text{ dB}\underline{/-47.4°} \tag{5.28}$$

Dividing both numerator and denominator of equation (5.27) by 120.2 yields

$$\frac{\theta_{\text{out}}}{\theta_{\text{in}}} = \frac{1.033}{1 + j1.087} \tag{5.29}$$

In the vector conversion table in Appendix C we find

$$1 + j1.087 \approx 1 + j1.09 = 1.479\underline{/47.5°} \tag{5.30}$$

then $$\frac{\theta_{\text{out}}}{\theta_{\text{in}}} = \frac{1.033}{1.479\underline{/47.5°}} = 0.70\underline{/-47.5°} = -3.1 \text{ dB}\underline{/47.5°} \tag{5.31}$$

Plotting points of gain in decibels, and phase angle in degrees, we obtain from equations (5.24), (5.25), and (5.26) the curves shown in Fig. 5.3.

Let us analyze the information we gained from Fig. 5.3. Case III looks good on the graph because of its large bandwidth (ω_b) with the -3 dB point about 160 rad/sec = 25.5 c/s. This means that our servo will follow inputs varying faster than 25 c/s. Note that in Chapter 4 we considered *open-loop bandwidth* of individual components. In the chapters ahead we *never* consider the 3 dB down point of the Bode or open-loop diagram because we are dealing with

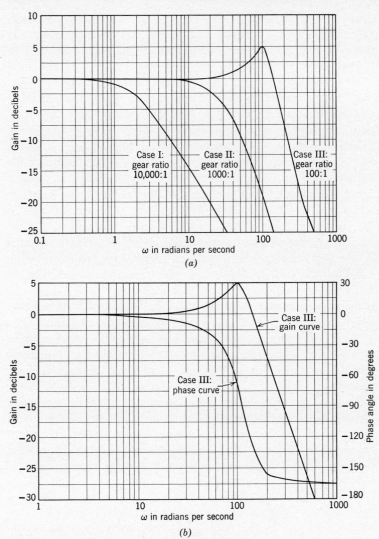

Fig. 5.3 (*a*) Closed-loop gain curves of all three systems. (*b*) Closed-loop gain and phase curves for Case III system.

closed-loop systems. From now on *bandwidth* refers only to *closed-loop bandwidth* (ω_b) obtained from closed-loop gain curves such as those in Fig. 5.3 or from mathematical equations developed in Chapter 6.

However, along with its good features this system has some bad ones. Note that the output of Case III does not respond in a 1:1 ratio to the input, as Case I and Case II do from zero frequency until they start to drop off at the right; Case III magnitude starts to climb at about 10 rad/sec until around 100 rad/sec ($= \omega_m$, the frequency at which maximum gain occurs.) At this frequency the output/input ratio climbs to a maximum of 5.0 dB = 1.78 (usually called M_m, maximum magnitude). At this point output responds almost 2:1 to an input error. This leads to overcorrection, which the instrument tries to counteract by a reverse correction, and the result is a tendency to hunt or oscillate continuously. Some hunting is desirable when coming to balance after a large error correction, but it must be quickly damped out, and it must not continue indefinitely. Experience indicates that a closed-loop peak of 1.4 or 3 dB is the maximum magnitude ratio that can be tolerated in a power servo, and 1.5 or 3.5 dB in an instrument servomechanism.

There are other considerations besides stability in choosing a system, as we learned in Section 5.2. We want the pen of our course recorder to move fast enough to follow rapid changes in plane heading.

We note in the motor speed-torque curves shown in the manufacturer's catalog that the maximum output speed of the motor we chose is about 6600 r/min. If we gear this down 10,000:1, the motor output shaft will turn at a maximum speed of 0.66 r/min. The recorder pen driven by this output shaft through a system of small pulleys will be very slow. If gear ratio is 1000:1, the motor turns at the rate of 6.6 r/min. With a 100:1 gear ratio the motor drives at 66 r/min or about 1 r/sec, which is much better. In addition, it would be well to consider the amount of error it takes to drive the motor at a certain speed—the *velocity error coefficient*, or *velocity lag error*. It is the reciprocal of the system *velocity gain constant* K_v, which has the dimension 1/sec.

$$\textit{Case I:}\quad \frac{K_v}{N} = 1.9/\text{sec}; \qquad \frac{N}{K_v} = \frac{10,000}{19,000}\ \text{sec} = \frac{1\ \text{rev}}{1.9\ \text{r/sec}} \qquad (5.32)$$

Changing the dimensions to deg/r/min we have

$$\frac{N}{K_v} = \frac{1 \text{ rev}}{1.9 \text{ r/sec}} \times \frac{1 \text{ min}}{60 \text{ sec}} \times \frac{360 \text{ deg}}{\text{rev}} = 3.16 \frac{\text{deg}}{\text{r/min}} \quad (5.33)$$

Case II: Because $N/K_v = 1/19$ sec, this velocity error coefficient will be 1/10 that of Case I, or 0.316 deg/r/min.

Case III: The coefficient here is one tenth that of Case II, or 0.0316 deg/r/min. This means that a system error (between compass and course recorder pen) of only 0.0316 deg will drive the motor at a speed of 1 r/min in the proper direction to correct the error.

We conclude that the output shaft speed and velocity lag error of Case III are by far the best. On the other hand, Case II is stable because its output/input ratio never exceeds 1. There is no hunting or oscillation. In fact, this system is too stable; we want a "livelier" one. In addition, as we have seen, Case II is slow (6.6 r/min maximum speed of output shaft) and only 1/10th as sensitive to an error signal as Case III. By looking at the magnitude curve of Case II we see another fault; it has a 3 dB down point at about 25 rad/sec or 4 c/s. (This is a bandwidth of 4 cycles.) At frequencies higher than 4 c/s the system will hardly respond. To solve the problem, we turn in Section 5.4 to another method of analysis.

First let us sum up the advantages of the closed-loop curves:

1. They are curves of actual closed-loop system performance, and almost all servo systems are closed loop.
2. They display closed loop
   (*a*) maximum system gain or magnitude M_m
   (*b*) frequency at which maximum system gain occurs ω_m
   (*c*) system bandwidth ω_b
   (*d*) phase at all gains

PROBLEMS

5.1. Using equations (5.1) and (5.2) and given the equation:
   Motor starting voltage = 5% of rated control phase voltage
   (*a*) Calculate amplifier gain if motor rated control phase voltage = 35 V, desired dead band = 0.1 deg, control transformer sensitivity = 0.393 V/-deg.
   (*b*) Calculate dead band in degrees if motor rated control phase voltage = 26 V, amplifier gain = 40 dB = 100, control transformer sensitivity = 1.000 V/deg.

5.2. Using equations (5.1) and (5.2), and given the equation

   Motor starting voltage = 5% of rated control phase voltage

(a) Calculate amplifier gain if motor rated control phase voltage = 33 V, desired dead band = 0.5 deg, control transformer sensitivity = 0.411 V/deg.

(b) Calculate dead band in degrees if motor rated control phase voltage = 40 V, amplifier gain = 40 dB = 100, control transformer sensitivity = 0.377 V/deg.

Note: Save your answers (numerical and Bode diagrams) to the rest of the problems in this chapter. You will be asked to compare results of changes in system design in this and the next two chapters.

5.3. For the system shown in Fig. 5.2, the component specifications given in the manufacturer's catalog are:

$$\text{Motor rated control phase voltage} = 36 \text{ V}$$

$$
\begin{aligned}
K_s &= 1.00 & &\text{V/deg} = 57.3 \text{ V/rad} \\
K_{vm}' &= 26 & &\text{rad/V-sec} \\
T_m' &= 0.04 & &\text{sec} \\
B' &= 25 & &\text{dyn-cm/(rad/sec)} \\
J &= 1.00 & &\text{gm-cm}^2 \\
N &= 3000 & & \\
K_a &= 120 & &
\end{aligned}
$$

and let

(a) Calculate system dead band in degrees.

(b) Correct the foregoing data (see equations (5.16) through (5.21)) and find the open-loop transfer function θ_{out}/E (see equation (5.4)).

(c) Find the closed-loop equation of this system (see equations (5.9) and (5.24a)), and convert it to the torque constant form (see equations (5.10) and (5.24b)).

5.4. Draw the closed-loop gain and phase curves—similar to Fig. 5.3b —of the closed-loop transfer function (torque constant form) found in Prob. 5.3(c). What is the maximum gain or magnitude (M_m), and what is the frequency (ω_m) at which this maximum occurs? Is the M_m too large? Why? What is the phase angle at ω_m? What is the system closed-loop bandwidth ω_b (3 dB down or −3 dB point)?

5.5. For the system shown in Fig. 5.2 the component specifications given in the manufacturer's catalog are

$$\text{Motor rated control phase voltage} = 180 \text{ V}$$

$$
\begin{aligned}
K_s &= 0.393 & &\text{V/deg} = 22.5 \text{ V/rad} \\
K_{vm}' &= 4.00 & &\text{rad/V-sec} \\
T_m' &= 0.015 & &\text{sec} \\
B' &= 60 & &\text{dyn-cm/(rad/sec)}
\end{aligned}
$$

$$J = 0.90 \quad \text{gm-cm}^2$$
$$N = 800$$
and let $\quad K_a = 1350$

(a) Calculate system dead band in degrees.

(b) Correct the foregoing data (see equations (5.16) through (5.21)), and find the open-loop transfer function θ_{out}/E (see equation (5.4)).

(c) Find the closed-loop equation of this system (see equations (5.9) and (5.24a)), and convert it to the torque constant form (see equations (5.10) and (5.24b)).

5.6. Draw the closed-loop gain and phase curves—similar to Fig. 5.3b —of the closed-loop transfer function (torque constant form) found in Prob. 5.5c. What is the maximum gain or magnitude (M_m), and what is the frequency (ω_m) at which this maximum occurs? Is the M_m too large? Why? What is the phase angle at ω_m? What is the system closed-loop bandwidth ω_b (3 dB or −3 dB point)?

5.4   CONTROL SYSTEM ANALYSIS BY OPEN-LOOP FREQUENCY RESPONSE

We would like to improve the stability of Case III while preserving its good points. To do this we can alter certain constants (such as gain) of the amplifier or add stabilizing elements. To analyze the results of each change we could draw new closed-loop curves such as those shown in Fig. 5.3. But these curves are cumbersome and require too much time-consuming mathematics and plotting of points. We therefore seek a fast and easy way to analyze our systems, and we find it in open-loop curves such as we drew in Chapters 3 and 4. Closed-loop curves are the natural curves that describe a closed-loop system. Open-loop curves are more artificial and remote from reality, but they are far easier and faster to draw.

If we fully understand the open-loop curves we can use them for most of our servo design work. We therefore inquire into the meaning and significance of open-loop analysis. To do this we open the loop (break the feedback path) in our course recorder instrument servomechanism. We break the feedback path from the motor gear train to the CT rotor by loosening the Allen set screw of the gear connecting the output shaft to the CT rotor. This procedure breaks the dashed line below the gear train in Fig. 5.1a, which is the same as the feedback line in Fig. 5.1b and c. The forward path is left intact and unchanged.

Assume that the CX rotor is exactly lined up with the CT rotor. If the CX rotor is turned 10° clockwise, voltages induced in the CT rotor and amplified by the amplifier would cause the motor to accelerate in one direction. If the CX rotor is turned backwards (counterclockwise) through a 20° arc so that it is 10° away from the CT rotor null in the opposite direction, the motor will accelerate in the opposite direction. We can leave the CT rotor fixed and move the CX rotor in a sine-wave pattern at various frequencies. For each frequency we can record output/input amplitude and phase and plot these values on a graph. This is the procedure we used with the automobile steering system to obtain frequency-response data in Chapter 1, and is the *experimental* or *laboratory* method.

The same results—frequency-response data and graph of same— are much easier to achieve by the *mathematical* method, chiefly by the Laplace transfer function and its graph, the Bode diagram. Using either method we have found that when the phase of the open loop output lags the input by 180°, closing the loop would cause positive feedback. If at that time the open-loop output/input magnitude ratio was greater than 1, closing the loop would cause increasing oscillations, that is, complete instability.

We therefore use the open-loop mathematical approach to our course recorder. Equation (5.4) of our open-loop transfer function is

$$\frac{\theta_{out}}{E} = \frac{K_s K_a K_{vm}/N}{s(1 + T_m s)} \tag{5.4}$$

In equation (5.23) we stated that $K_s K_a K_{vm} = 19,000$. Then the open-loop transfer functions for our three systems are, substituting $j\omega$ for s and putting in the value of our time constant $T_m = 0.0153$ sec, for

Case I: $N = 10,000$,

$$\frac{\theta_{out}}{e} = \frac{1.9}{j\omega(1 + j0.0153\omega)} = \frac{1.9}{j\omega(1 + j\omega/65.4)} \tag{5.34}$$

Case II: $N = 1000$

$$\frac{\theta_{out}}{e} = \frac{19}{j\omega(1 + j0.0153\omega)} = \frac{19}{j\omega(1 + j\omega/65.4)} \tag{5.35}$$

Case III: $N = 100$

$$\frac{\theta_{out}}{e} = \frac{190}{j\omega(1 + j0.0153\omega)} = \frac{190}{j\omega(1 + j\omega/65.4)} \tag{5.36}$$

These Bode plots may easily be sketched in by the methods described in Chapter 3. In each case we have a corner frequency of $1/0.0153 = 65.4$ rad/sec and an initial slope of -20 dB/decade. This slope crosses the 0 dB axis at $\omega = 1.9$ for Case I, at $\omega = 19$ for Case II, and at $\omega = 190$ for Case III. At $\omega_c = 65.4$ there is a breakpoint, to the right of which we have a -40 dB/decade slope. In other words, before $\omega_c = 65.4$ we have essentially $K/j\omega$, a -20 dB/decade slope; after $\omega_c = 65.4$ we have essentially $K/(j\omega)^2$, a -40 dB/decade slope. The phase curve starts at $-90°$ (because of the $1/j\omega$), passes through $-135°$ at the corner frequency, and finishes at nearly $-180°$. The straightline approximation is drawn in from $-90°$ at $\omega = 6.54$ to $-180°$ at $\omega = 654$. Before 6.54 the approximation is $-90°$; after 654 it is $-180°$. The corrections are added, as shown in Table 3.3 and Fig. 3.9 (Section 3.3). All three cases have the same phase curve because all three differ only by a constant. (To calculate the exact phase angle at any point, merely add $-90°$ to minus the angle of $1 + j0.0153\omega$ when the value of ω is given. The angle can be found in the vector conversion table in the appendix. For example, if $\omega = 20$, we have $1 + j0.0153 \times 20 = 1 + j0.306$. From the table we see that for $\omega T = 0.30$, angle $\theta = 16.7°$, and for $\omega T = 0.31$ angle $\theta = 17.2$, so our angle is about $17°$. Thus the phase angle is $-90° - 17° = -107°$.) The three Bode diagrams are shown in Fig. 5.4.

A critical measurement is the *phase margin*. We found this to be an angle equal to $180°$ minus the absolute value of the phase angle at the frequency where the gain line crosses the zero decibel line, the *gain crossover frequency*. In Sections 3.6 and 4.8 we learned that phase margins of from $40°$ to $60°$ are acceptable. In Case I the gain line crosses 0 dB at $\omega = 1.9$ where the phase angle is $92°$, so the phase margin is $180° - 92° = 88°$. In Case II we have $\omega = 19$ at the gain crossover, the phase angle is $107°$, and the phase margin is $180° - 106° = 74°$. In Case III the phase margin is $180° - 150° = 30°$.

Since a phase margin of $40°$ is an absolute minimum, $30°$ is definitely too small; $150°$ is too close to $180°$ when the gain is 1 (0 dB), and this situation leads to a "jittery" servo. In addition, for stability it is a good rule to have the gain curve slope at -20 dB per decade where it crosses the 0 dB line (gain crossover). In Case III we have a gain crossover slope of -40 dB per decade, indicating instability.

Another important measurement is the *gain crossover frequency*, which is an indication of the input signal frequency that the servo

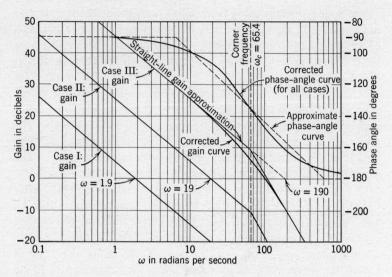

Fig. 5.4 Open-loop plot or Bode diagram of systems shown in Fig. 5.3.

Case I:

$$\frac{\theta_{\text{out}}}{E} = \frac{1.9}{j\omega(1 + j0.0153\omega)} = \frac{1.9}{j\omega(1 + j\omega/65.4)}$$

Case II:

$$\frac{\theta_{\text{out}}}{E} = \frac{19}{j\omega(1 + j0.0153\omega)} = \frac{1.9}{j\omega(1 + j\omega/65.4)}$$

Case III:

$$\frac{\theta_{\text{out}}}{E} = \frac{190}{j\omega(1 + 0.0153\omega)} = \frac{190}{j\omega(1 + j\omega/65.4)}$$

system can follow. Case I gain crossover frequency is less than 2 rad/sec, Case II is less than 20 rad/sec, and Case III is 112 rad/sec or 17.8 c/s. The gain crossover frequency is close to the natural frequency of the system, which is discussed in Chapter 6. The natural frequency of our Case III system is 111.4 rad/sec—very close to 112 rad/sec. The gain crossover frequency is not always this close, but it is always a good approximation.

PROBLEMS

5.7. The open-loop transfer function of the course recorder developed in this chapter is given by equation (5.4) as

$$\frac{\theta_{out}}{E} = \frac{K_v/N}{s(1 + T_m s)} = \frac{K_v/N}{j\omega(1 + jT_m\omega)}$$

The constants of this transfer function are given in equations (5.21) and (5.23) as: $T_m = 0.0153$ sec, and $K_v = 19,000$. Various gear ratios were tried, and we obtained equations (5.34), (5.35), and (5.36), whose Bode diagrams are shown in Fig. 5.4.

Use the same constants for T_m and K_v, but use a gear ratio of 500 to 1 ($N = 500$) to develop a new transfer function. Draw the Bode diagram of your transfer function. Is the system phase margin satisfactory? Is the slope at gain crossover (where the gain curve crosses the zero decibel line) satisfactory? Is the system stable? Is it too stable? Give reasons for your answers. What is the gain crossover frequency?

5.8. The open-loop transfer function of the course recorder developed in this chapter is given by equation (5.4) as

$$\frac{\theta_{out}}{E} = \frac{K_v/N}{s(1 + T_m)} = \frac{K_v/N}{j\omega(1 + jT_m\omega)}$$

The constants of this transfer function are given in equations (5.21) and (5.23) as: $T_m = 0.0153$ sec, and $K_v = 19,000$. Various gear ratios were tried, and we obtained equations (5.34), (5.35) and (5.36), whose Bode diagrams are shown in Fig. 5.4.

Use the same constants for T_m and K_v, but use a gear ratio of 750 to 1 ($N = 750$) to develop a new transfer function. Draw the Bode diagram of your transfer function. Is the system phase margin satisfactory? Is the slope at gain crossover (where the gain curve crosses the zero decibel line) satisfactory? Is the system stable? Is it too stable? Give reasons for your answers. What is the gain crossover frequency?

5.9. Draw the Bode diagram of the open-loop transfer function found as your answer to Prob. 5.3(*b*). What is the phase margin of the system? What is the slope of the gain curve at gain crossover? What is the gain crossover frequency? Is the system stable? Is it too stable? Give reasons for your last two answers.

5.10. Draw the Bode diagram of the open-loop transfer function found as your answer to Prob. 5.5(*b*). What is the phase margin of the system? What is the slope of the gain curve at gain crossover? What is the gain crossover frequency? Is the system stable? Is it too stable? Give reasons for your last two answers.

5.5   CONTROL SYSTEM COMPENSATION BY A RATE GENERATOR

We generally try to pick the best system and alter or *compensate* it to achieve an acceptable result. What can we do to compensate the Case III system? We are limited by available "hardware" or components, not by mathematical ideas. In this and the next two sections we shall discuss four possibilities of adding components to the loop to stabilize the system.

First, we can add a rate generator built into the same housing in line with the motor and driven at motor speed (see Fig. 4.31, Section 4.7). Naturally, the generator output is proportional to motor speed, and the generator is connected so that its output voltage opposes the amplifier input signal. The schematic diagram is shown in Fig. 5.5a. The potentiometer at the output of the generator enables us to adjust the amount of rate action. The effect of the rate generator on the motor can be experienced by removing the power from the control transformer primary and shorting the control transformer rotor leads (shorting the amplifier input). With the power on the rest of the system, if the motor rotor is turned, the generator feedback to the amplifier opposes the motor proportionally to its speed, causing a viscous drag. This action damps any motor oscillations, and the transfer function of our system with the added rate generator will illustrate this fact.

The block diagram of the system shown in Fig. 5.1 with the rate generator added is shown in Fig. 5.5b. A *mechanical switch* is shown in the original feedback loop, and we will analyze the system with this loop open. A second summing point is added where the generator loop closes; this is merely a wire connection. Note that θ_{out} going through the gear train backwards becomes $N\theta_{out}$ at the motor shaft (not the gear train output shaft). The quantity fed back is then $N\theta_{out}$ multiplied by the generator transfer function, $K_g s$. For the motor transfer function we return to the torque constant form given in Section 4.5, equation (4.23).

The system open-loop transfer function without the generator is

$$\frac{\theta_{out}}{E} = \frac{K_s K_a K_{tm}}{N(Js^2 + Bs)} \; ; \qquad K_{tm} = \text{motor } \textit{torque} \text{ constant} \qquad (5.37)$$

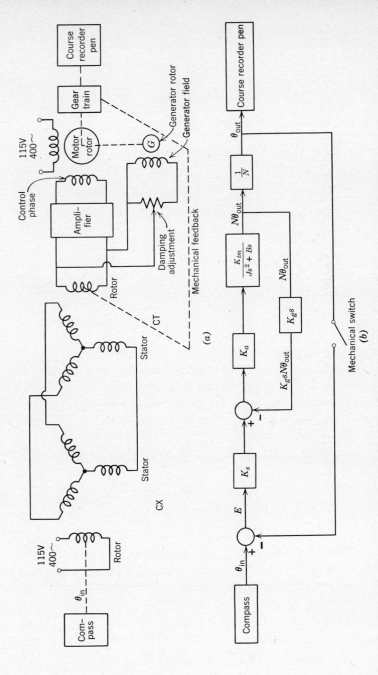

Fig. 5.5 System compensated by addition of a rate generator. (*a*) Schematic diagram. (*b*) Transfer function block diagram.

141

Let $K_s K_a K_{tm} = K_t$. Then

$$\frac{\theta_{\text{out}}}{E} = \frac{K_t}{N(Js^2 + Bs)} \tag{5.38}$$

With the generator loop we have from Fig. 5.5b

$$\theta_{\text{out}} = (EK_s - K_g s N \theta_{\text{out}}) \frac{K_a K_{tm}}{N(Js^2 + Bs)} \tag{5.39}$$

$$\theta_{\text{out}} N(Js^2 + Bs) = EK_s K_a K_{tm} - K_a K_{tm} K_g s N \theta_{\text{out}} \tag{5.40}$$

$$\theta_{\text{out}} N(Js^2 + Bs + K_a K_{tm} K_g s N \theta_{\text{out}}) = EK_s K_a K_{tm} = EK_t \tag{5.41}$$

$$\frac{\theta_{\text{out}}}{E} = \frac{K_t}{N(Js^2 + Bs + K_a K_{tm} K_g s)} = \frac{K_t/N}{Js^2 + s(B + K_a K_{tm} K_g)}$$

$$= \frac{K_t/N}{s(Js + B + K_a K_{tm} K_g)} \tag{5.42}$$

By comparing equation (5.42) with equation (5.38) we see that the preceding intuitive approach was correct; we have indeed added viscous damping $K_a K_{tm} K_g$ to our motor viscous damping B and nothing else. We shall soon see that this does damp out some tendency to oscillate, as proven by an increase in phase margin. Let us assume that we alter K_g by means of the potentiometer across the generator output (see Fig. 5.5a) and make $B + K_a K_{tm} K_g = 200$. For values to substitute in equation (5.42) we find from equation (5.18)

$$B' = 130.8 \text{ dyn-cm/rad/sec}; \qquad B = 65.4 \text{ dyn-cm/rad/sec} \tag{5.43}$$

and since $K_t/B = K_v$

$$\frac{K_t}{N} = \frac{K_v B}{N} = \frac{19{,}000 \times 65.4}{100} = 12{,}420 \tag{5.44}$$

In equation (5.19) the J of the motor rotor was 1.0 gm-cm^2. To this we must add 0.1 gm-cm^2—the added inertia of the drag cup fastened to the motor rotor shaft (see Fig. 4.31). Then motor plus rate generator

$$J = 1.1 \text{ gm-cm}^2 \tag{5.45}$$

Our new viscous damping is

$$B + K_a K_{tm} K_g = 200 \text{ dyn-cm/(rad/sec)} \tag{5.46}$$

Then our transfer function is, from equation (5.42) and substituting $j\omega$ for s,

$$\frac{\theta_{out}}{E} = \frac{12,420}{j\omega(1.1j\omega + 200)} = \frac{12,420/200}{j\omega(1.1j\omega/200 + 1)}$$

$$= \frac{62.1}{j\omega(1 + j0.0055\omega)} = \frac{62.1}{j\omega(1 + j\omega/181.8)} \quad (5.47)$$

This transfer function is plotted in Fig. 5.6. By comparing Fig. 5.4 Case III with Fig. 5.6 we see that with the rate generator added (*a*) the gain is lowered because the generator output is a feedback term lowering the overall gain of the amplifier, (*b*) the corner frequency is almost tripled, and (*c*) the phase curve is raised. Because the gain is cut to about one-third, we can see from equation (5.1) solved for dead band that our dead band will be nearly tripled.

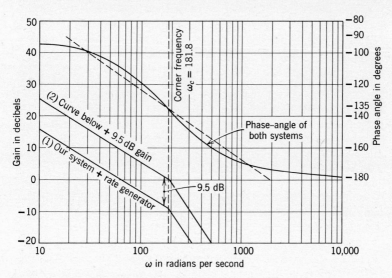

Fig. 5.6 Our system with a rate generator added (curve 1), and the same system with 9.5 dB added gain (curve 2).

(1)
$$\frac{\theta_{out}}{E} = \frac{62.1}{j\omega(1 + j0.0055\omega)} = \frac{62.1}{j\omega(1 + j\omega/181.8)}$$

(2)
$$\frac{\theta_{out}}{E} = \frac{3 \times 62.1}{j\omega(1 + j0.0055\omega)} = \frac{186.3}{j\omega(1 + j\omega/181.8)}$$

Velocity lag error is $1/K_v$ (equation (5.33)), and K_v includes K_a, the amplifier gain. By cutting our numerator term to one-third its former value we have tripled velocity lag error. But it is easy to turn up the gain control or add a stage to our amplifier to triple the gain by raising it 9.5 dB. This puts our curve up to where it was, as shown by the gain curve in Fig. 5.6. Now we find that our phase margin is 44°, which is satisfactory. And the gain crossover frequency 186 rad/sec is over 50% higher than the uncompensated system.

PROBLEMS

5.11. Compensate the system given in Prob. 5.3 (open-loop transfer function found as your answer to part (*b*)) by adding a rate generator. As explained in Section 5.6, this will add to viscous damping *B* and to rotor inertia *J*. Assume that adding the generator will cause *B* to increase 6 times and increase rotor inertia by 10%. Then your new *B* will equal 6 times the *B* of Prob. 5.3, and your new *J* will be 1.1 times the *J* of Prob. 5.3. Draw the Bode diagram of the new open-loop transfer function. Have we helped the system by the addition of the rate generator? How? To answer these questions compare your Bode diagram for this problem with your Bode diagram solution to Prob. 5.9. Raise your gain curve 10 dB. Is the system still stable? What have we done to the phase margin? to the gain crossover frequency? to the slope at gain crossover? to K_v/N? Is the new system better or worse? Why? Would another gain have been a better choice? If so, what would be the preferred gain? Why is this gain better?

5.12. Compensate the system given in Prob. 5.5 (open-loop transfer function found as your answer to part (*b*)) by adding a rate generator. As explained in Section 5.6, this will add to viscous damping *B* and to rotor inertia *J*. Assume that adding the generator will cause *B* to increase 5 times and increase rotor inertia by 10%. Then your new *B* will equal 5 times the *B* of Prob. 5.5, and your new *J* will be 1.1 times the *J* of Prob. 5.5. Draw the Bode diagram of the new open-loop transfer function. Have we helped the system by the addition of the rate generator? How? To answer these questions compare your Bode diagram for this problem with your Bode diagram solution to Prob. 5.10. Raise your gain curve 10 dB. Is the system still stable? What have we done to the phase margin? to the gain crossover frequency? to the slope at gain crossover? to K_v/N? Is the new system better or worse? Why? Would another gain have been a better choice? If so, what would be the preferred gain? Why is this gain better?

5.6 CONTROL SYSTEM COMPENSATION BY NETWORKS

We can also achieve our goal by insertion of a network between the control transformer and the amplifier. Two such networks are shown in Section 4.7, Figs. 4.32 and 4.33. These are dc networks, and our servosystem is ac throughout. We therefore must use some means of converting ac to dc, a demodulator, following the control transformer, and a modulator to reconvert the dc to ac following the network. A dual chopper will do this nicely. The transfer functions of these two added elements are simple constants K_d for the demodulator and K_m for the modulator. The Bode diagram of these networks is shown in Fig. 5.7. As we saw in Chapter 3, Bode diagram curves add, and we can see what such networks would do to our transfer function. Our new open-loop block diagram is shown in Fig. 5.8. If we assume that the losses K_d and K_m are negligible, we can omit them from our transfer function, which is then

$$\frac{\theta_{\text{out}}}{E} = \frac{K_s K_a K_{vm}/N}{j\omega(1 + jT_m\omega)} \frac{1 + jT_1\omega}{1 + jT_2\omega} = \frac{K_v/N}{j\omega(1 + jT_m\omega)} \frac{1 + jT_1\omega}{1 + jT_2\omega} \quad (5.48)$$

This equation is equation (5.4) with the network added.

We want to design first a lag network of the form $(1 + jT_1\omega)/(1 + jT_2\omega)$. In Section 4.7 we considered the lag network shown in Fig. 4.32, and we developed the Laplace transfer function of this network equation (4.51)

$$\frac{E_{\text{out}}}{E_{\text{in}}} = \frac{1 + sCR_2}{1 + sC(R_1 + R_2)} = \frac{1 + sT_1}{1 + sT_2}$$

We want this network to have $T_2 = 10T_1$, as shown in Fig. 5.7. By substituting these values in equation (4.51) and by letting $T_1 = 1$ we get the network transfer function

$$\frac{E_{\text{out}}}{E_{\text{in}}} = \frac{1 + 1s}{1 + 10s} = \frac{1 + j1\omega}{1 + j10\omega} \quad (5.49)$$

To construct the network shown in Fig. 4.32 which conforms to equation (5.49), we could use a capacitor C of 1 microfarad (μF), a resistor R_2 of 1 MΩ, and a resistor R_1 of 9 MΩ. Then CR_2 would have a time constant of 1 sec and $C(R_1 + R_2)$ would have a time constant of 10 sec, resulting in the transfer function of equation (5.49).

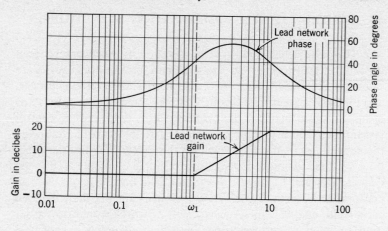

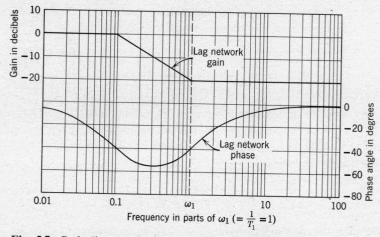

Frequency in parts of ω_1 $(= \frac{1}{T_1} = 1)$

Fig. 5.7 Bode diagram of a lead network and a lag network.

$$\frac{E_\text{out}}{E_\text{in}} = \frac{1 + jT_1\omega}{1 + jT_2\omega} \qquad \begin{array}{l} \text{Lag network:} \ T_2 = 10T_1 \\ \text{Lead network:} \ T_2 = \frac{1}{10}T_1 \end{array}$$

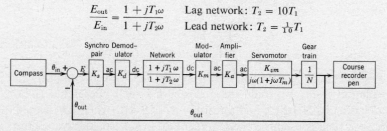

Fig. 5.8 System compensated by addition of dc network.

Our course-recorder system (equation (5.36)) when compensated by the lag network then becomes

$$\frac{\theta_{out}}{E} = \frac{190}{j\omega(1 + j0.0153\omega)}\frac{(1 + j1\omega)}{(1 + j10\omega)} = \frac{190(1 + j\omega)}{j\omega\left(1 + \dfrac{j\omega}{65.4}\right)\left(1 + \dfrac{j\omega}{0.1}\right)}$$

(5.50)

which is plotted in Fig. 5.9. This gives us a very large phase margin (71°). It also gives us two problems. First, the bandwidth is lowered, since the system drops off at a lower frequency at the high end, crossing the zero decibel line (gain crossover frequency) at about $\omega = 19$ instead of $\omega = 112$; second, if the gain is ever lowered so that the zero decibel crossing is made at $\omega = 0.2$, the phase margin would be $180° - 145° = 35°$, and the system would be unstable. This type of system is known as a *conditionally stable* system, that is, it is stable only if the gain never falls below a certain value. This is somewhat like a boy on a bicycle; they are stable unless the speed

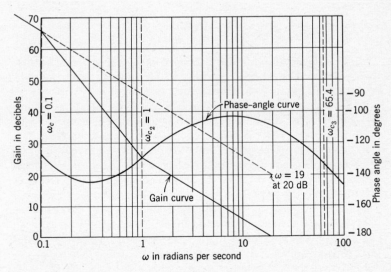

Fig. 5.9   Our system compensated by a lag network $\dfrac{1 + j\omega}{1 + j10\omega}$.

$$\frac{\theta_{out}}{E} = \frac{190}{j\omega(1 + j0.0153\omega)}\frac{1 + j\omega}{1 + j10\omega} = \frac{190(1 + j\omega)}{j\omega(1 + j\omega/65.4)(1 + j\omega/0.1)}$$

falls below a certain value. The gain crossover frequency is only 19 rad/sec, which means that our system will not follow a signal faster than about 3 c/s.

Note that in this and the next network compensated systems, the Bode diagram phase curve is plotted point by point; straightline approximation is not practicable. Note also that $\omega = 190 = K_v/N$, the point at which we would normally "aim" our initial slope, is not on the graph. This initial -20 dB/decade slope runs through 0.19 at 60 dB, 1.9 at 40 dB, 19 at 20 dB, and 190 at 0 dB. We choose $\omega = 19$ at 20 dB for accuracy. Finally note that the initial -20 dB/decade slope ends at the left-hand edge of the graph, and the -40 dB/decade slope starts there at $\omega = 0.1$.

PROBLEMS

5.13. Given the lag-network transfer function constructed like Fig. 4.32, with $T_1 = 0.5$ sec and $T_2 = 10$ sec:

$$\frac{1 + jT_1\omega}{1 + jT_2\omega}$$

(a) Find the network transfer function, and suggest one set of possible values for the resistors and capacitors in the network. Check your RC time constants against your transfer function values.

(b) Compensate the system given in Prob. 5.3 (open-loop transfer function found as your answer to part (b)) by adding the lag network of part (a) to the system. Your transfer function will be of the form of equation (5.48) and similar to equation (5.50).

(c) Draw the Bode diagram of the compensated system transfer function you found in part (b). Give the phase margin and the gain crossover frequency. Did the addition of the network help to stabilize the system whose Bode diagram you drew as your solution to Prob. 5.9? How? Is the system with the lag network added entirely satisfactory? If not, can you adjust the gain to make it so? Is the system conditionally stable? If so, what precautions must be taken when the system is used?

5.14. Given the lag-network transfer function constructed like Fig. 4.32, with $T_1 = 0.25$ sec and $T_2 = 5$ sec:

$$\frac{1 + jT_1\omega}{1 + jT_2\omega}$$

(a) Find the network transfer function, and suggest one set of possible values for the resistors and capacitors in the network. Check your RC time constants against your transfer function values.

(b) Compensate the system given in Prob. 5.5 (open-loop transfer function found as your answer to part (b)) by adding the lag network of part (a) to your system. The transfer function will be of the form of equation (5.48) and similar to equation (5.50).

(c) Draw the Bode diagram of the compensated system transfer function you found in part (b) Give the phase margin and the gain crossover frequency. Did the addition of the network help to stabilize the system whose Bode diagram you drew as your solution to Prob. 5.10? How? Is the system with the lag network added entirely satisfactory? If not, can you adjust the gain to make it so? Is the system conditionally stable? If so, what precautions must be taken when the system is used?

The transfer function of the lead network shown in Fig. 4.33 was developed in Section 4.7 as equation (4.52).

$$\frac{E_{out}}{E_{in}} = \frac{R_2}{R_1 + R_2} = \frac{sCR_1 + 1}{sC\dfrac{R_1R_2}{R_1 + R_2} + 1} = \frac{R_2}{R_1 + R_2}\frac{sT_1 + 1}{sT_2 + 1} \tag{4.52}$$

We want this network to have $T_2 = 0.1T_1$, as shown in Fig. 5.7. Substituting in equation (4.52) the time-constant values $T_1 = 0.02$ sec and $T_2 = 0.1T_1 = 0.002$ sec we can calculate possible values of R_1, R_2, and C for our lag network.

Given:
$$T_1 = R_1C = 0.02 \quad \text{sec} \tag{5.51}$$

Let $T_2 = \dfrac{R_1R_2}{R_1 + R_2}C = T_1\dfrac{R_2}{R_1 + R_2} = 0.1T_1 = 0.002 \quad \text{sec} \tag{5.52}$

Let $C = 1 \ \mu F$. Then:
$$T_1 = R_1C = 0.02 \qquad \therefore R_1 = 0.02 \ M\Omega$$

$$T_2 = 0.1T_1 = T_1\frac{R_2}{R_1 + R_2}$$

$$\therefore 0.1 = \frac{R_2}{R_1 + R_2} = \frac{R_2}{0.02 + R_2} \tag{5.53}$$

Clearing the right-hand portion of equation (5.53) of fractions gives
$$0.002 + 0.1R_2 = R_2; \qquad 0.002 = 0.9R_2;$$

$$R_2 = \frac{0.02}{9} = 0.00222 \ M\Omega = 2222 \ \Omega \tag{5.54}$$

Substituting these values into the second quantity in equation (5.52) yields 0.002, which proves our algebra.

The lead network equation (4.52) with $T_1 = 0.02$ sec and $T_2 = 0.002$ sec is then

$$\frac{E_{\text{out}}}{E_{\text{in}}} = \frac{R_2}{R_1 + R_2} \frac{sT_1 + 1}{sT_2 + 1} = \frac{0.00222}{0.02 + 0.00222} \frac{j0.02\omega + 1}{j0.002\omega + 1}$$

$$= \frac{1}{10} \frac{j0.02\omega + 1}{j0.002\omega + 1} = \frac{1}{10} \frac{j\omega/50 + 1}{j\omega/500 + 1} \qquad (5.55)$$

We raise the gain of our amplifier by a factor of 10 to cancel the $1/10$ in equation (5.55). Then using the lead network for compensation, the transfer function equation (5.48) becomes with the values of equation (5.36)

$$\frac{\theta_{\text{out}}}{e} = \frac{190(1 + j0.02\omega)}{j\omega(1 + j0.002\omega)(1 + j0.0153\omega)} = \frac{190\left(1 + \dfrac{j\omega}{50}\right)}{j\omega\left(1 + \dfrac{j\omega}{500}\right)\left(1 + \dfrac{j\omega}{65.4}\right)}$$

$$(5.56)$$

The Bode diagram is shown in Fig. 5.10, and has a phase margin of $180° - 114° = 66°$, and our bandwidth is increased because our gain crossover frequency is raised from $\omega = 112$ to $\omega = 247$.

PROBLEMS

5.15. Given the lead-network transfer function treated in equations (4.52) and (5.51) to (5.55) and constructed like Fig. 4.33, with $T_1 = 0.045$ sec and $T_2 = 0.0045$ sec:

$$\frac{1 + jT_1\omega}{1 + jT_2\omega}$$

(*a*) Find the network transfer function, and suggest one set of possible values for the resistors and capacitors in the network. Check your *RC* time constants against your transfer function values.

(*b*) Compensate the system given in Prob. 5.3 (open-loop transfer function found as your answer to part (*b*)) by adding the lead network of part (*a*) above to your system. Your transfer function will be of the form of equation (5.48) and similar to equation (5.56).

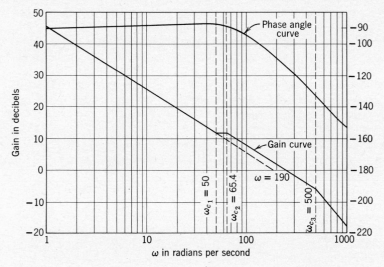

Fig. 5.10　Our system compensated by lead network $\dfrac{1 + j0.02\,\omega}{1 + j0.002\,\omega}$.

$$\frac{\theta_{out}}{E} = \frac{190}{j\omega(1 + j0.0153\omega)} \frac{1 + j0.02\omega}{1 + j0.002\omega}$$

$$= \frac{190(1 + j\omega/50)}{j\omega(1 + j\omega/65.4)(1 + j\omega/500)}$$

(*c*) Draw the Bode diagram of the compensated system transfer function you found in part (*b*). Give the phase margin and the gain crossover frequency. Did the addition of the network help to stabilize the system whose Bode diagram you drew as your solution to Prob. 5.9? How? Is the system with the lead network added entirely satisfactory? If not, can you adjust the gain to make it so?

5.16. Given the lead-network transfer function treated in equations (4.52) and (5.51) to (5.55) and constructed like Fig. 4.33, with $T_1 = 0.017$ sec and $T_2 = 0.0017$ sec:

$$\frac{1 + jT_1\omega}{1 + jT_2\omega}$$

(*a*) Find the network transfer function, and suggest one set of possible values for the resistors and capacitors in the network. Check your *RC* time constants against your transfer function values.

(*b*) Compensate the system given in Prob. 5.5 (open-loop transfer function found as your answer to part (*b*)) by adding the lead network of part

(a) above to your system. Your transfer function will be of the form of equation (5.48) and similar to equation (5.56).

(c) Draw the Bode diagram of the compensated system transfer function you found in part (b). Give the phase margin and the gain crossover frequency. Did the addition of the network help to stabilize the system whose Bode diagram you drew as your solution to Prob. 5.10? How? Is the system with the lead network added entirely satisfactory? If not, can you adjust the gain to make it so?

5.7   COMPENSATION BY USE OF AN INERTIALLY DAMPED SERVOMOTOR (IDSM)

In Section 4.7 we described the inertia-damped servomotor (IDSM). The IDSM is a servomotor with a mechanical "network" added; let us see what it will do for our course-recorder system. The following specifications are given in the manufacturer's catalog for the same servomotor we have used in our system so far, but with the inertia damper added (see Fig. 4.35):

> No-load speed: 2680 r/min
> Control phase voltage: 115 V
> Corner frequencies: 0.40, 2.75, 466 c/s

We use the same gear ratio ($N = 100$), amplifier gain ($K_a = 150$), and control transformer sensitivity ($K_s = 22.5$ rad/sec).

We change the corner frequency values to radians per second by multiplying by 2π, which gives

> Corner frequencies: 2.51, 17.3, and 293 rad/sec

and our time constants are $1/2.51$, $1/17.3$, and $1/293 = 0.398$, 0.00578, and 0.00341. By equation (4.41) our

$$K_{vm} = 2 \times \frac{\text{no-load speed}}{\text{control phase voltage}} \times \frac{2\pi}{60} \qquad (5.57)$$

$$= 2 \times \frac{2680}{115} \times \frac{2\pi}{60} = 4.87$$

Our $\quad K_v/N = \dfrac{K_s K_a K_{vm}}{N} = \dfrac{22.5 \times 150 \times 4.87}{100} = 164 \qquad (5.58)$

And our transfer function is

$$\frac{\theta_{\text{out}}}{E} = \frac{K_V/N(1 + jT_2\omega)}{j\omega(1 + jT_1\omega)(1 + jT_3\omega)}$$

$$= \frac{164\left(1 + \dfrac{j\omega}{17.3}\right)}{j\omega\left(1 + \dfrac{j\omega}{2.51}\right)\left(1 + \dfrac{j\omega}{293}\right)} = \frac{164(1 + j0.0578\omega)}{j\omega(1 + j0.398\omega)(1 + j0.00341\omega)}$$

$$(5.59)$$

This transfer function is plotted in Fig. 5.11. Note the phase curve; it is very similar to the lag-network-compensated system shown in Fig. 5.9. It is a good idea to place the gain crossover near the

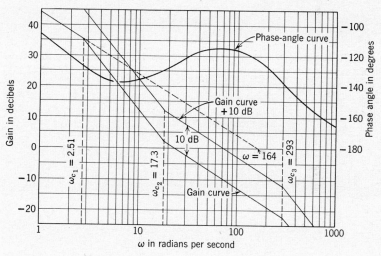

Fig. 5.11 Our system using an inertially damped motor.

Lower:

$$\frac{\theta_{\text{out}}}{\theta_{\text{in}}} = \frac{164(1 + j0.0578\omega)}{j\omega(1 + j0.398)(1 + j0.00341\omega)} = \frac{164(1 + j\omega/17.3)}{j\omega(1 + j\omega/2.51)(1 + j\omega/293)}$$

Upper (raised 10 dB):

$$\frac{\theta_{\text{out}}}{\theta_{\text{in}}} = \frac{518(1 + j0.0578\omega)}{j\omega(1 + j0.398\omega)(1 + j0.00341\omega)}$$

$$= \frac{328(1 + j\omega/17.3)}{j\omega(1 + j\omega/2.51)(1 + j\omega/293)}$$

highest point of the phase-margin curve. To determine the frequency at this point we find on the Bode diagram the midpoint between ω_{c2} and ω_{c3} as measured by a ruler; in Fig. 5.11 this midpoint is found by this method to be $\omega = 71$. We can mathematically find this point as $\sqrt{\omega_{c2}\omega_{c3}}$, which for the IDSM system in Fig. 5.11 is $\sqrt{17.3 \times 293} = 71.2$. Raising the gain curve by 10 dB (a gain of 3.16) accomplishes this result. Then $K_v/N = 3.16 \times 164 = 518$. The phase margin is now 65°, and the gain crossover frequency is now 75 rad/sec. Note that the phase curve at its lowest point, 6 rad/sec, dips to 42°, so that we have stability even at this point. This is not always true of IDSM systems, which can be *conditionally stable* (see Section 5.6).

PROBLEMS

5.17. Use an inertially damped servomotor IDSM, instead of the standard servomotor used in the system given in Prob. 5.3. An IDSM of the same size as the standard servomotor used and interchangeable with it has the following constants given by the manufacturer:

> No load speed = 9000 r/min
> Control phase voltage = 36 V
> Time constants: $T_1 = 1$ sec; $T_2 = 0.2$ sec; $T_3 = 0.01$ sec

Use the following constants given in Prob. 5.3:

$$K_s = 1.00 \text{ V/deg}$$
$$N = 3000$$
$$K_a = 120$$

(a) Find the corner frequencies, K_{vm}, and K_v/N (see equations (5.57) and (5.58)).

(b) Give the open-loop system transfer function (similar to equation (5.59)).

(c) Draw the Bode diagram.

(d) What is the frequency of the highest point on the phase curve? Raise or lower the gain curve until the gain crossover is at this frequency.

(e) With this new curve is the system stable? Why? Is it conditionally stable? Is the Bode diagram of this system similar to that of any other system found in this chapter? What does this tell us about the two systems? Which is the better system? Why?

5.18. Use an inertially damped servomotor, IDSM, instead of the standard servomotor used in the system given in Prob. 5.5. An IDSM of the same size as the standard servomotor used and interchangeable with it has the following constants given by the manufacturer:

No load speed = 7000 r/min
Control phase voltage = 180 V
Time constants: $T_1 = 0.5$ sec; $T_2 = 0.06$ sec; $T_3 = 0.005$ sec

Use the following constants given in Prob. 5.5:

$$K_s = 0.40 \text{ V/deg}$$
$$N = 800$$
$$K_a = 1350$$

(a) Find the corner frequencies, K_{vm} and K_v/N (see equations (5.57) and (5.58)).

(b) Give the open-loop system transfer function (similar to equation (5.59)).

(c) Draw the Bode diagram.

(d) What is the frequency of the highest point on the phase curve? Raise or lower the gain curve until the gain crossover is at this frequency.

(e) With this new curve, is the system stable? Why? Is it conditionally stable? Is the Bode diagram of this system similar to that of any other system found in this chapter? What does this tell us about the two systems? Which is the better system? Why?

5.8   EFFECTS OF LOAD INERTIA AND VISCOUS FRICTION

Thus far we have not mentioned any loading effect on a servomotor. For an instrument servo the load is light, is geared down, and can often be ignored. Let us look at the load inertia from the point of view of the motor rotor shaft. J_{Lr} is the inertia of the load "reflected back" from the load through the gear train to the rotor shaft. It can be proved that the ratio of reflected load inertia to the actual load inertia J_L is the gear ratio squared. Then

$$J_{Lr} = \frac{J_L}{N^2} \tag{5.60}$$

Similarly, load viscous friction or damping reflected back to the rotor shaft B_{Lr} is

$$B_{Lr} = \frac{B_L}{N^2} \tag{5.61}$$

It seems advisable to make the gear ratio as large as possible, but by the use of the calculus we can prove that acceleration is maximized when

$$N = \sqrt{J_L/J} \qquad (5.62)$$

that is, when the gear ratio is the square root of load inertia divided by motor rotor inertia.

From the point of view of the motor, the biggest load inertia that it has to accelerate is usually the rotor and the gear attached to the rotor shaft. For this reason, the motor output shaft often has gear teeth cut into it, thus eliminating the inertia of the first gear. Friction of the rotor is also kept to a minimum by the use of ball bearings.

Let us take an example of an inertia load that is not negligible. In the example given in Section 5.4 assume a load of 5000 gm-cm². The gear ratio N was 100, therefore $N^2 = 10,000$. Then

$$J_{Lr} = J_L/N^2 = 5000/10,000 = 0.5 \text{ gm-cm}^2 \qquad (5.63)$$

Motor rotor inertia was given as $J = 1.0$ gm-cm². Then the total inertia of the rotor and load is $J + J_{Lr} = 1.0 + 0.5 = 1.5 \times 1.0 = 1.5J$. We therefore have to accelerate the rotor plus a load of one-half the rotor inertia. The only constant in our system transfer function affected by the increase in inertia will be the time constant T_m. This is because in equations (4.24) through (4.26) we saw that J appears only in the time constant T_m, which is J/B. Our new time constant will then be 1.5 times the one given in equation (5.21). This means that if we take Case III equations (5.4) and (5.36) and alter them to the new conditions, this yields

$$\frac{\theta_{\text{out}}}{E} = \frac{K_v/N}{j\omega(1 + j1.5T_m\omega)} \qquad (5.64)$$

$$\frac{\theta_{\text{out}}}{E} = \frac{190}{j\omega(1 + j1.5 \times 0.0153\omega)} = \frac{190}{j\omega(1 + j0.0230\omega)}$$

$$= \frac{190}{j\omega(1 + j\omega/43.6)} \qquad (5.65)$$

The Bode diagram is drawn in Fig. 5.12. The phase margin is 23°. This is worse than the phase margin of the system with no-load inertia, Fig. 5.4 Case III, which was 30°. This makes sense because

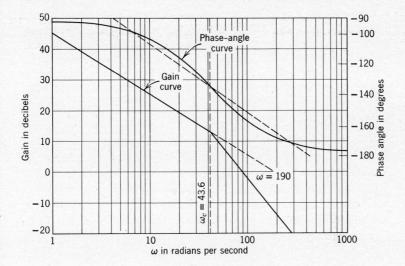

Fig. 5.12 Our system with appreciable load inertia.

$$\frac{\theta_{\text{out}}}{E} = \frac{190}{j\omega(1 + j0.0230\omega)} = \frac{190}{j\omega(1 + j\omega/43.6)}$$

any increase in inertia causes flywheel effect, overshooting, over-correction, and consequent hunting and oscillations. In trying to correct an error we store energy in an inertia element, and we then cannot stop this element at the control point without the release of the stored energy, which causes overshooting. In addition, the slope at gain crossover is -40 dB, a further indication of instability. The gain crossover frequency is 90 rad/sec.

PROBLEMS

5.19. Assume that in the system given in Prob. 5.3 there is reflected load inertia, J_{Lr}, equal to that of the motor rotor. To show this in your transfer function double the J value given. Draw the Bode diagram of the resulting open-loop transfer function. Is this system more or less stable than the one found in your answer to Prob. 5.9? When designing a servo is it a good idea to make the load inertia large or small? What about the servomotor rotor inertia—should it be made large or small? Give reasons for your answer.

5.20. Assume that in the system given in Prob. 5.5 there is reflected load inertia, J_{Lr}, equal to that of the motor rotor. To show this in your transfer function double the J value given. Draw the Bode diagram of the resulting open-loop transfer function. Is this system more or less stable than the one found in your answer to Prob. 5.10? When designing a servo is it a good idea to make the load inertia large or small? What about the servomotor rotor inertia—should it be made large or small? Give reasons for your answers.

The loading effect of viscous friction is the same as adding a rate generator, with one exception. The rate generator sends an electrical *signal* back that does not load up the servomotor. But actual viscous friction, although increasing stability, is a power loss, heats up the servomotor, causes a loss of no-load speed, and increases velocity lag error. Therefore viscous-damped servomotors (Section 4.7) are not popular.

5.9 SUMMARY OF SYSTEM COMPENSATION RESULTS

Table 5.1 gives the performance criteria of all the systems we have developed in this chapter. The first four columns of system values are calculated; the last four columns of values are derived from the Bode diagrams of the systems. We have described these criteria before in this chapter: (*a*) the velocity lag error is a dynamic measure of system ability to correct for a fast-changing error signal; (*b*) dead band is the maximum static error the system will not recognize and correct for; (*c*) phase margin is a measure of stability, as is (*d*) slope at gain crossover; and (*e*) ω at gain crossover is a measure of the upper frequencies the system will follow.

PROBLEMS

5.21. From the numerical answers and the Bode diagrams you found in working out Prob. 5.3, 5.9, 5.11, 5.13, 5.15, 5.17 and 5.19 make a chart similar to Table 5.1.

5.22. From the numerical answers and the Bode diagrams you found in working out Prob. 5.5, 5.10, 5.12, 5.14, 5.16, 5.18 and 5.20 make a chart similar to Table 5.1.

5.10 DRAWING CLOSED-LOOP DIAGRAMS FROM OPEN-LOOP DATA

We see that exploring improvements by using the open-loop Bode diagram is fast and leads to very useful results. Often this is sufficient for the servo designer. But the closed-loop diagrams of Fig. 5.3 add some information: the general configuration of the gain and phase curves, maximum closed-loop gain M_m, frequency ω_m at M_m, and closed-loop bandwidth (the 3 dB down point). The system operates as a closed loop, so these diagrams represent the operating system. However, we would like to avoid the work we did to produce these curves at the beginning of this chapter. We can do so by the procedure that follows.

A Nichols chart is enclosed in the back cover of this book. On this chart are two sets of scales: one set for the open-loop system, transfer function KG; and one set for the closed-loop system, transfer function $\dfrac{KG}{1 + KG}$. The open-loop data of KG is referred to the two axes: the horizontal axis, entitled "Phase angle in degrees"; and the vertical axis, entitled "Gain in decibels." The closed-loop data of $\dfrac{KG}{1 + KG}$ is referred to two sets of lines. The half-ellipses and other lines labeled with plus and minus numbers (no dimensions) are the gains in decibels; the line labeled Gain $\dfrac{KG}{1 + KG}$ is the -0.5 dB line. The lines radiating from the 0 point of the left margin and labeled with minus numbers followed by a degree sign are the phase angles in degrees; the line labeled Phase $\dfrac{KG}{1 + KG}$ is the $-10°$ line.

Thus the enclosed Nichols chart will enable us to plot closed-loop curves from open-loop curve data. The basic cross-section graph paper on which this chart is plotted has 10×10 squares to the inch. (This common graph or cross-section paper may be purchased at a stationery or engineering supply store.) On the cross-section paper we mark the vertical "gain" and horizontal "phase-angle" scale numbers just as they appear on the Nichols chart. We then refer to the open-loop Bode diagram of the system whose closed-loop plot we wish. We correct our straight-line Bode diagram

Table 5.1 *Values of Constants of Systems Analyzed in This Chapter*

Fig.	System Compensation	K_v/N	Velocity Lag Error (degrees per rpm)	K_a	Dead Band	Phase Margin	Values at Gain Crossover			Remarks
							ω (rad per sec)	ω (cycles per sec)	Slope (dB/decade)	
5.4	Uncompensated	190	0.0316	150	0.2	30°	112	17.8	−40	Unstable
5.6	Rate Generator plus 9.5 dB gain	186.3	0.0322	147	0.2°	44°	186	29.6	−20	High frequency
5.9	Lag network plus 10 dB gain	190	0.0316	150	0.2°	71°	19	3.02	−20	Low frequency Conditionally stable
5.10	Lead network	190	0.0316	150	0.2°	66°	247	39.3	−20	High frequency
5.11	IDSM plus 10 dB gain	518	0.0116	473	0.06°	65°	75	11.93	−20	Highest K_v
5.12	Uncompensated plus load inertia	190	0.0316	150	0.2°	26°	90	14.32	−40	Load inertia decreases stability

The values in this table are obtained as follows:

K_v/N is obtained from the transfer function; $N = 100$, and $NK_v/N = K_v$.

The velocity lag error is

$$\frac{N}{K_v} \times 6 = \frac{1}{K_v/N} \times 6 \, \frac{\text{deg}}{\text{r/min}}$$

(see Section 5.3, equations (5.32) and (5.33));

$$K_a = \frac{K_v}{K_s K_{vm}} = \frac{K_v}{22.5 \times 5.64}$$

(see Section 5.3, equation (5.23)), *except*

$$K_a \text{ of IDSM} = \frac{K_v}{22.5 \times 4.87}$$

The dead band is

$$\frac{2 \times \text{motor starting voltage}}{K_a K_s{}^*} = \frac{2 \times 5.75}{K_a \times 0.393}$$

$$K_s{}^* = K_s \text{ in V/deg}$$

(see Section 5.2, equations (5.1) and (5.2)),

The phase margin, ω at gain crossover, and slope at gain crossover are all found on the Bode diagram (see Section 5.4).

161

(see Section 3.3 and Fig. 3.10) by a 3 dB correction at the corner
frequency and a 1 dB correction at half and at twice the corner
frequency; *this is a must* for reasonably accurate results. Then at a
series of frequencies we plot the gain and phase of our Bode diagram
on the cross-section paper, using the same scale values as on the
Nichols chart. Figure 5.13 shows the plotted data taken from our
Case III original open-loop Bode diagram *corrected* (Fig. 5.4).
Note that each point plotted is labeled with its frequency ω. The
Nichols chart is placed over this gain-phase plot in exact register;

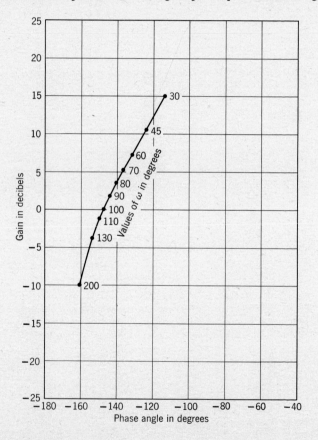

Fig. 5.13 Gain-phase plot for use with Nichols chart. (Data for gain-phase
points obtained from Fig. 5.4 corrected phase-angle curve and corrected Case
III gain curve.)

because the Nichols chart is semi-transparent, we can read lines of both graphs clearly (Fig. 5.14). Then at each ω of the gain-phase plot we read the value of gain in decibels indicated by the ellipse or between ellipses on the Nichols chart at that point, and the angle indicated by the other set of markings on the Nichols chart. As we

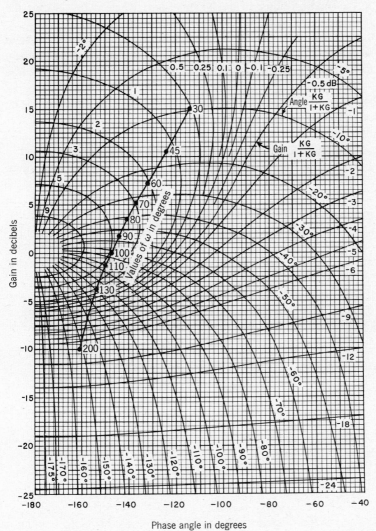

Fig. 5.14 Nichols chart overlay on top of Fig. 5.13.

read the closed-loop gain and phase results we plot them on semilog paper. Our result would be the Case III curve (Fig. 5.3), which we so laboriously plotted before. Note that the gain-phase and closed-loop plots should have many points in the critical area where the closed-loop plot peaks, which is where the gain-phase plot is tangent to the smallest ellipse of the Nichols chart which it touches, or the highest decibel value it reaches between ellipses.

We might be interested in the closed-loop response of our system with a lower or a higher gain, or with a certain M_m value. We can find any of these by moving our plotted gain-phase data curve vertically up or down with respect to the Nichols chart. Many designers like an M_m of 1.4 or 3 dB. If we wish to see what our system would look like with this M_m, we would place the Nichols chart over our plotted data with left margins in register and with the plotted curve tangent to the 3 dB ellipse of the Nichols chart, as shown in Fig. 5.15 and we would then take data as before and plot our closed-loop curves. We note that when the plotted curve is tangent to the 3 dB ellipse of the Nichols chart, the 0 dB horizontal line of the plot is over −4.5 dB of the Nichols chart. This means that in order to lower our system M_m to 3 dB we have to lower the system (amplifier) gain −4.5 dB = 0.6 gain ratio. This means we use 0.6 or 60% of our previous gain (K_a) of 150; the new gain will be 0.6 × 150 = 90.

We would expect this lowered gain to increase our system dead band. To find out how much effect this has we go back to equations (5.1) and (5.2). We solve the equation for dead band and then use the new gain value to discover the new dead band. We find

$$\text{Dead band} = \frac{2 \times \text{motor starting voltage}}{\text{amplifier gain} \times \text{control transformer sensitivity}}$$

$$(5.66)$$

Substituting the following values: (1) motor starting voltage = 5% of rated control phase voltage = 5% of 115 V = 5.75 V, (2) amplifier gain = K_a = 90 (from Nichols chart calculation), (3) control transformer sensitivity = K_s = 0.393 V/deg yields

$$\text{Dead band} = \frac{2 \times 5.75 \text{ V}}{90 \times 0.393 \text{ V/deg}} = 0.33 \quad \text{deg} \quad (5.67)$$

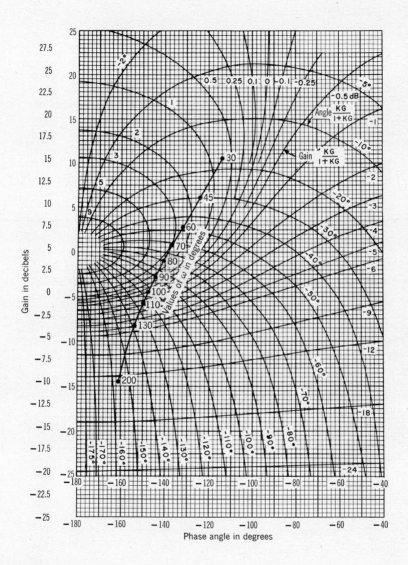

Fig. 5.15 Nichols chart overlay on top of Fig. 5.13 but moved up so that 3 dB ellipse is tangent to curve. Vertical axes are kept in register.

Our system dead band is therefore increased from 0.2° to 0.33°, a degradation that cannot be tolerated.

PROBLEMS

Instructions for problems 5.25–5.29 (see also Section 5.10): Buy cross-section (graph) paper with 10 x 10 squares to the inch. Remove the Nichols chart from the back cover of this book and copy the gain and the phase-angle scale numbers (along the left side and the bottom of the chart) onto your cross-section paper exactly as shown. When you put the Nichols chart on top of your cross-section paper each Nichols chart number in the margin should be on top of the same number marked on your graph. (Be sure that the cross-section area of your graph is 7 inches wide by 10 inches high, the same size as the Nichols chart.) Draw your gain-phase plot on a sheet of cross-section paper by the following procedure: At one value of ω check your Bode diagram gain and phase-angle curves for the gain and phase values at that frequency. Then plot this pair of gain and phase-angle values as one point on your cross-section paper. Before you forget, label the point with the value of ω applying to it. Plot other points and draw a smooth curve (see Fig. 5.13). Then superimpose the Nichols chart on your gain-phase plot. If you cannot see clearly the curve you drew, make it heavier. Your result will look like Fig. 5.14 for Probs. 5.25 and 5.27. Your work for Probs. 5.26 and 5.28 will look like Fig. 5.15, except that you will move the Nichols chart the exact distance to make your curve tangent to the 3 dB ellipse, making sure that the left edges of the Nichols chart and your graph cross-section area are carefully aligned.

5.23. From Fig. 5.14 plot the closed-loop gain and phase curves. Check these curves against Case III in Fig. 5.3. Your results should be identical or nearly so.

5.24. From Fig. 5.15 plot the closed-loop gain and phase curves. What is the bandwidth compared to Case III in Fig. 5.3, which is the same system before the gain was lowered?

5.25. Using the Bode plot you obtained in Prob. 5.9, draw the closed-loop gain and phase curves according to the procedure described in Section 5.10, beginning with the second paragraph and as shown in Figs. 5.13 and 5.14.

5.26. Lower the gain of the curve obtained in Prob. 5.25 until M_m is 3 dB (as shown in Fig. 5.15 and as described in Section 5.10). By how much did you lower the amplifier gain? Compare the original system dead band with the new dead band. Draw the closed-loop gain and phase curves.

5.27. Using the Bode plot obtained in Prob. 5.10, draw the closed-loop gain and phase curves according to the procedure described in Section

5.10, beginning with the second paragraph and as shown in Figs. 5.13 and 5.14.

5.28. Lower the gain of the curve obtained in Prob. 5.27 until M_m is 3 dB (as shown in Fig. 5.15 and as described in Section 5.10). By how much did you lower amplifier gain? Compare the original system dead band with the new dead band. Draw the closed-loop gain and phase curves.

5.29. Design a servo system to steer a model boat, airplane, or car; to position a TV antenna; to operate an instrument; or any other idea you may have. Decide on your performance specifications. Obtain catalogs from manufacturers (see Appendix D), and use commercially available component data. Analyze your system and compensate it if necessary.

SUMMARY

In this chapter we have seen that graphs of Laplace transform transfer functions of open-loop and closed-loop systems give us the information we need to meet specifications when designing automatic control systems. We have now completed our study of frequency-response methods of analysis and synthesis. Frequency response we found to be a powerful, fast, and therefore very useful tool for the control system designer. We now turn back to the time domain to see what happens to our control system immediately after a disturbance, and we examine the resulting transient carefully. We leave the *steady state* and return to the *transient*.

6.

Transient analysis

Thus far we have been concerned with what is called the *steady state* of control systems. For example, the amplifier in Chapter 1 was tested by a sine wave of one frequency followed by one of slightly higher frequency. In doing this testing we did not analyze the output response the first few microseconds or milliseconds after the sine-wave generator was switched on; we "waited" until the transients had died out before making our measurements. Any measurements we made were on an active system that had the same continuous input and would have the same steady-state output as long as we did not change anything. Theoretically these conditions could continue forever. This steady-state analysis is extremely important since, as we have seen, it gives us much valuable information about a control system.

Now we turn to another type of analysis—*transient* analysis. In this case we are interested in exactly the portion of the output wave we neglected before—the first few moments after we apply our input to the system. We can apply any wave shape—a sine wave, a unit step, a pulse, or a ramp (Fig. 6.1). The most common input is the unit step. The application of a step voltage to the capacitor shown in Fig. 2.2 and the resulting exponential decrease of the current, which we studied in Section 2.2, is a classical example of transient analysis, and it would be well to review that section. We used a step voltage E and then maintained this applied voltage forever. Theoretically the output current decreases forever, but we say that practically it reaches its final value in four or five time constants.

168

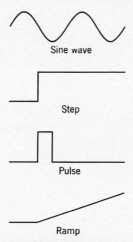

Fig. 6.1 Transient-initiating waveshapes.

6.1 CONTROL SYSTEM RESPONSE TO A STEP INPUT

To illustrate a typical system response we will use the same course-recorder system we analyzed in Chapter 5. Let us use the first system, Case III, before we improved it; we know that it was not a very successful system at that stage. We will naturally use the closed-loop transfer function. The open-loop system is an artificial one we use in frequency-response analysis; at all other times we consider our system as it really is, that is, closed-loop. Our system was presented in Chapter 5 in terms of the Laplace transform, a frequency function. For *transient* analysis we need a *time* function; what is more transient than time? The procedure we follow is the same as that outlined in Section 2.2: we find the Laplace transform and then the corresponding time function. This time function of our control system is then plotted, on graph paper, with time the abscissa and amplitude the ordinate.

The Case III closed-loop Laplace transfer function is given in equation (5.26) and is rearranged as equation (6.1)

$$\frac{\theta_{\text{out}}}{\theta_{\text{in}}} = \frac{12{,}420}{-\omega^2 + j65.4\omega + 12{,}420} \tag{6.1}$$

We want this equation in its Laplace transform form; thus we let $j\omega = s$. Then $-\omega^2 = s^2$, and equation (6.1) becomes

$$\frac{\theta_{\text{out}}}{\theta_{\text{in}}} = \frac{12,420}{s^2 + 65.4s + 12,420} \qquad (6.2)$$

This is a *second-order system* because the second power s^2 is the highest power of the variable in the characteristic equation, that is, in the denominator.

In order to generate a transient we repeat what we did in Section 2.2; we use a unit step input as our excitation function. This is what would happen if the airplane were parked on the ground and our course recorder were drawing a straight line at due North, and if we suddenly turned the compass transmitter synchro by hand to due West and held it there. The course-recorder pen would move from due North and eventually line out at due West on the chart. But before it settled down there would be a *transient*. The pen might creep into balance, it might move quickly to a slight overshoot or two and then balance out, or it might oscillate back and forth for quite a time before settling down. Which of these effects actually does take place the system response to a unit step input will tell us, mathematically and graphically.

The Laplace transform of a unit step is $1/s$. It is a rule of control system mathematics that *system response transform = excitation function transform × system transfer function transform*. (This is similar to $E = IR$ if we think of I as the *excitation* applied to a simple system of one resistor and E as the result or *response* of our system.) Therefore we have for our system shocked by a unit step

$$\frac{1}{s} \times \frac{12,420}{s^2 + 65.4s + 12,420} = \frac{12,420}{s(s^2 + 65.4s + 12,420)} \qquad (6.3)$$

We must find the inverse transform or time function of this equation. We look in a table of Laplace transforms and find an odd-looking pair of functions that might fit our case. The Laplace transform in the table* is

$$\frac{1}{s\left(\dfrac{s^2}{\omega_n{}^2} + \dfrac{2zs}{\omega_n} + 1\right)} \qquad (6.4)$$

* Eq. No. 00.101 in Nixon, *Handbook of Laplace Transformation*, see Bibliography, Appendix E.

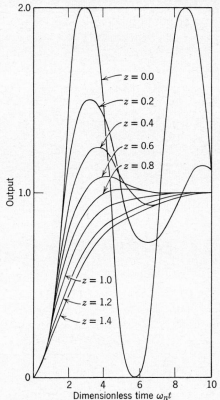

Fig. 6.2   Response of second-order system to a unit step.

The ω_n is the *natural frequency*, sometimes called undamped frequency, of the system. Many classes of objects "ring" or vibrate at or near their natural frequency when struck or shocked; for example, bells, piano strings, mechanical systems, electrical circuits, and many others. The relative damping or damping factor is z. The z, or ζ (the Greek letter zeta), is the most important criterion of transient response. It is a measure of the speed of decay or dying out of transient oscillations. Some universal curves showing transient response for several values of z are given in Fig. 6.2. Note that for $z = 0$ we have a sine wave that lasts forever, for $z < 1$ we have an underdamped system; for $z = 1$ we have critical damping. Usually the system designer keeps his damping factor z larger than 0.4 to assure adequate system stability.

Equation (6.3) can be put in the form of equation (6.4) if we first divide both numerator and denominator by 12,420, which gives us

$$\frac{1}{s\left(\dfrac{s^2}{12,420} + \dfrac{65.4s}{12,420} + 1\right)} = \frac{1}{s\left(\dfrac{s^2}{\omega_n{}^2} + \dfrac{2zs}{\omega_n} + 1\right)} \qquad (6.5)$$

We see from the first denominator term that $\omega_n{}^2 = 12,420$. Then

$$\omega_n = \sqrt{12,420} = 111.4 \qquad \text{rad/sec} \qquad (6.6)$$

The system's natural frequency is 111.4 rad/sec, or $111.4/2\pi =$ about 18 c/s.

The middle terms of equation (6.5) must be equal, thus

$$\frac{2zs}{\omega_n} = \frac{65.4s}{12,420} = \frac{65.4s/111.4}{12,420/111.4} = \frac{0.586s}{111.4} = \frac{2 \times 0.293s}{111.4} \qquad (6.7)$$

Note that we divided both numerator and denominator by 111.4 so that the denominator would become 111.4, or ω_n. Note also that $z = 0.293$.

Our system Laplace transform is then

$$\frac{1}{s\left(\dfrac{s^2}{\omega_n{}^2} + \dfrac{2zs}{\omega_n} + 1\right)} = \frac{1}{\left(\dfrac{s^2}{(111.4)^2} + \dfrac{2(0.293)s}{111.4} + 1\right)} \qquad (6.8)$$

The time-function half of this pair is given in Laplace transform tables:

$$1 + \frac{1}{\sqrt{1 - z^2}}\, e^{-z\omega_n t} \sin\left(\omega_n \sqrt{1 - z^2}\, t - \arctan \frac{\sqrt{1 - z^2}}{-z}\right) \qquad (6.9)$$

The substitution or 111.4 for ω_n and 0.293 for z in equation (6.9) gives us the time-domain equation of our system. We find that

$$\sqrt{1 - z^2} = 0.956 \quad \text{and} \quad \frac{1}{\sqrt{1 - z^2}} = \frac{1}{0.956} = 1.046 \quad (6.10)$$

and

$$\omega_n \sqrt{1 - z^2} = 111.4 \times 0.956 = 106.7 = \omega_d \qquad (6.11)$$

ω_d is the frequency of our transient, the *damped* sine wave. It is therefore called the *damped frequency*.

For the last term of equation (6.9)

$$\arctan \frac{\sqrt{1-z^2}}{-z} = \arctan \frac{0.956}{-0.293} = \arctan(-3.26) = -107°$$

$$(6.12)$$

since $\tan 107° = -3.26$. Equation (6.9) then becomes

$$1 + 1.046e^{-32.6t} \sin(106.7t - 107°) \qquad (6.13)$$

This is the time function of our system shocked by a unit step. It looks complex, so we will break it up into its parts. The 1 is the unit step. The rest is the transient; it is of the form

$$K_1 e^{-K_2 t} \sin(K_3 t - \theta) \qquad (6.14)$$

By omitting the exponential term we have $K_1 \sin(K_3 t - \theta)$, which is of the form $E_{max} \sin(\omega t - \theta)$. This expression represents any sine wave with amplitude K_1, frequency ω or 2π equal to K_3; and phase-shift angle (lagging) of θ. The exponential term $e^{-K_2 t}$ causes the wave to die out. Figure 6.3a shows the sine wave and the exponential elements of the curve. Figure 6.3b shows the damped sinusoid, which is 1 plus the product of 1.046 and the two curves in Fig 6.3a. In Fig. 6.3b the exponential curves are construction curves only; they show the "envelope" of the sinusoid.

6.2 PLOTTING THE TRANSIENT-RESPONSE CURVE OF THE UNCOMPENSATED COURSE RECORDER SYSTEM

If we go through the steps of plotting this curve, given in equation (6.13), we will understand it better. We recognize $\sin(106.7t - 107°)$ as $\sin(\omega t - \phi)$. The value of ω is 106.7 rad/sec, slightly less than 111.4, rad/sec, the *natural frequency* ω_n. We call this 106.7 rad/sec the *damped frequency* ω_d; it is the actual frequency of our transient curve. The *period* T of any wave $\sin \omega t$ is $2\pi/\omega$: $T = 1/f$; $\omega = 2\pi f = 2\pi/T$; $T = 2\pi/\omega$. Therefore our damped sine-wave period is

$$\frac{2\pi}{\omega_d} = \frac{2\pi}{106.7} = 0.0589 \text{ sec} \qquad (6.15)$$

At $t = 0$ equation (6.13) of the transient curve becomes

$$f(t) = 1 + 1.046e° \sin(0 - 107°)$$
$$= 1 + 1.046(-0.956) = 1 - 1 = 0 \qquad (6.16)$$

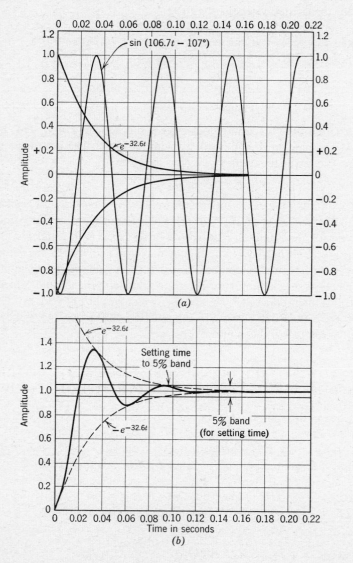

Fig. 6.3 Uncompensated course recorder system transient response to a unit step. (*a*) Elements whose product $e^{-32.6t} \sin (106.7t - 107°)$ is part of the transient shown in (*b*). (*b*) Heavy line is the transient:

$$1 + 1.046e^{-32.6t} \sin (106.7t - 107°)$$

To find the maximum and minimum points of the complete curve shown in Fig. 6.3b we can differentiate the equation of the curve (6.13) and then equate the result to zero.

$$\frac{d}{dt}[1 + 1.046e^{-32.6t}\sin(106.7t - 107°)] = 0 \qquad (6.17)$$

$$0 + 1.046[-32.6e^{-32.6t}\sin(106.7t - 107°)$$
$$+ 1.046\cos(106.7t - 107°)] = 0 \quad (6.18)$$

$$1.046e^{-32.6t}[-32.6\sin(106.7t - 107°)$$
$$+ 106.7\cos(106.7t - 107°)] = 0 \quad (6.19)$$

$$32.6\sin(106.7t - 107°) = 106.7\cos(106.7t - 107°) \quad (6.20)$$

$$\frac{\sin(106.7t - 107°)}{\cos(106.7t - 107°)} = \frac{106.7}{32.6} = 3.27 \qquad (6.21)$$

$$\tan(106.7t - 107°) = 3.27 \qquad (6.22)$$

$$106.7t - 107° = \arctan 3.27 = -107°, 73°, 253°, 433°, \ldots \quad (6.23)$$

$$106.7t = 0°, 180°, 360°, 540°, \ldots = n\pi \text{ rad}; n = 0,1,2,3\ldots \quad (6.24)$$

Equation (6.24) shows that at each maximum and minimum point

$$106.7t = \omega_d t = n\pi; n = 0,1,2,3,\ldots \qquad (6.25)$$

With this substitution the exponential term of equation (6.9) becomes, using equation (6.11),

$$e^{-z\omega_n t} = e^{-z\omega_d t/(1-z^2)} = e^{-zn\pi/\sqrt{1-z^2}}; n = 0,1,2,3,\ldots \quad (6.26)$$

The general equation (6.9) becomes at maximum and minimum points, using equations (6.25) and (6.26)

$$1 + \frac{1}{\sqrt{1 - z^2}} e^{-z\pi n/\sqrt{1-z^2}} \sin\left(n\pi - \arctan\frac{\sqrt{1 - z^2}}{-z}\right);$$
$$n = 0,1,2,3,4,\ldots \quad (6.27)$$

at each minimum and maximum we have

$$\frac{1}{\sqrt{1 - z^2}}\sin\left(n\pi - \arctan\frac{\sqrt{1 - z^2}}{-z}\right) = 1.046\sin(n\pi - 107°)$$
$$= \pm 1; n = 0,1,2,3,\ldots \quad (6.28)$$

which can be shown as follows: The term $1.046 \sin(n\pi - 107°)$ has been calculated when $n = 0$ in equation (6.16) as -1. When $n = 1$, we have $1.046 \sin(180° - 107°) = 1.046 \sin 73° = +1$. When $n = 2$, we have $1.046 \sin(360° - 107°) = 1.046 \sin 253° = -1$. Thus this term is -1 at each minimum and $+1$ at each maximum.

Substituting the results of equation (6.28)—± 1—into equation (6.27), at each minimum the transient equation becomes:

$$1 - e^{-zn\pi/\sqrt{1-z^2}}; \qquad n = 0,1,2,3, \ldots \qquad (6.29a)$$

and at each maximum of the transient equation we have:

$$1 + e^{-zn\pi/\sqrt{1-z^2}}; \qquad n = 0,1,2,3, \ldots \qquad (6.29b)$$

After we calculate the time t of each minimum and maximum we will find it easier to go back to the general expression for the exponential term, $e^{-z\omega_n t} = e^{-32.6t}$, rather than to use equations (6.29a) and (6.29b). We then calculate our transient minimum values by

$$1 - e^{-z\omega_n t} = 1 - e^{-32.6t}; \qquad t = \text{all minimum values} \quad (6.29c)$$

and our maximum values by

$$1 + e^{-z\omega_n t} = 1 + e^{-32.6t}; \qquad t = \text{all maximum values.} \quad (6.29d)$$

The time at each transient maximum and minimum is, from equation (6.25)

$$t = \frac{n\pi}{\omega_d} = \frac{n\pi}{106.7} = \frac{0}{106.7}, \frac{\pi}{106.7}, \frac{2\pi}{106.7}, \frac{3\pi}{106.7}, \ldots \quad (6.30a)$$

Calculation gives the minimum and maximum values:

$$t = n\frac{\pi}{\omega_d} = n \times 0.02944 = 0, 0.02944, 0.0589, 0.0883, \ldots \quad (6.30b)$$

Each t is separated by 0.02944 sec $= 1/2$ of 0.0589 sec, which we calculated in equation (6.15) as the time of one period of our damped sine wave. Therefore *the first maximum is 1/2 period after t = 0, and all minima and maxima occur midway in the cycle.* Therefore we can find the values of equation (6.30b) from equation (6.15). Using the results of equations (6.29c), (6.29d), and (6.30a) as formulas, we do not need to repeat the preceding calculus to plot any second-order transient wave.

The crossings of the 1.0 amplitude line in Fig. 6.3b will occur when

$$1 + 1.046e^{-32.6t} \sin (106.7t - 107°) = 1 \qquad (6.31)$$

or $\quad 1.046e^{-32.6t} \sin (106.7t - 107°) = 0, 180°, 360°, \ldots \qquad (6.32)$

This happens when the sine term = 0, that is, when

$$106.7t - 107° = 0 \qquad (6.33)$$

Then when $106.7t - 107° = 0$

$$106.7t = 107 \text{ deg} \times \frac{1 \text{ deg}}{57.3 \text{ rad}} = 1.87 \qquad \text{rad} \qquad (6.34a)$$

$$t = \frac{1.87}{106.7} = 0.0175 \qquad \text{sec} \qquad (6.34b)$$

and 1.0 crossings occur every 0.02944 sec thereafter, or when

$t = 0.0175, 0.0470, 0.0764, 0.1059, 0.1353, 0.1647,$ and 0.1942 sec

$$(6.35)$$

The general equation for time at the 1.0 crossings is

$$t = \frac{-\arctan(\sqrt{1 - z^2}/-z)}{57.3\omega_d} + \frac{n\pi}{\omega_d}; \qquad n = 0, 1, 2, 3, \ldots \qquad (6.36)$$

We can now calculate points so that we can plot the curve of equation (6.13). The results are shown in Fig. 6.3b, and Table 6.1 shows tabulation of points for plotting curves of Fig. 6.3b.

6.3 ANALYSIS OF TRANSIENT-RESPONSE CURVE AND ITS CONSTANTS

Transient Data

The curve shown in Fig. 6.3b is universal in nature, and therefore typical of all control systems. What does it tell us about our system? First, we cannot have a system that "overshoots" or deviates from the control point by too large an amount. The pen on our course recorder must, if it is to be "alive," have some overshoot but not too much. Generally anything over 25% *maximum overshoot* is too much; we have 38.2% in our curve of Fig. 6.3b, which is unacceptable. Again, we want the pen to stop oscillating as quickly as possible;

Table 6.1 *Tabulation of Points for Plotting Curves of Fig. 6.3b*

Points		1.0	Max	1.0	Min	1.0	Max	1.0	Min	1.0	Max	1.0	Min	1.0	Max
Time	0	0.0175	0.0294	0.0470	0.0589	0.0764	0.0883	0.1059	0.1178	0.1353	0.1472	0.1647	0.1767	0.1942	0.2061
$-32.6t$	0		0.961		1.92		2.88		3.84		4.80		5.76		6.72
$e^{-32.6t}$	1		0.383		0.147		0.056		0.022		0.008		0.003		0.001
$1 + e^{-32.6t}$			1.383		1.0		1.056		1.0		1.008		1.0		1.001
$1 - e^{-32.6t}$	0		1.0		0.853		1.0		0.978		1.0		0.997		

that is, we want the oscillations to die out as quickly as possible. For the *settling time* we see that on the graph oscillations die out to within a 5% band either side of 1.0 in 0.09 sec after a little more than $1\frac{1}{2}$ cycles or oscillations. We can see the speed of response from the *rise time*—usually the time the system requires to go from 10% of the unit step to 90% of the unit step. We find from the curve it is $0.017 - 0.007 = 0.01$ sec. The *time to the first peak or maximum overshoot* is 0.0294 sec. Thus the transient curve shows us many things the Bode diagram did not tell us and gives us many criteria valuable in control system analysis and design.

We solved the *specific* second-order equation in order to plot the transient curve of Fig. 6.3. There are a number of very useful formulas based on the *general* second-order equation

$$\frac{\theta_{\text{out}}}{\theta_{\text{in}}} = \frac{1}{\dfrac{s^2}{\omega_n{}^2} + \dfrac{2zs}{\omega_n} + 1} \tag{6.4}$$

As we have seen, the defining constants of a specific second-order equation such as equation (6.2) are z and ω_n. We therefore must first find these two values, as indicated in equations (6.38), (6.39), and (6.40). In each of these equations the general formula is given first, and then we substitute the specific values of the uncompensated course recorder for which the open-loop transfer function is

$$\frac{\theta_{\text{out}}}{E} = \frac{K_v/N}{s(1 + T_m s)} = \frac{19{,}000/100}{s(1 + 0.0153s)} \tag{6.37}$$

$$\omega_n = \sqrt{K_v/NT_m} = \sqrt{19{,}000/(100 \times 0.0153)}$$

$$= \sqrt{12{,}420} = 111.4 \, \frac{\text{rad}}{\text{sec}} \tag{6.38}$$

$$z = \tfrac{1}{2}\sqrt{N/K_v T_m} = \tfrac{1}{2}\sqrt{100/(19{,}000 \times 0.0153)} = 0.293 \tag{6.39}$$

To check the foregoing calculations of z and ω_n we can use the following equation:

$$z = \frac{1}{2T_m \omega_n} = \frac{1}{2 \times 0.0153 \times 111.4} = 0.293 \tag{6.40}$$

These values of z and ω_n are keys to other formulas:

Damped frequency $= \omega_d = \omega_n \sqrt{1 - z^2} = 106.7$ rad/sec   (6.41)

Time of one period $= \dfrac{2\pi}{\omega_n \sqrt{1 - z^2}} = \dfrac{2\pi}{\omega_d} = 0.0589$ sec   (6.42)

Time to reach maximum overshoot $= \dfrac{1}{2} \dfrac{2\pi}{\omega_n \sqrt{1 - z^2}}$

$$= \dfrac{\pi}{\omega_d} = 0.02944 \quad\text{sec}\quad (6.43)$$

Maximum deviation or overshoot $= e^{-z\pi / \sqrt{1-z^2}} = 0.382$ (6.44)

Settling time within 5% band $= \dfrac{3.0}{z\omega_n} = 0.092$ sec   (6.45)

Number of oscillations before preceding settling time

$$= \dfrac{1.5 \sqrt{1 - z^2}}{z\pi} = 1.56 \quad (6.46)$$

Note that we derived equations (6.41), (6.42), (6.43), and (6.44) in calculating our transient.

Closed-Loop Data from z and ω_n

It is interesting to note that although time and frequency characteristics are handled separately, they are intimately related, as will be shown very effectively by the root locus method discussed in Chapter 7. We can also see this relationship by developing closed-loop frequency response data from the same z and ω_n we used to construct the transient curves in Fig. 6.3. Using the values $z = 0.293$ and $\omega_n = 111.4$, derived in equations (6.38) and (6.39) we can find three very important closed-loop constants. First, we calculate the value of the *closed-loop peak frequency* ω_m, the frequency at which the maximum magnitude occurs, as follows:

$$\omega_m = \omega_n \sqrt{1 - 2z^2} = 111.4 \sqrt{0.828} = 101.2 \quad\text{rad/sec}\quad (6.47)$$

By comparing this value with the closed-loop plot, Fig. 5.3, we see that it is quite accurate.

Second, we calculate M_m, the closed-loop maximum magnitude. We substitute $j\omega$ for s in equation (6.2) (giving us equation (5.26)), and then use 101.2, the value of ω_m for ω. Then we have

$$M_m = \frac{\theta_{out}}{\theta_{in}} = \frac{12{,}420}{12{,}420 - \omega^2 + j65.4\omega}$$

$$= \frac{12{,}420}{12{,}420 - 10{,}240 + j6620} = \frac{12{,}420}{2180 + j6620}$$

$$= \frac{12{,}420}{6980\underline{/71.8^\circ}} = 1.785\underline{/-71.8^\circ} = 5.0 \text{ dB}\underline{/-71.8^\circ} \quad (6.48)$$

This value checks our Case III maximum amplitude value M_m and phase angle at M_m in Fig. 5.3b very closely.

Third, we calculate ω_b, the *closed-loop bandwidth* (bandwidth is the half-power or 3 dB down point), and we use the equation

$$\omega_b = \omega_n \sqrt{1 - 2z^2 + \sqrt{2 - 4z^2 + 4z^4}} = 162.5 \qquad \text{rad/sec} \quad (6.49)$$

This frequency value is very close to that of Case III at -3 dB in Fig. 5.3. Thus we can calculate three key closed-loop values to help us plot the curve, or we could possibly avoid plotting the curve altogether if all we needed were values of ω_m, M_m, and ω_b.

Tables of Transient and Frequency-Response Data

Table 6.2 gives values of z and corresponding values of other constants depending directly on z (columns 2 and 3) or on z and ω_n (the last three columns). In the latter case, simply multiply the value given by ω_n; for example, if $z = 0.45$ and $\omega_n = 100$ rad/sec, then $\omega_d = 89.3$ rad/sec, $\omega_b = 133$ rad/sec, and $\omega_m = 76.8$ rad/sec.

In Chapter 5 only three of our systems were second order: the uncompensated system with which we began (equation (6.37)), the rate-generator compensated system (equation (5.47)), and the system with load inertia (equation (5.65)). All other systems were third order, and their transients will be dealt with in Chapter 7. In Table 6.3 we have constants for all three systems, found by plugging values of these systems into equations (6.38) through (6.46). Note that the maximum overshoot, time to first maximum, and time of one period are all necessary to plot our transient curve of Fig. 6.3b, while the settling time within a 5% band and number of oscillations before settling can be used to check the plotted curve after it is drawn. In addition all values in Table 6.3 can be roughly checked by interpolation of Table 6.2.

Table 6.2   *Constants of Second-Order Systems as a Function of z*

z	Maximum Overshoot (decimal fraction)*	Number of Oscillations to Settle to ±5%*	$\dfrac{\omega_d}{\omega_n}$	$\dfrac{\omega_b}{\omega_n}$	$\dfrac{\omega_m}{\omega_n}$
0.0	1.00	∞	1	1.55	1
0.1	0.730	4.76	0.995	1.54	0.99
0.2	0.527	2.34	0.980	1.51	0.959
0.3	0.372	1.52	0.954	1.45	0.906
0.4	0.254	1.09	0.9165	1.39	0.825
0.45	0.205	0.95	0.893	1.33	0.768
0.5	0.166	0.82	0.866	1.27	0.707
0.6	0.0955	0.64	0.800	1.13	0.529
0.707	0.042	0.48	0.707	1.00	0.0
0.8	0.016	0.36	0.600	0.90	
0.9	0.0015	0.23	0.300	0.74	
1.0	0.0	0.0	0.0	0.64	

Note: Dimensions of time constants are seconds and of frequency constants (ω) are radians per second.
* Of initial step.

PROBLEMS

6.1. From the open-loop transfer functions you found in working out Probs. 5.3(*b*), 5.11, and 5.19, make a table similar to Table 6.2. Start by calculating z and ω_n, possibly by using equations (6.38) and (6.39) and by *checking* these values using equation (6.40), or you can check by putting the values you found into equation (6.4) and get back your original transfer function, as shown in equation (6.5). Check your values of ω_b and ω_m (closed-loop bandwidth and frequency of closed-loop maximum gain value) against your closed-loop plot drawn as your answer to Prob. 5.4. A rough check of your final values may be made if you interpolate in Table 6.1, using your values of z and ω_n.

6.2. From the open-loop transfer functions you found in working out Probs. 5.5(*b*), 5.12, and 5.20, make a table similar to Table 6.2. Start by calculating z and ω_n, possibly by using equations (6.38) and (6.39) and by *checking* these values using equation (6.40), or you can check by putting the values you found into equation (6.4) and get back your original transfer function, as shown in equation (6.5). Check your values of ω_b

Table 6.3 *Values of Constants of Three Second-Order Systems*

	z	Maximum Overshoot (decimal fraction)*	Number of Oscillations to Settle to $\pm 5\%$*	ω_n	Time to Maximum Overshoot π/ω_d	Time of One Period $2\pi/\omega_d$	Settling Time to $\pm 5\%$*	ω_d	ω_b	ω_m
Uncompensated system	0.293	0.382	1.56	111.4	0.0294	0.0589	0.092	106.7	162.5	101.2
Rate-generator system	0.494	0.169	0.84	184.0	0.0196	0.0392	0.030	160.1	237.0	132.0
System with load inertia	0.239	0.461	1.94	91.0	0.0355	0.0711	0.138	88.4	136.0	85.6

* Of initial step.

and ω_m (closed-loop bandwidth and frequency of closed-loop maximum gain value) against your closed-loop plot drawn as your answer to Prob. 5.6. A rough check of your final values may be made if you interpolate in Table 6.1, using your values of z and ω_n.

6.3. (*a*) The closed-loop equation you found for Prob. 5.3(*c*) is in velocity constant (K_v) form. Change your equation as indicated in equations (5.10) and (5.24*b*) by multiplying the numerator and the denominator of the closed-loop equation by the value of $1/T_m$. Your equation will then have the torque constant (K_t) form of equations (6.1) and (6.2).

(*b*) Multiply your equation obtained in (*a*) by $1/s$, as in equation (6.3). Then divide the numerator and the denominator by the numerator value. Obtain the values of ω_n and z as shown in equation (6.5) and check your answers in Prob. 6.1.

6.4. (*a*) The closed-loop equation you found for Prob. 5.5(*c*) is in velocity constant (K_v) form. Change your equation as indicated in equations (5.10) and (5.24*b*) by multiplying the numerator and the denominator of your closed-loop equation by your value of $1/T_m$. Your equation will then have the torque constant (K_t) form of equations (6.1) and (6.2).

(*b*) Multiply the equation you obtained in (*a*) by $1/s$, as in equation (6.3). Then divide the numerator and denominator by the numerator value. Obtain the values of ω_n and z as shown in equation (6.5), and check your answers of Prob. 6.2.

6.5. (*a*) Using equation (6.9) as the inverse Laplace transform or time equivalent of the equation found in the answer to Prob. 6.3(*b*) and the values of ω_n and z, find the transient equation of the system. Calculate the phase angle *carefully*. Your equation will have the form of equation (6.13).

(*b*) Calculate the values necessary to plot the curves of the system and draw the curves similar to those shown in Fig. 6.3*b*.

(*c*) Find on the transient curve: the rise time from 10% to 90% of 1.0 amplitude; the settling time to within a 5% band; the number of oscillations before settling within a 5% band. Check these values against your calculated values of this system in your answer to Prob. 6.1.

6.6. (*a*) Using equation (6.9) as the inverse Laplace transform or time equivalent of your equation found in your answer to Prob. 6.4(*b*) and your values of ω_n and z, find the transient equation of the system. Calculate the phase angle *carefully*. Your equation will have the form of equation (6.13).

(*b*) Calculate the values necessary to plot the curves of the system and draw the curves similar to those shown in Fig. 6.3*b*.

(*c*) Find on your transient curve: the rise time from 10% to 90% of 1.0 amplitude; the settling time within a 5% band; the number of oscillations before settling within a 5% band. Check these values against your calculated values of this system in the answer to Prob. 6.2.

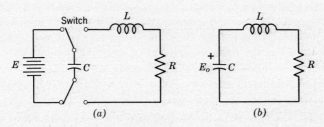

Fig. P6.7.

6.7. (*a*) In Fig. P6.7*a* $E = 2000$ V, $L = 0.0125$ H, $R = 100$ Ω. At time $t = 0$; the double-pole switch is thrown from the left to the right, giving the circuit shown in Fig. P.67*b*, with the capacitor initially charged to 2000 V. The current in the circuit is then

$$i = \frac{CE}{LC\sqrt{\dfrac{1}{LC} - \dfrac{R^2}{4L^2}}} e^{-\frac{tR}{2L}} \sin \sqrt{\dfrac{1}{LC} - \dfrac{R^2}{4L^2}}\, t \qquad \text{(P6.7.1)}$$

This is of the form

$$i = I_0 e^{K_1 t} \sin K_2 t \qquad \text{(P6.7.2)}$$

which is similar to equation (6.14). Substitute the values just given for R, L, and C in equation (P6.7.1) and find a numerical expression for i.

(*b*) Draw the transient curve of i. (The curve will be similar to Fig. 6.4.)

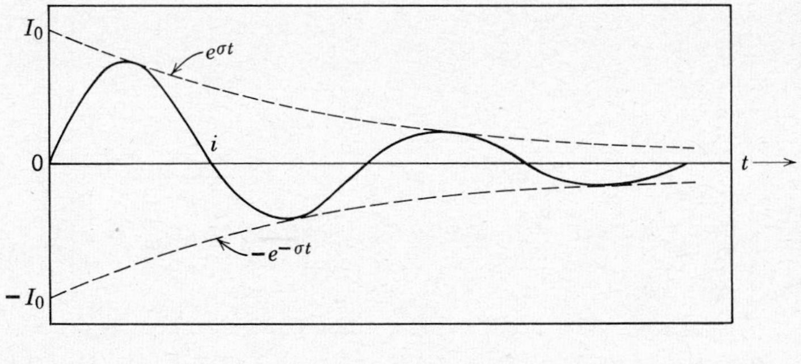

Fig. 6.4   Typical curve of decaying oscillations.

$$i = I_0\, e^{\sigma t} \sin \omega t$$

The transient curve found as the answer to Prob. 6.9(*b*) is of the form of Fig. 6.4. (This curve is different from that of Fig. 6.3*b* in that there is no initial step; the Fig. 6.4 curve always returns to the same zero axis.) Figure 6.4 is the form of damped or decaying oscillations if there is no external power applied to the oscillating device after $t = 0$; the device could be an active oscillator from which power has been suddenly removed as the curve passes through zero. It could also be an oscillator at rest until it has been given a very short sharp rap or *impulse*. If we hit a pendulum at rest sharply in the direction of its normal travel but do not "follow through," the pendulum will describe the curve shown in Fig. 6.4. The initial capacitor voltage suddenly switched into the circuit in Prob. 6.7 is a form of impulse given to an *RLC* oscillating system. If in this *RLC* circuit instead of the charge on the capacitor we had supplied an external dc voltage in series with R, L, and C, and suddenly replaced it with a short circuit at time $t = 0$, the transient current curve would have been like Fig. 6.5, which is essentially the same as Fig. 6.4, but starts at I_0 instead of 0. The transient curves of Figs. 6.4 and 6.5 are those of an *RLC* circuit, a child's swing, a pendulum, a galvanometer, a vibrating string, a tuning fork, the balance wheel of a watch, or an underdamped servosystem—when these are (*a*) at rest and given an impulse or are displaced and suddenly let go, or are (*b*) oscillating uniformly and the external power source is suddenly removed. In both cases oscillations decay naturally as friction or resistance reduce the amplitude of each succeeding oscillation.

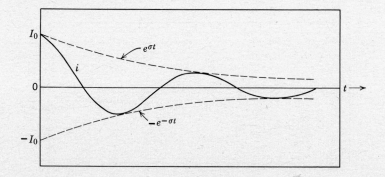

Fig. 6.5 Typical curve of decaying oscillations.

$$i = I_0 e^{\sigma t} \cos \omega t$$

6.4 COMPLEX S-PLANE ANALYSIS

In order to explore further the transient curve we seek a general equation of damped curves such as Fig. 6.3*b*, Fig. 6.4, and Fig. 6.5. Let us examine carefully the equation of the curve shown in Fig. 6.5; it is

$$i = I_0 e^{\sigma t} \cos \omega t \tag{6.50}$$

This equation has three parts: I_0, $e^{\sigma t}$, and $\cos \omega t$. If $t = 0$ we have only I_0, a dc value that is always positive or negative and does not change with time. If $\omega = 0$ we have $I_0 e^{\sigma t}$, a decaying exponential curve similar to a capacitor discharge if σ is negative, and an exponentially increasing curve if σ is positive. If $\sigma = 0$, we have $I_0 \cos \omega t$, a cosine wave with amplitude I_0.

We would gain more mathematical insight into equation (6.50) if we could find an exponential expression for $\cos \omega t$, for then $e^{\sigma t} \cos \omega t$ would all be expressed as e to some power. We know that to describe a steady-state sine or cosine wave we can use the projection of a steadily rotating phasor, as shown in Fig. 6.6, where ω is the angular velocity. If angular velocity ω is increased, we could have Fig. 6.7. For a slower angular velocity (a smaller ω) we could have Fig. 6.8.

It can be shown mathematically (by infinite series) that

$$e^{j\theta} = \cos \theta + j \sin \theta \tag{6.51}$$

where e is the base of the natural system of logarithms and has a numerical value of 2.71828. Now e^{θ} has numerical meaning if θ is a number in radians. But $e^{j\theta}$ has no meaning as a number; it has meaning only as an *operator* rotating a phasor by an angle θ, as shown in Fig. 6.9. Thus $e^{j\pi}$ rotates a phasor 180° because π radians = 180°.

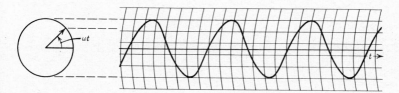

Fig. 6.6 Generation of a sine or cosine wave by a rotating phasor. If angular velocity ω is increased, we could have Fig. 6.7.

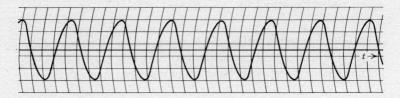

Fig. 6.7 Cosine wave generated by a vector moving at a higher velocity than in Fig. 6.6.

And $e^{i\theta}$ is similar to $+$, $-$, and $\times$ in that it indicates an operation to be performed. From Fig. 6.9 we conclude that

$$1e^{i\theta} = 1\cos\theta + 1j\sin\theta \tag{6.52}$$

or

$$e^{i\theta} = \cos\theta + j\sin\theta \tag{6.53}$$

This is called Euler's formula. In a similar manner we can show that parallel to equation (6.51) we have

$$e^{-i\theta} = \cos\theta - j\sin\theta \tag{6.54}$$

Adding equations (6.53) and (6.54) gives

$$e^{i\theta} + e^{-i\theta} = 2\cos\theta \tag{6.55}$$

or

$$\frac{e^{i\theta} + e^{-i\theta}}{2} = \cos\theta \tag{6.56}$$

and when $\theta = \omega t$

$$e^{j\omega t} + e^{-j\omega t} = 2\cos\omega t; \qquad \frac{e^{j\omega t} + e^{-j\omega t}}{2} = \cos\omega t \tag{6.57}$$

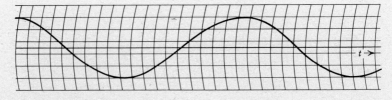

Fig. 6.8 Cosine wave generated by a vector moving at a lower velocity than in Fig. 6.6.

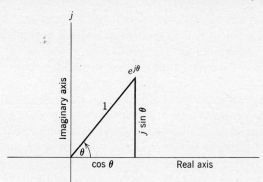

Fig. 6.9 Rotation of phasor of length 1 by the operator $e^{j\theta}$.

We have now achieved our goal, which was to express all cosine waves mathematically by exponentials, as in equation (6.57). Graphically we can find all cosine waves on the *complex frequency* or *s plane*, which is shown in Fig. 6.10. On this plane the vertical axis or ordinate is the $j\omega$ axis, j signifying that the axis is rotated 90° from the horizontal. Each cosine wave is represented in Fig. 6.10 by *two* points

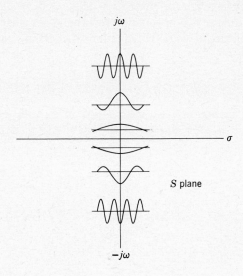

Fig. 6.10 Cosine waves found on the *s* complex frequency or *s* plane along the *j*ω axis.

on the axis, $j\omega$ and $-j\omega$ corresponding to $e^{j\omega t}$ and $e^{-j\omega t}$ in equation (6.57). Note that it is the exponent of e which is plotted, or rather the s in e^{st}, where $s = j\omega$.

In Fig. 6.10 the points illustrated are *frequency* points, but the *time* representations of cosine waves are pictured; that is, points along the vertical axis are in terms of $j\omega$, but the waves shown are in terms of t. The *points* $j\omega$ and $-j\omega$ at which the waves are shown are correct, but the *waveshapes* shown are a compromise with reality: they are 180° out of phase, to represent $j\omega$ and $-j\omega$. But as the form of equation (6.57) shows us, it takes *both* $e^{j\omega t}$ and $e^{-j\omega t}$ ($s = j\omega$ and $s = -j\omega$) to make one cosine wave. We can fold the plane along the σ axis and combine any two points that lie next to one another on the $j\omega$ axis to get one cosine wave. (We shall see later that this is also true of all points off the horizontal (σ) axis.)

In equation (6.57) we did not define the amplitude of the cosine wave. To specify the amplitude we need a real multiplier K or I_0 so that

$$I_0(e^{j\omega t} + e^{-j\omega t}) = 2I_0 \cos \omega t \qquad (6.58)$$

The value of I_0 is not indicated on the complex plane. At the origin $\omega = 0$, and we have dc; for given $I_0 e^{j\omega t}$ and $\omega = 0$, we have I_0, a dc value. (Substitute $\omega = 0$ in equation (6.58) and see what happens.)

This section began with the equation of the transient curve in Fig. 6.5

$$i = I_0 e^{\sigma t} \cos \omega t \qquad (6.59)$$

We have already dealt with I_0 and $\cos \omega t$; $e^{\sigma t}$ remains, where σ is a real number. In Fig. 6.11 we see a graph of $e^{\sigma t}$ with σ a negative number. If $t = 0$, $e^{\sigma t} = e^0 = 1$, as shown. If σ is a larger negative

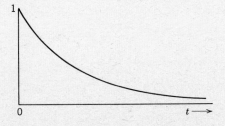

Fig. 6.11   Graph of exponentially decreasing function $e^{\sigma t}$. At $t = 0$, $e^{\sigma t} = 0$, as shown at the left.

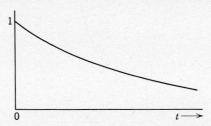

Fig. 6.12   Same as Fig. 6.11 but with smaller negative value of σ.

number, Fig. 6.12 results. If σ is a smaller negative number, Fig. 6.13 results. Of course, if σ were positive, $e^{\sigma t}$ would be an increasing instead of decreasing exponential, as shown in Fig. 6.14. Note that this curve is boundless; it is headed for infinity.

Note that σ, like $j\omega$, has dimensions of $1/t$, the same as ω and f. Therefore σ is mathematically a form of frequency, and we can truthfully call the s plane the *complex frequency plane*. On this plane we locate Figs. 6.11 through 6.14 along the horizontal or σ axis, as shown in Fig. 6.15. At $\sigma = 0$ we again have $I_0 e_0 = I_0 = $ dc. Note that as the values of σ we show *time* equivalents $e^{\sigma t}$. We also have waves along the $j\omega$ axis displayed.

Points on the s plane off the axes are combinations of cosine waves and exponentials. We found that to designate a cosine wave we need $s = j\omega$ and $s = -j\omega$ (time function $e^{j\omega t} + e^{-j\omega t} = 2 \cos \omega t$). For each wave off the axes we would expect to have a pair of points $s = \sigma + j\omega$ and $s = \sigma - j\omega$. The corresponding time function would then be

$$\frac{I_0}{2} \left[e^{(\sigma + j\omega)t} + e^{(\sigma - j\omega)t} \right] = \frac{I_0}{2} e^{\sigma t}(e^{j\omega} + e^{-j\omega t}) = I_0 e^{\sigma t} \cos \omega t \quad (6.60)$$

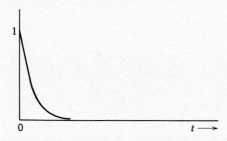

Fig. 6.13   Same as Fig. 6.11 but with larger negative value of σ.

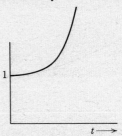

Fig. 6.14 Graph of exponentially increasing function $e^{\sigma t}$, $\sigma =$ a positive number.

which is the curve we started with (Fig. 6.5). Therefore the complex s plane can be used to display all transients of the form of equation (6.60). The s of $e^{st} = e^{(\sigma+j\omega)t}$ takes on all values, such as $2 + j3$, -2, $j5$, $-2 - j4$. These complex frequency values give rise to all the waveforms shown in Fig. 6.16. Again as we saw with cosine waves in Fig. 6.10, points off the axes where the waves shown are correct, but the waveshapes shown are a compromise with reality.

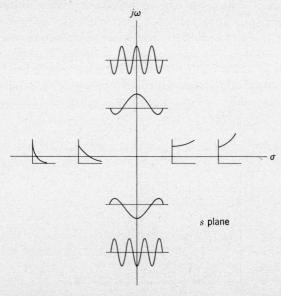

Fig. 6.15 Waveshapes found along the σ and $j\omega$ axes of the complex frequency or s plane.

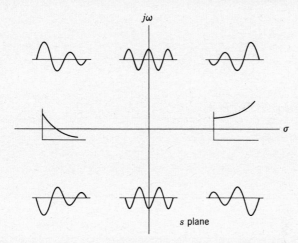

Fig. 6.16   Waveshapes found in various parts of the complex frequency or *s* plane.

We need both $s = \sigma + j\omega$ and $s = \sigma - j\omega$ to give a transient cosine wave. The waveshapes shown in Fig. 6.16 are *time*-domain representations of the *frequency* variable *s*. Therefore for each wave we have two points equidistant above and below the σ axis. We see that *s is two-dimensional; it includes radian frequency and rate of decay of the transient. Therefore* $I_0(e^{s_1 t} + e^{s_2 t})$ *can be used to represent the steady state and the transient state in compact form, as shown in Fig. 6.17.*

SUMMARY

Frequency-response transfer functions and graphs of these transfer functions (Bode diagrams) gave us much valuable information about control system *steady state behavior*. In all this work we limited the value of *s* to $j\omega$; in other words we have in preceding chapters restricted ourselves to the $j\omega$, or vertical axis, in the *s* plane. In this chapter we have added a new dimension to our analysis—*transient* analysis—and we have thus ventured off the $j\omega$ axis into all parts of the *s* plane. On this plane, letting $s = \sigma + j\omega$ we have found all dc, exponential, cosine, and decaying cosine curves. A graphic procedure that gives

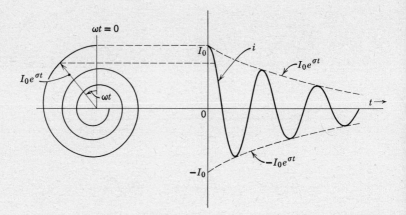

Fig. 6.17 Generation of a damped cosine wave by a two-dimensional (rotating: $e^{j\omega t}$, and shrinking: $e^{\sigma t}$) phasor.

$$i = I_0 e^{\sigma t} \cos \omega t = \frac{I_0}{2} e^{\sigma t}(e^{j\omega t} + e^{-j\omega t}) = \frac{I_0}{2}(e^{s_1 t} + e^{s_2 t})$$

both *steady-state and transient* information and uses the entire complex s plane is the *root locus* method, which we investigate in Chapter 7.

7.

Root locus

7.1 INTRODUCTION

Characteristic Equation

In any transfer function, such as

$$\frac{\theta_{out}}{E} = KG = \frac{\text{Numerator}}{\text{Denominator}} = \frac{K(s+2)}{(s+1)(s+3)} \qquad (7.1)$$

the *characteristic equation* is the denominator of the function equated to zero

$$\text{Denominator} = (s+1)(s+3) = 0 \qquad (7.2)$$

whose roots are $s = -1$ and $s = -3$. That this equation contains the most important *characteristic* parts of the function in equation (7.1) is demonstrated by breaking the transfer function into partial fractions

$$\frac{s+2}{(s+1)(s+3)} = \frac{A}{s+1} = \frac{B}{s+3} = \frac{A(s+3) + B(s+1)}{(s+1)(s+3)} \qquad (7.3)$$

(Note that we have dropped the constant K to make the result easier to see.)

$$s + 2 = A(s+1) + B(s+3) \qquad (7.4)$$

Let $s = -1$ in equation (7.4). Then

$$1 = 2A; \qquad A = \tfrac{1}{2} \qquad (7.5)$$

Let $s = -3$ in equation (7.4). Then

$$-1 = -2B; \qquad B = \tfrac{1}{2} \qquad (7.6)$$

Combining (7.3), (7.4), and (7.5), we obtain

$$\frac{s+2}{(s+1)(s+3)} = \frac{\frac{1}{2}}{s+1} + \frac{\frac{1}{2}}{s+3} \qquad (7.7)$$

We can check our answer by the reverse process of adding the partial fractions

$$\frac{\frac{1}{2}}{s+1} = \frac{\frac{1}{2}}{s+3} = \frac{\frac{1}{2}(s+3) + \frac{1}{2}(s+2)}{(s+1)(s+3)}$$

$$= \frac{\frac{1}{2}s + \frac{3}{2} + \frac{1}{2}s + \frac{1}{2}}{(s+1)(s+3)} = \frac{s+2}{(s+1)(s+3)} \qquad (7.8)$$

From equation (7.7) it can be seen that the denominator determines the form of the function. The elements of this equation, which are shown at the right, are made up of the denominator of the transfer function and two constants. Furthermore, if $s = -1$, then $s + 1 = 0$, and the entire transfer function in equation (7.1) becomes infinite; likewise if $s = -3$, then $s + 3 = 0$, and the transfer function becomes infinite. We say that $s = -1$ and $s = -3$ are the *poles* of the transfer function in equation (7.1) and the *roots* of the characteristic equation (7.2). Thus *the characteristic equation determines the behavior of the function.* The numerator, $s + 2$, is in control only if $s = -2$, when $s + 2 = 0$. Then the whole transfer function becomes zero, and $s = -2$ is called a *zero* of the function. Poles and zeros determine the behavior of every transfer function, and thus of the system described by the function.

PROBLEMS

7.1. Separate the following fraction into the sum of two partial fractions. Prove your answer by adding the two partial fractions to obtain the original fraction.

$$\frac{s+3}{(s+2)(s+4)}$$

7.2. Separate the following fraction into the sum of two partial fractions. Prove your answer by adding the two partial fractions to obtain the original fraction.

$$\frac{s+3.5}{(s+2.5)(s+4.5)}$$

Routh Test

Figures 6.15 and 6.16 show that in the part of the complex plane left of the vertical ($j\omega$) axis transients die out, and that transients to the right of the vertical axis increase—theoretically forever, actually until saturation is reached or until some component breaks. This instability is due to *poles* in the right half of the complex plane (abbreviated RHP), and these poles are indicated by characteristic equation *positive real roots* or *complex roots with positive real parts*. The characteristic equation would contain factors such as $s - 1$ or $s - 1 \pm j3$ in such a case, with roots of $s = +1$ and $s = +1 \pm j3$ respectively. Therefore *absolute instability is indicated by a positive real root or a positive real part of a complex root of the characteristic equation.*

The characteristic equation

$$(s - 1)(s + 2)(s + 3) = 0 \tag{7.9}$$

obviously has one root ($s = +1$) in the RHP, which indicates an unstable system. The characteristic equation

$$s^2 + 2s + 2 = (s - 1 - j1)(s - 1 + j1) = 0$$

has no roots with positive real parts, which indicates a system that is not absolutely unstable. But what about equations such as

$$s^3 + 6s^2 + 11s + 6 = 0 \tag{7.10}$$

and $$s^3 + s^2 + 4s + 30 = 0 \tag{7.11}$$

One of these equations has a positive real root; the other does not. How can we tell in such cases and in cases of equations of higher degree?

First there are two cases we can distinguish immediately as having roots in the RHP. The first is any equation with a minus sign in it. If the unfactored characteristic equation has *any* negative terms, it has at least one root in the RHP. An example is

$$s^2 + s - 2 = (s - 1)(s + 2) = 0 \tag{7.12}$$

and we see that we need not worry about classifying such equations;

they all indicate unstable systems. The second case is an unfactored equation lacking one or more powers of the variable s. Thus

$$s^3 + 1 = (s + 1)\left(s - \frac{1}{2} + j\sqrt{\frac{3}{2}}\right)\left(s - \frac{1}{2} - j\sqrt{\frac{3}{2}}\right) \qquad (7.13)$$

has two complex roots with positive real parts ($s = +\frac{1}{2} \pm j\sqrt{3}/2$), which we would know by inspection because the s^2 term is missing.

We shall now use the Routh test to determine whether equations (7.10) and (7.11) have roots in the RHP. These equations are of the general form

$$a_0 s^n + a_1 s^{n-1} + a_2 s^{n-2} + \cdots + a_n = 0 \qquad (7.14)$$

Equation (7.10) then has the form

$$a_0 s^3 + a_1 s^2 + a_2 s + a_3 = 0 \qquad (7.15)$$

with $a_0 = 1$, $a_1 = 6$, $a_2 = 11$, and $a_3 = 6$. The Routh array for testing is

$$\begin{array}{ccc} a_0 & a_2 & a_4 \\ a_1 & a_3 & a_5 \\ b_1 & b_2 & b_3 \\ c_1 & c_2 & \\ d_1 & d_2 & \\ e_1 & & \end{array} \qquad (7.16)$$

and the rule is: *There are no roots in the RHP if all elements of the left-hand column of the Routh array (a_0, a_1, b_1, c_1, d_1, etc.) are all positive and nonzero.* The elements b_1, b_2, etc. are calculated as follows:

$$b_1 = \frac{a_1 a_2 - a_0 a_3}{a_1} \qquad b_2 = \frac{a_1 a_4 - a_0 a_5}{a_1}$$

$$c_1 = \frac{b_1 a_3 - a_1 b_2}{b_1} \qquad c_2 = \frac{b_1 a_5 - a_1 b_3}{b_1} \qquad (7.17)$$

$$d_1 = \frac{c_1 b_2 - b_1 c_2}{c_1} \qquad e_1 = \frac{d_1 c_2 - c_1 d_2}{d_1}$$

To calculate the Routh array for testing equation (7.10), we use the values $a_0 = 1$, $a_1 = 6$, $a_2 = 11$, $a_3 = 6$; then

$$b_1 = \frac{6 \times 11 - 1 \times 6}{6} = 10, \quad \text{and} \quad c_1 = \frac{10 \times 6 - 0}{10} = 6$$

All other constants of (7.16) are zero. The Routh array is

$$\begin{array}{ll} 1 & 11 \\ 6 & 6 \\ 10 & \\ 6 & \end{array}$$

The left-hand column elements—1, 6, 10, 6—are all positive and nonzero; therefore there are no roots in the RHP and the system is not absolutely unstable. The factors of equation (7.10) prove that all roots are negative and therefore in the left half plane (LHP).

$$s^3 + 6s^2 + 11s + 6 = (s + 1)(s + 2)(s + 3) = 0 \quad (7.18)$$

For equation (7.11) with $a_0 = 1$, $a_1 = 1$, $a_2 = 4$, $a_3 = 30$, $b_1 = 4 - 30/1 = -26$, and $c_1 = 30$, the Routh array is

$$\begin{array}{ll} 1 & 4 \\ 1 & 30 \\ -26 & \\ 30 & \end{array}$$

The fact that -26 is a negative number shows us that there are roots of equation (7.11) with positive real parts. This is proven by the factored equation

$$s^3 + s^2 + 4s + 30 = (s - 1 - j3)(s - 1 + j3)(s + 3) = 0 \quad (7.19)$$

The roots are $s_1 = +1 + j3$, $s_2 = +1 - j3$, $s_3 = -3$. Both roots s_1 and s_2 have positive real parts (the number 1) and are found in the RHP. The system is therefore *absolutely* unstable.

The value of the Routh test is shown when higher-degree equations are tested, as for example the equation

$$s^4 + 2s^3 + 3s^2 + 8s + 2 = 0 \quad (7.20)$$

The Routh array is, with $a_0 = 1$, $a_1 = 2$, $a_2 = 3$, $a_3 = 8$, $a_4 = 2$,

$$\begin{array}{lll} 1 & 3 & 2 \\ 2 & 8 & \\ -1 & 2 & \\ 12 & & \\ 2 & & \end{array}$$

There is a negative sign in the left-hand column, so there is at least one root in the RHP, and the system is *absolutely* unstable.

PROBLEMS

Using the Routh test, check the following characteristic equations to see if there are any roots in the right half-plane; if there are, the system is absolutely unstable.

7.3. $s^3 + 4s^2 + 5s + 2 = 0$

7.4. $s^3 + 5s^2 + 8s + 4 = 0$

7.5. $s^3 + s^2 + 11s + 51 = 0$

7.6. $s^3 + 2s^2 + 17s + 100 = 0$

7.7. $s^4 + 3s^3 + 5s^2 + 4s + 1 = 0$

7.8. $s^4 + 2s^3 + 3s^2 + 5s + 2 = 0$

7.9. $s^4 + 2s^3 + s^2 + 3s + 2 = 0$

7.10. $s^4 + 2s^3 + 4s^2 + 2s + 2 = 0$

7.2   ROOT LOCUS DERIVATION

The *root locus* is the path of the roots of the characteristic equation when one parameter or variable of the system transfer function is changed. The usual variable is K_a, the gain of the servo amplifier. During design it is always easily increased or reduced. For on-the-job changes of gain, in the system amplifier there is usually a gain control knob or a shaft with screwdriver slot which adjusts a potentiometer in the first or second stage of the amplifier. Strip-chart servo-driven recorders are a common example of this technique. In such a recorder we can usually raise the gain until the servo becomes unstable— oscillates continuously. We can then turn the control knob back until oscillations just stop. Following this we usually test the recorder with a step input and reduce the gain a little further until after a step change oscillations die out rapidly. We then have the best speed of response compatible with a straight pen line for a fixed input.

In Section 7.1 it was stated that the characteristic equation is the denominator of the closed-loop transfer function, and that *the roots of the characteristic equation are the poles of the closed-loop system.* In discussing the root locus, however, we use the terms *poles* and *zeros* when we refer to the *open-loop system*, and the term *roots* when we refer to the *closed-loop system*. As the value of the system gain K_a varies, the roots of the characteristic equation also vary, and *the root locus is the path of these roots in the complex plane as* *the system K_a varies.* The gain K_a is usually part of a lumped constant K_v or K_r, which then varies as K_a varies. We shall see this in the systems analyzed in this chapter; naturally the systems are presented in order of complexity.

First-Order System

We start with a first-order system, that is, a system whose denominator contains s to the first power only. This first-order system could be an amplifier and a lead network in series. The system block diagram is shown in Fig. 7.1, and the open-loop transfer function is

$$\frac{E_{\text{out}}}{E_{\text{in}}} = KG = K_a \frac{sT_1 + 1}{sT_2 + 1} = K_a \frac{T_1}{T_2} \frac{s + 1/T_1}{s + 1/T_2} \tag{7.21}$$

For mathematical reasons we have changed the form of the factors of equation (7.21) from $sT + 1$ to $s + 1/T$, which we shall do with all root locus transfer functions. The network of Fig. 7.1 is shown by equation (7.21) to have a pole at $1/T_2$ and a zero at $1/T_1$. Let us assume the values of the time constants to be $T_1 = 1$ and $T_2 = \frac{1}{3}$. Then we have

$$KG = K_a \frac{T_1}{T_2} \frac{s + 1/T_1}{s + 1/T_2} = 3K_a \frac{s + 1}{s + 3} \tag{7.22}$$

and the pole and zero of our open-loop transfer function KG are -3 and -1 respectively. We can see that this is so because when $s = -3$, $KG = \infty$; and when $s = -1$, $KG = 0$. As is customary in root locus plots, Fig. 7.2 shows the pole by a cross and the zero by a circle.

Let us see what happens when we close the loop, as shown in Fig. 7.3. Using equation (5.12) with $H = 1$ (unity feedback), we have from the open-loop equation (7.22)

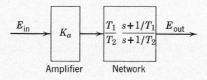

$$E_{\text{in}} \longrightarrow \boxed{K_a} \longrightarrow \boxed{\frac{T_1}{T_2} \frac{s + 1/T_1}{s + 1/T_2}} \xrightarrow{\;E_{\text{out}}\;}$$

$$\text{Amplifier} \qquad\qquad \text{Network}$$

Fig. 7.1 Block diagram of first-order system.

$$\frac{E_{\text{out}}}{E_{\text{in}}} = KG = K_a \frac{T_1}{T_2} \frac{s + 1/T_1}{s + 1/T_2}$$

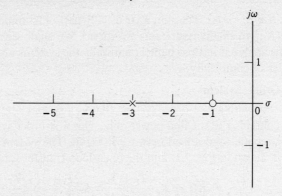

Fig. 7.2 Open-loop pole and zero of first-order system.

$$\frac{E_{\text{out}}}{E_{\text{in}}} = KG = 3K_a\frac{s+1}{s+3}$$

$$\frac{E_{\text{out}}}{E_{\text{in}}} = \frac{KG}{1 + KG} = \frac{3K_a\dfrac{s+1}{s+3}}{1 + 3K_a\dfrac{s+1}{s+3}} = \frac{\dfrac{3K_a(s+1)}{s+3}}{\dfrac{s+3+3K_a(s+1)}{s+3}}$$

$$= \frac{3K_a(s+1)}{s+3+3K_a s+3K_a} \tag{7.23}$$

The characteristic equation is the denominator of the last expression of equation (7.23) equated to zero:

$$s + 3K_a s + 3 + 3K_a = s(1 + 3K_a) + 3 + 3K_a = 0 \tag{7.24}$$

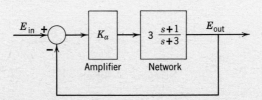

Fig. 7.3 Closed-loop equivalent of first-order system shown in Fig. 7.1 when $1/T_1 = 1$ and $1/T_2 = 3$.

$$\frac{E_{\text{out}}}{E_{\text{in}}} = \frac{3Ka(s+1)}{s+3+3K_a s+3K_a} = \frac{3K_a(s+1)}{s(1+3K_a)+3+3K_a}$$

Three different values of $3K_a$ will show us what happens to the roots of the characteristic equation as K_a varies. Let us start with the characteristic equation set equal not to zero but to y:

$$s(1 + 3K_a) + 3 + 3K_a = y \qquad (7.25)$$

and let us graph the results. When $K_a = 0$ we have Fig. 7.4a. The

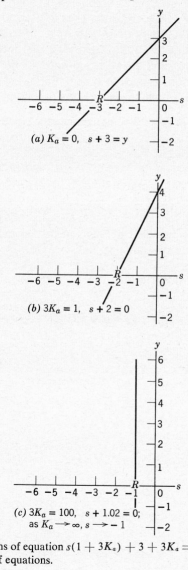

(a) $K_a = 0$, $s + 3 = y$

(b) $3K_a = 1$, $s + 2 = 0$

(c) $3K_a = 100$, $s + 1.02 = 0$;
as $K_a \rightarrow \infty$, $s \rightarrow -1$

Fig. 7.4   Graphs of equation $s(1 + 3K_a) + 3 + 3K_a = y$ for three values of K_a. R = roots of equations.

characteristic equation (7.24) is satisfied when $y = 0$, and this occurs when the slanting line of Fig. 7.4a crosses the horizontal axis at $s = -3$. When $3K_a = 1$ in equation (7.25), we have Fig. 7.4b; when $y = 0$ here, $s = -2$. When $3K_a = 100$, we have Fig. 7.4c; here $y = 0$ when $s = -1.02$, indicating that when $K_a = \infty$ and $y = 0$, $s = -1$.

Note that when $y = 0$, as K_a varies from 0 to ∞, s varies from -3 to -1. The *root locus* is the *path of these values of s*, values which are the *roots* of the characteristic equation. The root locus is shown in Fig. 7.5 by the heavy line between -3 and -1 on the horizontal axis, and is typical for this type of system. Following are the characteristics of first-order system root loci (the plural of *locus* is *loci*):

1. The *locus of the roots* of the characteristic equation is from the open-loop pole (when $K_a = 0$—see Fig. 7.4a) to the open-loop zero (when $K_a = \infty$—see Fig. 7.4c).

2. First-order systems have only one branch of the root locus, and only real values of s occur. The locus never leaves the horizontal axis.

3. Even with infinite gain, first-order systems with poles and zeros to the left of the $j\omega$ axis have all roots in the left half-plane (LHP) and are therefore always stable.

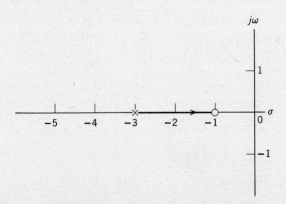

Fig. 7.5 Root locus of first-order system.

$$\frac{E_{\text{out}}}{E_{\text{in}}} = KG = 3K_a \frac{s+1}{s+3}$$

Second-Order System

Course Recorder. We next investigate a second-order system, that is, one with s^2 the highest power of s. For a second-order system we use our uncompensated course recorder, analyzed in Sections 5.3 and 5.4, and whose open-loop transfer function is equation (5.36). Substituting s for $j\omega$ in this equation we have

$$\frac{\theta_{out}}{E} = \frac{190}{j\omega(1 + j0.0153\omega)} = \frac{190}{s(1 + 0.0153s)} = \frac{K_v/N}{s(1 + s/65.4)} \quad (7.26)$$

since K_v/N of our system was 190. We change the form of this transfer function as follows:

$$\frac{\theta_{out}}{E} = \frac{K_v/N}{s(1 + s/65.4)} = \frac{65.4 K_v/N}{s(s + 65.4)} = \frac{K_r}{s(s + 65.4)} \; ; \; 65.4 K_v/N = K_r \quad (7.27)$$

Now if $s = -65.4$ in equation (7.27), our transfer function becomes

$$\frac{\theta_{out}}{E} = \frac{K_r}{0} = \infty \quad (7.28)$$

infinitely large, as shown in equation (7.28). If $s = 0$ the same thing happens. These two values of s are poles, one at the origin and one at -65.4 on the real axis, and they are marked with crosses, as shown in Fig. 7.6. When s in equation (7.27) becomes very large the transfer function will have a value approaching zero. Two zeros will be located at $K_r = \infty$. *There are always as many zeros as poles.* We are interested in the closed-loop transfer function of our system. If

$$\frac{\theta_{out}}{E} = KG = \frac{K_r}{s(s + 65.4)} = \frac{K_r}{s^2 + 65.4s} \quad (7.29)$$

then the closed-loop transfer function with 100% feedback is

$$\frac{\theta_{out}}{\theta_{in}} = \frac{KG}{1 + KG} = \frac{\dfrac{K_r}{s^2 + 65.4s}}{1 + \dfrac{K_r}{s^2 + 65.4s}} = \frac{K_r}{s^2 + 65.4s + K_r} \quad (7.30)$$

The denominator of the last expression in equation (7.30) yields the *characteristic equation*

$$s^2 + 65.4s + K_r = 0 \quad (7.31)$$

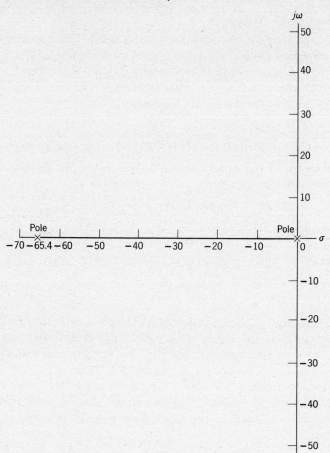

Fig. 7.6 Poles of

$$\frac{\theta_{\text{out}}}{E} = \frac{65.4K_v/N}{s(s + 65.4)} = \frac{K_r}{s(s + 65.4)}$$

but we will again graph this equation set not equal to zero but equal to y:

$$s^2 + 65.4s + K_r = y \qquad (7.32)$$

We will let K_r assume various values and find the roots of equation (7.32), which are also the roots of the characteristic equation (7.31). The graph of equation (7.32) is shown in Fig. 7.7. When $K_r = 0$

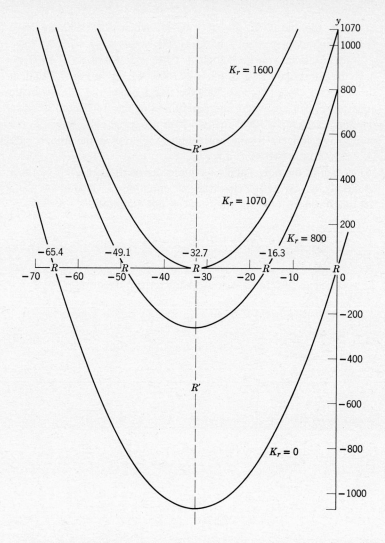

Fig. 7.7 Graphs of $s^2 + 65.4s + K_r = y$ for four values of K_r. Note that vertical scale is compressed. $R =$ roots of equations. $R' =$ complex roots of equation with $K_r = 1600$.

207

we have the parabola $y = s^2 + 65.4s$; when $K_r = 800$ we have another parabola $y = s^2 + 65.4s + 800$; when $K_r = 1070$ we have a third parabola $y = s^2 + 65.4s + 1070$, and when $K_r = 1600$ we have the parabola $v = s^2 + 65.4s + 1600$. We see in Fig. 7.7 that in the first two cases ($K_r = 0, 800$) the two *roots* of the characteristic equation (7.31) are where the parabolas cut the horizontal axis; in the third case ($K_r = 1070$) the two *roots* are equal and are where the parabola is tangent to the horizontal axis; and in the fourth case ($K_r = 1600$) the two *roots* are complex.

Let us find the horizontal axis intercepts or roots of each of these equations by solving the characteristic equation (7.31), and by using the quadratic formula for the roots of this equation:

$$s = \frac{-65.4 \pm \sqrt{65.4^2 - 4K_r}}{2} = -32.7 \pm \sqrt{1070 - K_r} \quad (7.33)$$

Thus we have two roots of our characteristic equation:

$$s_1 = -32.7 + \sqrt{1070 - K_r}; \qquad s_2 = -32.7 - \sqrt{1070 - K_r}$$
$$(7.34)$$

When $K_r = 0$

$$s_1 = -32.7 + 32.7 = 0; \qquad s_2 = -32.7 - 32.7 = -65.4 \quad (7.35)$$

When $K_r = 800$

$$s_1 = -32.7 + 16.4 = -16.3; \qquad s_2 = -32.7 - 16.4 = -49.1$$
$$(7.36)$$

When $K_r = 1070$

$$s_1 = -32.7; \qquad s_2 = -32.7 \quad (7.37)$$

When $K_r = 1600$

$$s_1 = -32.7 + \sqrt{1070 - 1600} = -32.7 + j23; \quad s_2 = -32.7 - j23$$
$$(7.38)$$

These and other values of the roots are given in Table 7.1.

Table 7.1   *Values of K_r and Roots of Equation (7.31)*

K_r	s_1	s_2
0	0	-65.4
800	-16.3	-49.1
1,070	-32.7	-32.7
1,444	$-32.7 + j19.3$	$-32.7 - j19.3$
1,600	$-32.7 + j23$	$-32.7 - j23$
3,025	$-32.7 + j44.2$	$-32.7 - j44.2$
12,420	$-32.7 + j106.5$	$-32.7 - j106.5$

We see again that in each case the *roots* of the characteristic equation are the points where the horizontal axis is cut by the parabolas of the equation $s^2 + 65.4s + K_r = y$ or are complex and are on the vertical dotted line equidistant above and below the horizontal (σ) axis. We are really interested only in the path or *locus* of these *roots*, so we draw the root locus in Fig. 7.8. From equation (7.37) and from Figs. 7.7 and 7.8 we see that when $K_r = 1070$ there are two equal real roots. At this point where $s_1 = s_2 = -32.7$ there is a *breakaway* point where the two branches of the root locus leave the horizontal or real axis, turn 90°, and take on complex values. These complex values are paired, with equal real parts and with complex parts of opposite sign.

The characteristics of second-order system root loci are as follows:

1. Second-order equations have two branches of the root locus.
2. The *locus* of the characteristic equation *roots* (= the root locus) consists of one branch from each of the two open-loop poles (when $K_r = 0$) along the real axis until the two branches meet at the midpoint between the two poles. Then the two branches move away from the real axis and become complex, one branch with positive imaginary parts going to a zero at positive infinity, the other branch with negative imaginary parts going to a zero at negative infinity.
3. Second-order systems with poles and zeros at the origin or in the left half-plane are never completely unstable because they never have roots in the right half-plane regardless of the values assumed by K_r.

Let us see what the root locus tells us about the uncompensated course-recorder system, which we analyzed in Chapters 5 and 6. In this system $K_r = 12,420$, so our particular closed-loop transfer function can be found from equation (7.30):

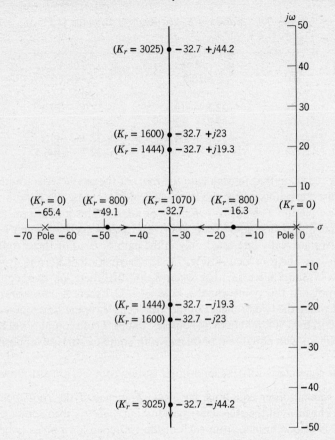

Fig. 7.8 Root locus plot of

$$\frac{\theta_{\text{out}}}{E} = \frac{65.4K_v/N}{s(s + 65.4)} = \frac{K_r}{s(s + 65.4)}$$

Characteristic equation: $s^2 + 65.4s + K_r = \sigma$. Note: In this and other figures in this chapter black dots along the root locus are used to point out specific roots discussed or illustrated.

$$\frac{\theta_{\text{out}}}{\theta_{\text{in}}} = \frac{K_r}{s^2 + 65.4s + K_r} = \frac{12,420}{s^2 + 65.4s + 12,420} \qquad (7.39)$$

which can be derived from equation (5.26) if s is substituted for $j\omega$ and s^2 for $-\omega^2$.

Figure 7.9 shows an extension of Fig. 7.8 on a smaller-scale plot. The value of $K_r = 111.4^2 = 12,420$ is shown, as well as the two roots at this point: $s_1 = -32.7 + j106.7$ and $s_2 = -32.7 - j106.7$. We recognize 111.4 as our system natural frequency ω_n, and we note the ordinate value of 106.7, which is our damped frequency ω_d.

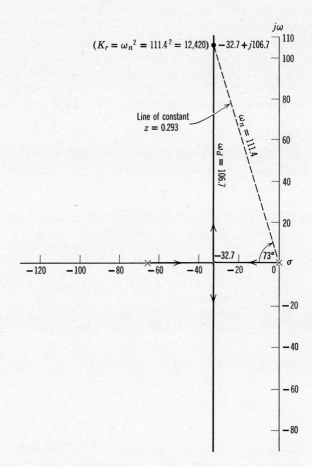

Fig. 7.9 Root locus plot of

$$\frac{\theta_{\text{out}}}{E} = \frac{K_r}{s(s + 65.4)}$$

with $K_r = 12,420$.

The damping factor z is equal to the cosine of the angle shown, 73°, and is 0.293. These same values were derived mathematically in Sections 6.1 and 6.2.

Note that as K_r increases above a value of 1070, the breakaway point, z decreases and ω_n increases. As z decreases $z/\sqrt{1-z^2}$ decreases, so the maximum overshoot and number of oscillations to settle both increase (equations (6.44) and (6.46)). The time to reach maximum overshoot decreases, and the settling time increases (equation (6.43) and (6.45)). Most important, in fact basic to the idea of the root locus, is the fact that at any value of K_r we can find the equation of our closed-loop system. For example, when $K_r = 12,420$ as it did in our original system, the roots at this point are

$$s_1 = -32.7 + j106.7 \quad \text{and} \quad s_2 = -32.7 - j106.7 \quad (7.40)$$

Our closed-loop system transfer function is always

$$\frac{K_r}{(s - s_1)(s - s_2)} \quad (7.41)$$

With $K_r = 12,420$ this transfer function becomes

$$\frac{12,420}{(s + 32.7 + j106.7)(s + 32.7 - j106.7)} = \frac{12,420}{s^2 + 65.4s + 12,420} \quad (7.42)$$

which is the same as equation (7.39).

Suppose that we want a system with more damping, that is, with a larger z, and let us pick a value of $z = 0.5$ as desirable. Then arc cos 0.5 = 60°. Figure 7.10 shows the root locus. K_r has a value of $65.4^2 = 4280$. Our new roots are

$$s_1 = -32.7 + j56.6 \quad \text{and} \quad s_2 = -32.7 - j56.6 \quad (7.43)$$

and our new closed-loop transfer function is

$$\frac{K_r}{(s - s_1)(s - s_2)} = \frac{K_r}{(s + 32.7 + j56.6)(s + 32.7 - j56.6)}$$

$$= \frac{4280}{s^2 + 65.4s + 4280} \quad (7.44)$$

When we examine this system we see that by raising the value of z from 0.293 to 0.5 we have reduced the maximum overshoot from

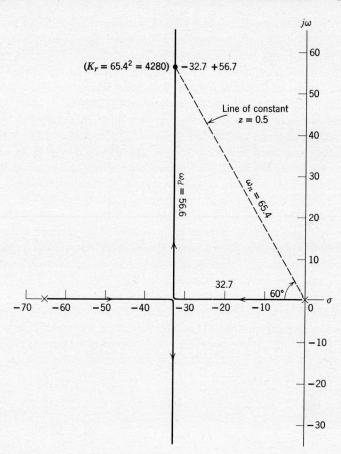

Fig. 7.10   Root locus plot of

$$\frac{\theta_{\text{out}}}{E} = \frac{K_r}{s(s + 65.4)}$$

38.2% to 16.6% (see Table 6.2). But we have lowered K_r by a factor of $4280/12,420 = 0.344$ by lowering the amplifier gain by this same factor. Equation (5.2) tells us that

$$\text{Dead band} = \frac{2 \times \text{motor starting voltage}}{\text{amplifier gain} \times \text{control transformer sensitivity}}$$

$$(7.45)$$

so by reducing amplifier gain by 0.344 we have increased dead band by $1/0.344 = 2.91$. Our velocity lag error will also be increased by this same amount (see equations (5.32) and (5.33)). Therefore our system is not acceptable as is, and it will have to be compensated, as we found out from our frequency-response analysis of this system in Chapter 5 and our transient analysis in Chapter 6.

We can summarize our findings at this point by saying that the root locus plot is a locus of all the roots of the closed-loop system transfer function as K_r is varied. Note that the open-loop poles and zeros are fixed; the closed-loop poles (roots) move and generate the loci. Individual branches of the root locus have been identified as they turn off the real axis at the breakaway points in Figs. 7.8, 7.9, and 7.10. This has been done to show that there is an individual path or locus from each pole to each zero. This practice is very seldom followed and will not be continued in the rest of this chapter. But it is worthwhile remembering that *there is one individual root locus path from each pole to each zero.*

Course Recorder Compensated by a Rate Generator. We can now draw the root locus of our course recorder compensated by a rate generator, which we analyzed in Section 5.5 by frequency response (see Fig. 5.6 for Bode diagram). The open-loop transfer function is given in equation (5.47), from which we derive the root locus form in equation (7.46).

$$\frac{\theta_{out}}{E} = \frac{K_v/N}{j\omega(1 + j\omega/181.8)} = \frac{181.8\,K_v/N}{j\omega(j\omega + 181.8)} = \frac{K_r}{s(s + 181.8)} \quad (7.46)$$

Here we have poles at 0 and 181.8, and two zeros at infinity. The locus leaves the σ or real axis at $181.8/2 = 90.9$, and one branch goes "north," the other "south," as shown in Fig. 7.11. We will not indicate which branch is which by carefully sketching the breakaway point from the real axis as we did in Figs. 7.8, 7.9, and 7.10. Since all root loci are symmetric about the real axis we need draw only the upper half of the locus.

Let us again use a z of 0.5 (maximum overshoot 16.6%) and see what performance we obtain. Figure 7.11 shows the dashed line of constant $z = 0.5$. We see that for this system $\omega_n = 181.8$ and $\omega_d = 158.5$. For any second-order system $K_r = \omega_n^2$, so our $K_r = 181.8^2 = 33,100$. In Fig. 5.6 for our system gain raised 9.5 dB we

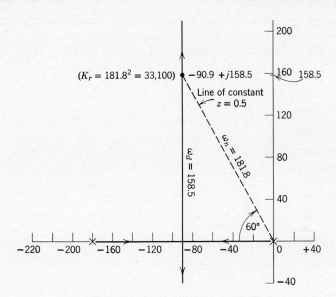

Fig. 7.11 Root locus plot of rate-generator compensation.

$$\frac{\theta_{out}}{E} = \frac{K_r}{s(s + 181.8)}$$

had a K_v/N of 186.3. In equation (7.46) we see that $K_r = 181.8K_v/N$, so here our $K_r = 181.8 \times 186.3 = 33,800$, which is very close to 33,100. Therefore our system damping factor z of the system shown in Fig. 5.6 was almost 0.5—actually 0.494. Therefore our rate-generator compensated system, which passed the frequency-response test in Chapter 5, looks good when analyzed by the root locus method.

PROBLEMS

Note: For all root locus problems use 8½ by 11 graph (cross-section) paper with 10 x 10 divisions to the inch, or better 10 x 10 divisions to the half-inch. An engineer's scale (graduated in decimal parts of an inch), a compass, and a good protractor are useful for construction of the root locus.

7.11. From the data given in Prob. 5.3 and your answers to that problem:

(a) Find the open-loop root locus form of the transfer function (see equation (7.27)).

(b) Find the closed-loop root locus form of the transfer function (see equation (7.30)).

(c) Find the characteristic equation (see equation (7.31)).

(d) Factor this equation by the quadratic formula.

(e) Find the characteristic equation roots for one value of K_r in each of the following four cases (see equations (7.32) through (7.38)):

1. When $K_r = 0$.

2. When the value of K_r is such that the roots are real and unequal.

3. When the value of K_r is such that the roots are real and equal.

4. When the value of K_r is such that the roots are complex.

7.12. (a) On a sheet of cross-section paper 10 x 10 divisions to the inch or 10 x 10 divisions to the half-inch, mark and identify the poles (open-loop) of Prob. 7.11(a), as shown in Fig. 7.6.

(b) On the same sheet mark and identify the characteristic equation roots you found in Prob. 7.11(e). (See Fig. 7.8.)

(c) On the same sheet draw the root locus of your system, as shown in Fig. 7.8.

(d) Find the value of K_r corresponding to your system found as your answer to Prob. 5.3(c).

(e) Find the point on the root locus where the K_r of (d) above is located. It can be found by measuring $\sqrt{K_r} = \omega_n$ = the distance from the origin to the point on either branch of the root locus, as shown in Fig. 7.9. What is the value of ω_n? of ω_d? What is the angle between the horizontal (σ) axis and the line from the origin to the point on the root locus (= the line of constant z)? What is the value of z? What maximum overshoot will result from this value of z? (See equation (6.44).)

(f) For a z of 0.5 find ω_n, ω_d, K_r, and the maximum overshoot (see Fig. 7.10).

7.13. From the data given in Prob. 5.5 and your answers to that problem:

(a) Find the open-loop root locus form of the transfer function (see equations (7.26) and (7.27)).

(b) Find the closed-loop root locus form of the transfer function (see equations (7.29) and (7.30)).

(c) Find the characteristic equation (see equation (7.31)).

(d) Factor this equation by the quadratic formula.

(e) Find the characteristic equation roots for one value of K_r in each of the following four cases. (See equations (7.34) through (7.38).)

1. When $K_r = 0$.

2. When the value of K_r is such that the roots are real and unequal.

3. When the value of K_r is such that the roots are real and equal.

4. When the value of K_r is such that the roots are complex.

7.14. (*a*) On a sheet of cross-section paper 10 x 10 divisions to the inch or 10 x 10 divisions to the half-inch mark and identify the poles (open-loop) of Prob. 7.13(*a*), as shown in Fig. 7.6.

(*b*) On the same sheet mark and identify the characteristic equation roots you found in Prob. 7.13(*e*). (See Fig. 7.8.)

(*c*) On the same sheet draw the root locus of your system, as shown in Fig. 7.8.

(*d*) Find the value of K_r corresponding to your system found as your answer to Prob. 5.5(*c*).

(*e*) Find the point on the root locus where the K_r of (*d*) above is located. It can be found by measuring $\omega_n = \sqrt{K_r}$ = the distance from the origin to the point on either branch of the root locus, as shown in Fig. 7.9. What is the value of ω_n? of ω_d? What is the angle between the horizontal (σ) axis and the line from the origin to the point on the root locus (= the line of constant z)? What is the value of z? What maximum overshoot will result from this value of z? (See equation (6.44).)

(*f*) For a z of 0.5 find ω_n, ω_d, K_r, and the maximum overshoot. (See Fig. 7.10.)

7.15. Draw the root locus of the rate-generator compensated servo system whose constants are given in Prob. 5.11 (and Prob. 5.3). Use any shortcuts you can, but your final plot should be similar to Fig. 7.11. Use a z of 0.5. What is the value of your ω_n? ω_d? K_r?

7.16. Draw the root locus of the rate-generator compensated servo system whose constants are given in Prob. 5.12 (and Prob. 5.5). Use any shortcuts you can, but your final plot should be similar to Fig. 7.11. Use a z of 0.5. What is the value of your ω_n? ω_d? K_r?

7.3 THIRD-ORDER SYSTEM TRANSIENT RESPONSE VERSUS SECOND-ORDER SYSTEM TRANSIENT RESPONSE

In Chapter 6 and in this chapter so far, we have discussed only second-order systems. The rest of the examples in this chapter are third-order systems. In Chapter 6 we derived z, ω_n, and other constants for a second-order system, and we used these constants to analyze our system quite thoroughly. Can we do the same for the third-order systems found in Chapter 5? Let us find out.

A typical second-order system open-loop transfer function is of the form

$$\frac{\theta_{\text{out}}}{E} = \frac{K_r}{(s + d_1)(s + d_2)} \tag{7.47}$$

For example, our course recorder poles were $d_1 = 0$, $d_2 = 65.4$. A typical third-order system open-loop transfer function is

$$\frac{\theta_{out}}{E} = \frac{K_r(s + n_1)}{(s + d_1)(s + d_2)(s + d_3)} \tag{7.48}$$

We use n for zeros because they always appear in the *numerator* of the open-loop transfer function, and we use d for poles because they always appear in the transfer function *denominator*. Equation (7.48) is the form of the transfer functions of our course recorder compensated by a lag network, by a lead network, and by using an inertia-damped servomotor (IDSM). Now if in equation (7.48) $n_1 = d_2$, we have *mathematically* by canceling

$$\frac{K_r(s + n_1)}{(s + d_1)(s + d_2)(s + d_3)} = \frac{K_r}{(s + d_1)(s + d_3)} ; \quad n_1 = d_2 \tag{7.49}$$

a second-order transfer function. Figure 7.19 shows that the root locus of such a third-order system transfer function looks very much like that of a second-order system, although n_1 does not exactly equal d_2. Actually the physical situation never allows complete cancellation, but the cancellation concept can be used to analyze the situation if the limitations are kept in mind. In the lead-network examples and problems in this book the zero and one pole are sufficiently close together for us to analyze the systems as second-order.

When in equation (7.48) no pole has a value close to that of the zero, we have another situation. In this case it is customary to place one of the poles of equation (7.48) well to the left of the other two poles, as is the case in Figs. 7.17 and 7.20. In both cases we have two poles close together and relatively near the origin, and a third pole much farther to the left. An example of this type of system is our course recorder with an inertia-damped servomotor (IDSM), analyzed in Section 5.7. From equation (5.59) of this system we derive the root locus open-loop equation

$$\frac{\theta_{out}}{E} = KG = \frac{164(1 + s/17.3)}{s(1 + s/2.51)(1 + s/293)}$$

$$= \frac{164\left(\dfrac{2.51 \times 293}{17.3}\right)(s + 17.3)}{s(s + 2.51)(s + 293)}$$

$$= \frac{6960(s + 17.3)}{s(s + 2.51)(s + 293)} = \frac{K_r(s + z_1)}{(s + p_1)(s + p_2)(s + p_3)} \tag{7.50}$$

The closed-loop equation is then

$$\frac{\theta_{out}}{\theta_{in}} = \frac{KG}{1 + KG} = \frac{6960(s + 17.3)}{s(s + 2.51)(s + 293) + 6960s + 6960 \times 17.3}$$

$$= \frac{6960(s + 17.3)}{s^3 + 295.5s^2 + 7695s + 120,400} \qquad (7.51)$$

We want to find the transient response of this system so we shock it with a unit step; mathematically this means multiplying the equation by $1/s$. To obtain the time equation of this transient response we look in a table of Laplace transforms for equation (7.51) $\times$ $1/s$. After a fair amount of algebra, including factoring a cubic equation, we obtain the transient

$$10^{-6}[52.9 + 5.05e^{-268t} + 5.41e^{-13.5t} \sin (345t - 52°)] \qquad (7.52)$$

This transient-response equation of a third-order system with a remote pole far to the left of the others is of the form

$$K_1 + K_2e^{-K_3t} + K_4e^{-K_5t} \sin (K_6t - \theta) \qquad (7.53)$$

Comparing this with the transient response equation of a second-order system

$$K_1 + K_2e^{-K_3t}(\sin K_4t - \theta) \qquad (7.54)$$

we see that the second term of the third-order system equation (7.53), $K_2e^{-K_3t}$, does not appear in equation (7.54) of the second-order system. This term is a decaying exponential; if it were not present in equation (7.53) both equations would be of the same form. When we look at equation (7.52) we see that the second term, $5.05e^{-268t}$, has a time constant of $1/268 = 0.00373$ sec. The third term is a decaying sine wave, and the exponential factor of this sine wave, $5.41e^{-13.5t}$, has a time constant of $1/13.5 = 0.074$ sec, twenty times that of the second term. Final and most important is the fact that the second term makes no essential contribution after 0.015 sec (four time constants). After that the system reacts like a second-order system. An electromechanical servo-system transient response is relatively slow, and the part that interests us most takes place after 0.015 sec.

In summary, (1) if in a third-order system a pole and a zero are almost equal, they tend to "cancel" each other out, and a semi-second-order system results; and (2) if one pole has a value far greater than the one closest to it (say five times or more), there is a quickly decaying exponential term in the transient, plus a second-order system transient. In either case we can consider electromechanical systems as essentially second-order, and we can analyze the root locus the same way as the second-order systems we have already covered.

7.4 RULES FOR CONSTRUCTION OF THE ROOT LOCUS

The simple root loci we have drawn have been of first- and second-order systems. The rest of the examples and problems in this chapter are third-order systems, and to draw the root loci of these systems we need a few general rules, which apply to all systems:

RULE 1. The open-loop transfer function factors must be of the form $s + 1/T$. Convert transfer functions with factors $sT + 1$ to the proper form (see equation (7.21)).

RULE 2. Plot the poles of the open-loop transfer function on the complex plane, using crosses. Plot the finite zeros, if any, with circles. See Figs. 7.2 and 7.6 as examples.

RULE 3. Poles and zeros are called *singularities*—points where the function takes on a "singular" aspect, either infinity or zero. The root locus exists on the real axis only if the number of singularities (poles plus zeros) to the right is odd. In Fig. 7.12 we find the root locus on the real axis to the left of the first, third, and fifth (odd) singularities, but *not* to the left of the second and fourth (even) singularities.

RULE 4. The number of root locus branches is the number of poles. Fig. 7.5 has one pole and one branch; Fig. 7.8 has two poles and two branches.

RULE 5. Each branch of the root locus begins at a pole, where $K_r = 0$, and proceeds to a zero, where $K_r = \infty$. Figure 7.5 needs no comment; in Fig. 7.8 one branch starts at the pole at 0 and proceeds to the zero at plus infinity, and the other branch starts at the pole at -65.4 and proceeds to the zero at minus infinity.

RULE 6. All linear system root loci are symmetrical with respect to the real (horizontal) axis. Sometimes to save time and space or to

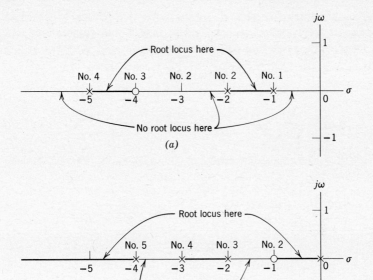

Fig. 7.12 Root locus on the real axis. Singularities (poles and zeros) are numbered. Note: the root locus off the real axis has been omitted.

use a larger scale we draw only the upper half of the locus. See Figs. 7.17 and 7.20.

RULE 7. The root locus branches that leave the real axis become asymptotic to straight lines when projected far enough. These straight lines are at angles to the real axis of

$$\frac{\pm 180°}{\text{total number of poles} - \text{total number of finite zeros}} \quad (7.55a)$$

(In more advanced work beyond the scope of this book we multiply the numerator of equation (7.55a) by K, K being an odd number—1, 3, 5, etc.) In Fig. 7.15 we have three poles and one finite zero, so equation (7.55a) becomes

$$\frac{\pm 180°}{3 - 1} = \frac{\pm 180°}{2} = \pm 90° \quad (7.55b)$$

and asymptotes at these angles to the real axis are drawn in as dashed lines. If the root loci were extended they would come closer and closer to these lines but never touch them.

RULE 8. The point on the real axis from which we draw the asymptotes at the angles found in Rule 7 above is given by the expression

$$\frac{\text{sum of pole values} - \text{sum of zero values}}{\text{total number of poles} - \text{total number of finite zeros}} \quad (7.56)$$

In Fig. 7.19 we have three poles at 0, -65.4, and -500 respectively, and one zero at -50. Then from equation (7.56) we have

$$\frac{-500 + (-65.4) + 0 - (-50)}{3 - 1} = \frac{-515.4}{2} = -257.7 \quad (7.57)$$

RULE 9. The root locus branches leave the real axis at the *breakaway point*, and we must find this point. In Fig. 7.15 the root locus branch that starts at the origin heads for the nearest pole at -1; there is no breakaway here. But between the poles at -2 and -4 there must be a breakaway point because the branch starting at -2 goes to the breakaway point and from there goes to a zero at plus infinity; the branch starting at -4 leaves the real axis at the same breakaway point and goes toward minus infinity. Let us call the breakaway point b. Then

$$\sum \frac{1}{b - d} = \sum \frac{1}{b - n} \quad (7.58)$$

n being a zero (numerator factor) and d being a pole (denominator factor). If all the poles and zeros are real and are negative or zero, equation (7.58) becomes, with signs on both sides of the equation reversed to reduce minus signs later,

$$\sum \frac{1}{|b| - |d|} = \sum \frac{1}{|b| - |n|} \quad (7.59)$$

Two examples will help us to understand how the breakaway point is found. Suppose that in Fig. 7.8 we did not know the breakaway point, and that we guessed at a value of -30 for b. Then we have, with two poles at 0 and -65.4 and no finite zeros, by substituting in equation (7.59),

$$\Sigma \frac{1}{|b| - |d|} = \frac{1}{30 - 0} + \frac{1}{30 - 65.4} \qquad (7.60)$$

$$\Sigma \frac{1}{|b| - |n|} = 0 \qquad (7.61)$$

Equating (7.60) and (7.61) we get

$$\frac{1}{30} + \frac{1}{30 - 65.4} \, ? \, 0$$

$$\frac{1}{30} + \frac{1}{-35.4} \neq 0$$

Try -32 for b in equation (7.59):

$$\frac{1}{32} + \frac{1}{32 - 65.4} \, ? \, 0$$

$$\frac{1}{32} + \frac{1}{-33.4} \neq 0$$

Try -32.7 for b.

$$\frac{1}{32.7} + \frac{1}{32.7 - 65.4} \, ? \, 0$$

$$\frac{1}{32.7} + \frac{1}{-32.7} = 0$$

Therefore the breakaway point is -32.7.

Figure 7.19 is a little more complicated. Here we have three poles —at 0, -65.4, and -500, and one zero—at -50. Then

$$\Sigma \frac{1}{|b| - |d|} = \frac{1}{280 - 0} + \frac{1}{280 - 65.4} + \frac{1}{280 - 500} \qquad (7.62)$$

$$\Sigma \frac{1}{|b| - |n|} = \frac{1}{280 - 50} \qquad (7.63)$$

Equating (7.62) and (7.63) we get

$$\frac{1}{280} + \frac{1}{280 - 65.4} + \frac{1}{280 - 500} \, ? \, \frac{1}{280 - 50}$$

$$\frac{1}{280} + \frac{1}{214.6} + \frac{1}{-220} \; ? \; \frac{1}{230}$$

$$0.00357 + 0.00465 - 0.00455 \; ? \; 0.00435$$

$$0.00368 \neq 0.00435$$

This is not the answer, so let us try -270:

$$\frac{1}{270 - 0} + \frac{1}{270 - 65.4} + \frac{1}{270 - 500} \; ? \; \frac{1}{270 - 50}$$

$$0.00370 + 0.00489 - 0.00435 \; ? \; 0.00455$$

$$0.00424 \neq 0.00455$$

This is closer, so let us try -260:

$$\frac{1}{260 - 0} + \frac{1}{260 - 65.4} + \frac{1}{260 - 500} \; ? \; \frac{1}{260 - 50}$$

$$0.00385 + 0.00514 - 0.00417 \; ? \; 0.00476$$

$$0.00482 \neq 0.00476$$

Because at -270 the value on the right (0.00455) is larger than the value on the left (0.00424), and at -260 the reverse is true, the breakaway is between -270 and -260, much closer to -260. We therefore try -262

$$\frac{1}{262 - 0} + \frac{1}{262 - 65.4} + \frac{1}{262 - 500} \; ? \; \frac{1}{262 - 50}$$

$$0.00382 + 0.00509 - 0.00420 \; ? \; 0.00472$$

$$0.00471 \approx 0.00472$$

This is close enough. From an examination of the figures we can see that at -260 there is a difference of 6 in the last figure, and at -270 a difference of 31 in the other direction. Therefore a difference of only 1 in the last figure means that we have achieved three-figure accuracy of our breakaway point. Note that had we started at the point where our asymptotes begin (-257.7), we would have been fairly close to the breakaway point.

RULE 10. After sketching in the root locus by rules 1 through 9, we can check each point of the locus off the real axis by the method

derived and outlined below. The general closed-loop equation of a
system was given in equation (5.12) and is repeated here:

$$\frac{\theta_{out}}{\theta_{in}} = \frac{KG}{1 + KGH} = \frac{KG}{1 + KG} \quad \text{when} \quad H = 1 \quad (100\% \text{ feedback})$$

$$(7.64)$$

Then the characteristic equation of the last expression in equation
(7.64) is

$$1 + KG = 0 \qquad (7.65)$$

which we can write as follows

$$KG = -1 \qquad (7.66)$$

Equation (7.66) is true if the following conditions are met:

$$|KG| = 1 \qquad (7.67)$$

and

$$\underline{/KG} = \pm 180° \qquad (7.68)$$

The proof of these two equations is demonstrated in Fig. 7.13,
which shows that a vector whose length or absolute value is 1 becomes -1 when rotated $\pm 180°$ from 0.

In feedback control systems we have expressions such as

$$KG = \frac{K_r(s + n_1)}{(s + d_1)(s + d_2)(s + d_3)} \qquad (7.69)$$

where s is any point on the plane, n_1 is the value of the zero of KG,
and d_1, d_2, and d_3 are values of the poles of KG. If the conditions of

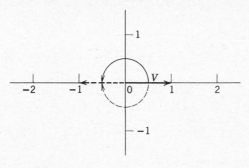

Fig. 7.13 The vector $|V| = 1$; after rotation through $\pm 180°$, $|V| = -1$.

equation (7.67) hold true, then from equations (7.67) and (7.69) we have

$$KG = \left| \frac{K_r(s + n_1)}{(s + d_1)(s + d_2)(s + d_3)} \right| = \frac{K_r|s + n_1|}{|s + d_1| \, |s + d_2| \, |s + d_3|} = 1$$

(7.70)

or

$$K_r = \frac{|s + d_1| \, |s + d_2| \, |s + d_3|}{|s + n_1|}$$

(7.71)

and from equations (7.68) and (7.69) we obtain

$$\underline{/KG} = \underline{\bigg/ \frac{K_r(s + n_1)}{(s + d_1)(s + d_2)(s + d_3)}}$$

(7.72)

$$= \underline{/s + n_1} - \underline{/s + d_1} - \underline{/s + d_2} - \underline{/s + d_3} = \pm 180°$$

since when vectors are multiplied their angles are added, and when vectors are divided their angles are subtracted. The term $|s + n_1|$ is the length of the vector $(s + n_1)$; the term $\underline{/s + n_1}$ is the angle of the same vector. At any point on the root locus the product of the pole vector lengths divided· by the zero vector lengths must equal K_r (equation (7.71)), and the sum of the angles of the vectors to the point must equal $\pm 180°$ (equation (7.72)).

We now try to find the root locus that satisfies these conditions. In Fig. 7.14 point s is a search point or trial point which might or might not lie on the root locus. To test the point we use equation (7.72) because adding angles is much easier than multiplying vector lengths. We use a good protractor, note the angles of each pole and each zero, and accept the point s as being on the root locus only if equation (7.72), restated in equation (7.73), holds.

$$\underline{/KG} = \theta_{n_1} - \theta_{d_1} - \theta_{d_2} - \theta_{d_3} = \pm 180°$$

(7.73)

Applied to Fig. 7.14 equation (7.73) becomes

$$\theta_{n_1} - \theta_{d_1} - \theta_{d_2} - \theta_{d_3} = 135° - 147° - 113° - 55° = -180°$$

(7.74)

for our trial point s shown at $-2.75 + 2j\omega$. Therefore s is on the root locus. If the sum of the angles is other than $\pm 180°$, we reject the point because it is not on the root locus. Beginning as in Fig. 7.14 and searching for other points on the root locus, we draw the

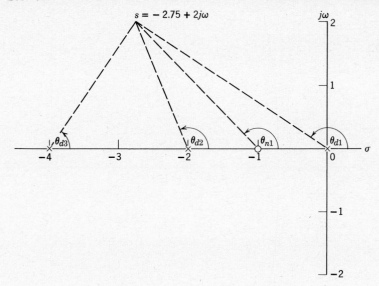

Fig. 7.14 Testing a point s to see if it is on the root locus.

$$\theta_{n1} - \theta_{d1} - \theta_{d2} - \theta_{d3} = 135° - 147° - 113° - 55° = -180°$$

Point s is on the root locus shown in Fig. 7.15.

root locus through the points that pass the test of equation (7.74), as shown in Fig. 7.15. Note that the locus of Fig. 7.15 leaves the real axis at the breakaway point and bends towards the asymptotes, then starts to straighten out. If projected further above and below, the root locus would approach closer and closer to the asymptotes but never touch them.

We can use a protractor for this procedure, but if we have a large amount of work with the root locus we can use a special root-searching angle-adding vector-multiplying device called the Spirule. This can be ordered from the Spirule Co., 9728 El Venado, Whittier, California. It costs $3.00 postpaid.

RULE 11. After we have sketched in the root locus we may want the value of K_r at some point on the locus. To find this value we go back to equation (7.71), which tells us that at any point on the locus

$$K_r = \frac{\text{product of distances from that point to each pole}}{\text{product of distances from that point to each finite zero}} \qquad (7.75)$$

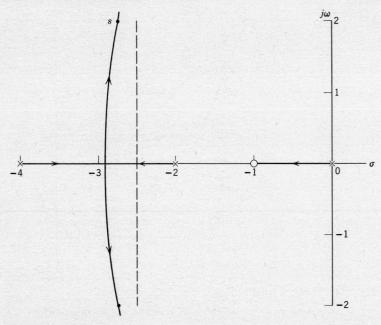

Fig. 7.15 Root locus plot of

$$\frac{\theta_{\text{out}}}{E} = \frac{K(s+1)}{s(s+2)(s+4)}$$

Point s is the point shown in Fig. 7.14.

We use an engineer's scale or the Spirule to measure the lengths from the point to each pole and each zero. Figure 7.16 shows the calculation of K_r at a point on the root locus; the complete root locus is shown in Fig. 7.19.

PROBLEMS

7.17. Given the open-loop transfer function

$$\frac{\theta_{\text{out}}}{E} = \frac{K_r(s+1)}{s(s+2)(s+3)}$$

Find: (a) the values of the poles
      (b) the values of the zeros

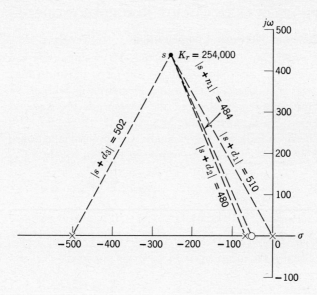

Fig. 7.16 Calculation of K_r at a point s on the root locus.

$$K_r = \frac{|s + d_1|\,|s + d_2|\,|s + d_3|}{|s + n_1|} = \frac{510 \times 480 \times 502}{484} = 254,000$$

(see also Fig. 7.19).

      (c) the number of branches of the root locus
      (d) where the root locus exists on the real axis
      (e) the angles of the asymptotes
      (f) the point of intersection of the asymptotes and the real axis
      (g) the breakaway point from the real axis
7.18. Given the open-loop transfer function

$$\frac{\theta_{\text{out}}}{E} = \frac{K_r(s + 2)}{s(s + 3)(s + 5)}$$

Find: (a) the values of the poles
      (b) the values of the zeros
      (c) the number of branches of the root locus
      (d) where the root locus exists on the real axis
      (e) the angles of the asymptotes
      (f) the point of intersection of the asymptotes and the real axis
      (g) the breakaway point from the real axis

7.5   ROOT LOCUS OF COURSE RECORDER COMPENSATED

(a) Phase-lag Network Compensation

This system was analyzed in Section 5.6 by frequency response (Bode diagram); see Fig. 5.9. Its root locus is shown in Fig. 7.17, which was plotted according to the rules given in Section 7.4. The procedure followed is given in the paragraphs below, which are numbered the same as the rules of Section 4.

1. The open-loop transfer function was given in equations (5.48) and (5.50). We convert this to root locus form in equation (7.76).

$$\frac{\theta_{out}}{E} = \frac{190(1 + s)}{s(1 + s/0.1)(1 + s/65.4)} = \frac{190 \dfrac{65.4 \times 0.1}{1} (s + 1)}{s(s + 0.1)(s + 65.4)}$$

$$= \frac{6.54K_v/N(s + 1)}{s(s + 0.1)(s + 65.4)} = \frac{K_r(s + 1)}{s(s + 0.1)(s + 65.4)} ;$$

$$K_r = 6.54K_v/N \qquad (7.76)$$

2. In Fig. 7.17 poles at 0, -0.1, and -65.4 and the zero at -1 are plotted. Note the enlargement of the region near the origin.

3. As shown in Fig. 7.17, the root locus exists to the left of $s = 0$ (singularity 1) but stops at $s = -0.1$ (2). It starts again at $s = -1$ (3) and stops at $s = -65.4$ (4).

4 and 5. There are three poles, and one branch begins at each pole. Therefore there are three branches and three zeros. One branch of the locus ends at the zero at -1. Two branches leave the breakaway point: one branch goes to the zero at plus infinity, and one branch goes to the zero at minus infinity. The circle at the origin is confusing, but the rule holds.

6. In Fig. 7.17 only the upper half of the root locus is drawn because a larger scale is possible, and because the other half is a mirror image about the real (horizontal) axis.

7. From equation (7.55a) we have

$$\frac{\pm 180°}{3 - 1} = \pm 90° \qquad (7.77)$$

and the two asymptotes at these angles are shown as dashed lines. Projected far enough, the root locus branches will come infinitesimally close to these dashed lines.

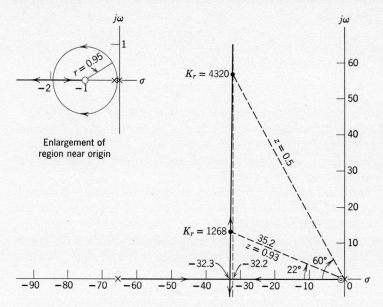

Fig. 7.17 Phase-lag network compensation

$$\frac{\theta_{\text{out}}}{E} = \frac{K_r(s + 1)}{s(s + 0.1)(s + 65.4)}$$

Note: the -32.3 point has been moved left to show the separation between the asymptotes and the root locus.

8. By equation (7.56) we have the intersection of the asymptotes and the real axis at

$$\frac{\text{sum of pole values} - \text{sum of zero values}}{\text{total number of poles} - \text{total number of finite zeros}} =$$

$$\frac{0 + (-0.1) + (-65.4) - (-1)}{3 - 1} = \frac{-64.5}{2} = -32.25 \quad (7.78)$$

9. By the method and the examples given in Section 7.4 and Rule 9, and by using equations (7.59), (7.60), and (7.61), we find by trial and error the breakaway point near -32.

The final and successful trial is with $b = -32.3$:

$$\sum \frac{1}{|b| - |d|} = \frac{1}{32.3 - 0} + \frac{1}{32.3 - 0.1} + \frac{1}{32.3 - 65.4}$$

$$= 0.0310 + 0.0310 - 0.0302 = 0.0318 \quad (7.79)$$

$$\sum \frac{1}{|b| - |n|} = \frac{1}{32.3 - 1} = 0.0319 \qquad (7.80)$$

Equating (7.79) and (7.80) we see that

$$0.0318 \approx 0.0319 \qquad (7.81)$$

and equation (7.59) is satisfied, so our breakaway point is -32.3. This point is so close to -32.2 that a true graph would not show any difference between the breakaway point and the asymptotes. Therefore the breakaway is moved slightly to the left to show the construction of the root locus.

There are two other breakaway points—one between 0 and 0.1 and one at about 2, as shown in Fig. 7.17 in the enlargement of the region near the origin. This circle can be determined by finding the two breakaway points and then their midpoint, which is the center of the circle. But wherever the leftmost pole is remote from the other poles and the zero—say well to the left of the geometrical center of the root locus, as in Fig. 7.17 and Fig. 7.20—an easy method of constructing the circle is available. This method is based on the assumption that the leftmost pole is at minus infinity. Figure 7.18 shows the exact root locus for such a case. The center of the circle is at the zero, and the radius is found by the formula

$$\text{Radius} = r = \sqrt{ab} \qquad (7.82)$$

where a is the distance from the zero to the nearest pole and b is the distance from the zero to the second pole.

In Fig. 7.17 our value of a is $1 - 0.1 = 0.9$, and our value of b is 1, so the radius of our circle is

$$r = \sqrt{1.0 \times 0.9} = \sqrt{0.9} = 0.95 \qquad (7.83)$$

Calculation of the exact breakaway point will show that this value is very close to -1.95, which we found the easy way. Also this part of the root locus is usually not very important for our calculations; we need to know only its shape and location.

10. We need plot no individual points. If we had to we would follow the procedure of Section 7.4 and Rule 10.

11. Application of Rule 11 to the point where the line of constant $z = 0.5$ intersects the root locus, as shown in Fig. 7.17, gives us the value of K_r at that point:

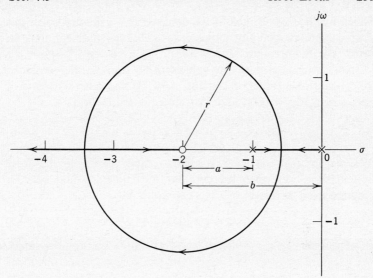

Fig. 7.18 Root locus of

$$\frac{\theta_{\text{out}}}{E} = \frac{K_r(s + 2)}{s(s + 1)}$$

Radius $r = \sqrt{ab} = \sqrt{1 \times 2} = 1.414.$

K_r at a point

$$= \frac{\text{product of distances from the point to each pole}}{\text{product of distances from the point to each finite zero}}$$

$$= \frac{64.8 \times 64.8 \times 65.2}{64.6} = 4230 \quad (7.84)$$

To find K_v/N at that point we use equation (7.76) for this system and we find

$$\frac{K_v}{N} = \frac{K_r}{6.54} = \frac{4230}{6.54} = 648 \quad (7.85)$$

This means that from a transient point of view our system gain K_v/N of 190 which we used in Chapter 5 could be increased considerably. Figure 5.11 also indicates that some increase is possible, since a phase margin of 71° is more than enough. However, we often design conservatively to allow for system changes during operation which might cause trouble if we designed too tightly. Also in this case conditional stability imposes an additional problem that we must take into account.

In our original problem our value of K_v/N was 190 after we added 10 dB gain (see Table 5.1 and Fig. 5.9). To find out what the z of this system was we first find K_r from equation (7.76)

$$K_r = \frac{6.54K_v}{N} = 6.54 \times 190 = 1242 \qquad (7.86)$$

We can see that the locus is almost exactly like a second-order system. If it were second-order, our K_r required would be at a distance from the origin of

$$\sqrt{K_r} = \sqrt{1242} = 35.2 \qquad (7.87)$$

as we can see on Figs. 7.9, 7.10, and 7.11—all second-order systems. We measure a vector 35.2 long from the origin to the root locus and mark the point, as shown on Fig. 7.17. Then we check K_r at this point and find, as in equation (7.84),

$$K_r = \frac{35.2 \times 35.2 \times 35.6}{34.8} = 1268; \quad \frac{K_v}{N} = \frac{1268}{6.54} = 194 \quad (7.88)$$

This is close enough to 1242 and to 190. If it were not we could move the point and try another calculation like equation (7.88), until we came within $\pm 5\%$ of the value we want. At this value of K_r and of K_v/N we find that the line of constant z from the origin to the point on the locus makes an angle of 22° with the horizontal, as we see in Fig. 7.17. The cosine of 22° is 0.93, which is the value of z for this K_v/N, the value we used in Chapter 5. This is a very stable system indeed from a transient point of view.

Reading the calculations of K_r for the next two systems (Section 7.5b, paragraph 11, and 7.5c, paragraph 11) would be helpful in solving the following problems.

PROBLEMS

7.19. (a) Starting with the open-loop transfer function you found as your answer to Prob. 5.13(b), find the open-loop root locus transfer function. (See equation (7.76).)

(b) Draw the root locus.

(c) Draw the line of constant $z = 0.5$, and mark the point where this line crosses the root locus branch that goes to plus infinity. Find the values of K_r and K_v/N at this point.

(d) Find a point on the root locus where K_v/N has almost the same value as in your answer to Prob. 5.13; use the final K_v/N value you decided on for best system performance. What is the angle of the line drawn from the origin to this point? What constant value of z does this line represent? What is the maximum overshoot? (See equation (6.44).) What is the exact K_v/N of this point?

7.20. (a) Starting with the open-loop transfer function you found as your answer to Prob. 5.14(b), find the open-loop root locus transfer function. (See equation (7.76).)

(b) Draw the root locus.

(c) Draw the line of constant $z = 0.5$, and mark the point where this line crosses the root locus branch that goes to plus infinity. Find the values of K_r and K_v/N at this point.

(d) Find a point on the root locus where K_v/N has almost the same value as in your answer to Prob. 5.14; use the final K_v/N value you decided on for best system performance. What is the angle of the line drawn from the origin to this point? What constant value of z does this line represent? What is the maximum overshoot? (See equation (6.44).) What is the exact K_v/N of this point?

(b) Phase-lead Network Compensation

To plot the root locus of this system, analyzed in Section 5.6 by frequency response (see Fig. 5.10), we again follow the rules of Section 7.4 and obtain Fig. 7.19.

1. The root locus form of the open-loop transfer function of the course recorder compensated by a phase-lead network is obtained from equations (5.55) and (5.56):

$$\frac{\theta_{out}}{E} = \frac{190(1 + s/50)}{s\left(1 + \dfrac{s}{65.4}\right)\left(1 + \dfrac{s}{500}\right)} = \frac{190\,\dfrac{65.4 \times 500}{50}(s + 50)}{s(s + 65.4)(s + 500)}$$

$$= \frac{654K_v/N(s + 50)}{s(s + 65.4)(s + 500)} = \frac{K_r(s + 50)}{s(s + 65.4)(s + 500)};$$

$$K_r = \frac{654K_v}{N} \quad (7.89)$$

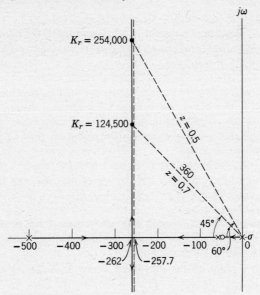

Fig. 7.19 Phase-lead network compensation.

$$\frac{\theta_{\text{out}}}{E} = \frac{K(s + 50)}{s(s + 65.4)(s + 500)}$$

2. The zero at -50 and the poles at 0, -65.4, and -500 are plotted in Fig. 7.19.

3. The root locus exists to the left of $s = 0$ (singularity 1) but stops at $s = -50$ (2). It starts again at $s = -65.4$ (3) and stops at $s = -500$ (4).

4 and 5. Because of the three poles there are three branches of the root locus: one from the pole at the origin to the zero at -50, one from the pole at -65.4 to the zero at plus infinity, and one from the pole at -500 to the zero at minus infinity.

6. The root locus is obviously symmetrical.

7. Our asymptotes are at $\pm 90°$, as shown in equation (7.55).

8. By equation (7.56) the asymptotes intersect the real axis at

$$\frac{0 + (-65.4) + (-500) - (-50)}{3 - 1} = \frac{-515.4}{2} = -257.7 \quad (7.90)$$

9. The breakaway point of this system was calculated as the second example in Section 7.4, Rule 9, where the value of -262 was found.

10. We need plot no individual points. If we had to we would follow the procedure of Section 7.4, Rule 10.

11. The K_r at the point where the line of constant $z = 0.5$ cuts the root locus is calculated and illustrated in Fig. 7.16. By equation (7.89) K_v/N at this point is equal to $K_r/654 = 254,000/654 = 389$. In our original problem the value of K_v/N was 190, which is a K_r of $654 \times 190 = 124,200$. To achieve this K_r we need to have a vector from the origin to the root locus of length $\sqrt{124,200} = 352$. Because the locus is a little to the left of center and because the vector to the zero at -50 is longer than the vector to the pole at -65.4, we make our vector from the origin to $K_r = 360$—a little longer than the 352 calculated on the basis of a second-order system (see Section 7.5a, paragraph 11). We then have

$$K_r = \frac{360 \times 322 \times 350}{326} = 124,500; \quad \frac{K_v}{N} = \frac{K_r}{654} = \frac{124,500}{654} = 190.5$$

$$(7.91)$$

This is very close indeed! The angle of this vector is $45°$, and the cosine of this angle $= z = 0.7$, as we see in Fig. 7.19. Again we see that our Chapter 5 system had a very satisfactory transient response.

PROBLEMS

7.21. (*a*) Starting with the open-loop transfer function you found as your answer to Prob. 5.15(*b*), find the open-loop root locus transfer function (see equation (7.89)).

(*b*) Draw the root locus.

(*c*) Draw the line of constant $z = 0.5$, and mark the point where this line crosses the root locus branch that goes to plus infinity. Find the values of K_r and K_v/N at this point.

(*d*) Find a point on the root locus where K_v/N has almost the same value (within $\pm 5\%$) as in your answer to Prob. 5.15; use the final K_v/N value you decided on for best system performance. What is the angle of the line drawn from the origin to this point? What constant value of z does this line represent? What is the maximum overshoot? (See equation (6.44).) What is the exact K_v/N of this point?

7.22. (*a*) Starting with the open-loop transfer function you found as your answer to Prob. 5.16 (*b*), find the open-loop root locus transfer function (see equation (7.89)).

(*b*) Draw the root locus.

(*c*) Draw the line of constant $z = 0.5$, and mark the point where this line crosses the root locus branch that goes to plus infinity. Find the values of K_r and K_v/N at this point.

(*d*) Find a point on the root locus where K_v/N has almost the same value (within $\pm 5\%$) as in your answer to Prob. 5.16; use the final value of K_v/N you decided on for best system performance. What is the angle of the line drawn from the origin to this point? What constant value of z does this line represent? What is the maximum overshoot? (Use equation (6.44).) What is the exact K_v/N of this point?

(c) Use of an Inertially Damped Servomotor (IDSM)

The root locus of this system, analyzed in Section 5.7 by frequency response (see Fig. 5.11), is given in Fig. 7.20. Again we start with the rules of Section 7.4. This system is very similar to the phase-lag compensated system, so we will not go into detail on every rule.

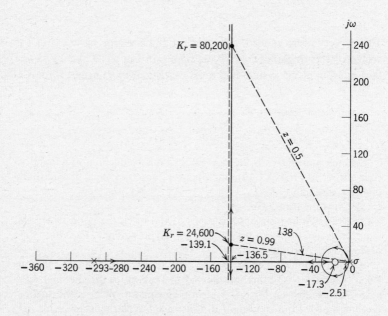

Fig. 7.20   Inertially damped servomotor system.

$$\frac{\theta_{\text{out}}}{E} = \frac{K_r(s + 17.3)}{s(s + 2.51)(s + 293)}$$

1. $$\frac{\theta_{out}}{E} = \frac{164\left(1 + \dfrac{s}{17.3}\right)}{s\left(1 + \dfrac{s}{2.51}\right)\left(1 + \dfrac{s}{293}\right)} = \frac{164\left(\dfrac{2.51 \times 293}{17.3}\right)}{s(s + 2.51)(s + 293)}$$

$$= \frac{42.5K_v/N(s + 17.3)}{s(s + 2.51)(s + 293)} = \frac{K_r(s + 17.3)}{s(s + 2.51)(s + 293)};$$

$$K_r = 42.5K_v/N \quad (7.92)$$

2. The poles and zeros are marked in Fig. 7.20.

3. The real axis root locus is marked in Fig. 7.20.

4 and 5. See Section 7.5a, paragraphs 4 and 5 (phase-lag compensation).

6. See Section 7.5a, paragraph 6.

7. See Section 7.5a, paragraph 7.

8. By equation (7.56) the real axis intercept of the asymptotes is

$$\frac{0 - 2.51 - 293 - (-17.3)}{3 - 1} = \frac{-295.5 + 17.3}{2} = -139.1 \quad (7.93)$$

9. The major breakaway point can be guessed at as near the asymptote intercept, -139.1, or as halfway between the zero at -17.3 and the pole at -293, about -138. By the method and examples given in Section 7.4, Rule 9, we find after a few trials that the breakaway point is at -136.5:

$$\frac{1}{136.5 - 0} + \frac{1}{136.5 - 2.51} + \frac{1}{136.5 - 293} \ ? \ \frac{1}{136.5 - 17.3}$$

$$0.00733 + 0.00746 - 0.00639 \ ? \ 0.00839$$

$$0.00840 \approx 0.00839$$

There is a circle near the origin, and we covered this situation in Fig. 7.18 and in Section 7.5a, paragraph 9. Using this same technique we find, using equation (7.82),

$$\text{Radius} = r = \sqrt{ab} = \sqrt{17.3 \times (17.3 - 2.51)} = 16.0 \quad (7.94)$$

We can test the accuracy of this method by checking one of the two points where the circle cuts the real axis. To the left of the zero the point cut by the circle is $-17.3 - 16.0 = -33.3$. Following the usual breakaway (in this case "break-in") method we find by trial and error that the point is actually at -35.8:

$$\frac{1}{35.8 - 0} + \frac{1}{35.8 - 2.51} + \frac{1}{35.8 - 293} \overset{?}{=} \frac{1}{35.8 - 17.3}$$

$$0.0540 \approx 0.0541$$

The error (-33.3 versus -35.8) is small, and we usually need not be too accurate in this part of the locus, so we use the method of Fig. 7.18 to save ourselves a lot of work.

10. We need plot no individual points. If we had to, we would follow the procedure of Section 7.4, Rule 10.

11. When $z = 0.5$

$$K_r = \frac{275 \times 274 \times 284}{267} = 80,200 \tag{7.95}$$

From equation (7.92) we have

$$\frac{42.5 \, K_v}{N} = K_r; \qquad \frac{K_v}{N} = \frac{K_r}{42.5} = \frac{80,200}{42.5} = 1890$$

This is better than 3×518, the value we finally chose for this system (see Table 5.1). But there are very good reasons for being conservative in designing this type of system, as we shall see.

With a value of 518, which we chose in Chapter 5,

$$K_r = 42.5 \times 518 = 22,000; \qquad \sqrt{22,000} = 148.3 \tag{7.96}$$

Because of the pole and zero locations 148.3 will probably give too high a figure, so let us try 140.

$$K_r = \frac{140 \times 137.5 \times 158.5}{124} = 24,600 \tag{7.97}$$

This is more than 5% above 22,000, so let us try 138.

$$K_r = \frac{138 \times 135.5 \times 157}{122} = 21,300 \tag{7.98}$$

This is close enough to 22,000. The angle is 7.5°, and cos 7.5° = z = 0.99, as we see in Fig. 7.20. This seems like too stable a system, but we have discussed reasons for designing conservatively, and the IDSM like the phase lag gives us a conditionally stable system. Finally the IDSM has, as we saw in Fig. 4.37, an enormous initial overshoot that our mathematics doesn't account for. Therefore it is well that our system z (damping) is high.

PROBLEMS

7.23. (*a*) Starting with the open-loop transfer function you found as your answer to Prob. 5.17(*b*), find the open-loop root locus transfer function (see equation (7.92)).

(*b*) Draw the root locus.

(*c*) Draw the line of constant $z = 0.5$, and mark the point where this line crosses the root locus branch that goes to plus infinity. Find the value of K_r and K_v/N at this point.

(*d*) Find a point on the root locus where K_v/N has almost the same value (within $\pm 5\%$) as in your answer to Prob. 5.17; use the final value you decided on for best system performance. What is the angle of the line drawn from the origin to this point? What constant value of z does this line represent? What is the exact K_v/N of this point?

7.24. (*a*) Starting with the open-loop transfer function you found as your answer to Prob. 5.18(*b*), find the open-loop root locus transfer function (see equation (7.92)).

(*b*) Draw the root locus.

(*c*) Draw the line of constant $z = 0.5$, and mark the point where this line crosses the root locus branch that goes to plus infinity. Find the value of K_r and K_v/N at this point.

(*d*) Find a point on the root locus where K_v/N has almost the same value (within $\pm 5\%$) as in your answer to Prob. 5.18; use the final value you decided on for best system performance. What is the angle of the line drawn from the origin to this point? What constant value of z does this line represent? What is the exact K_v/N of this point?

7.25. Using the root locus analyze the servo system you designed as your answer to Prob. 5.29. Follow the instructions of Prob. 7.24 as far as possible, referring of course to Prob. 5.29. Also calculate maximum overshoot (using equation (6.44)) and number of oscillations before settling within a 5% band (using equation (6.46)). See how you can use the root locus in other ways to analyze your system, or even to synthesize a better one.

SUMMARY

This book has attempted to help the student who is not proficient in the calculus and differential equations to attain a foundation in the most widely used techniques of control theory. If you have followed the work thus far and can work the problems, you will be able to read much of the literature on control system theory and understand most of what you read. I hope that you find control systems enjoyable.

Appendix **A.**

Servomechanism conversion factors

Multiply the left-hand entry by the value in the center column to obtain the unit of measure shown in the right-hand column. Single-letter abbreviations are: c = cycle, m = meter, r = revolution, s = second.

	Angular Measure	
deg	17.45	mils
deg	60.00	min
deg	1.745×10^{-2}	rad
mils	5.730×10^{-2}	deg
mils	3.438	min
mils	1.000×10^{-3}	rad
min	1.667×10^{-2}	deg
min	0.2909	mils
min	2.909×10^{-4}	rad
rad	57.30	deg
rad	1.000×10^{3}	mils
rad	3.438×10^{3}	min
	Angular Velocity	
deg/s	1.745×10^{-2}	rad/s
deg/s	0.1667	r/min
deg/s	2.778×10^{-3}	r/s
rad/s	57.30	deg/s
rad/s	9.549	r/min
rad/s	0.1592	r/s
r/min	6.000	deg/s
r/min	0.1047	rad/s
r/min	1.667×10^{-2}	r/s
r/s = c/s	360.00	deg/s
r/s = c/s	6.283	rad/s
r/s = c/s	60.00	r/min
Army mil	1/6400	revolutions

Damping

$\dfrac{\text{ft-lb}}{\text{rad/s}}$	20.11	$\dfrac{\text{oz-in.}}{\text{r/min}}$
$\dfrac{\text{oz-in.}}{\text{r/min}}$	4.974×10^{-2}	$\dfrac{\text{ft-lb}}{\text{rad/s}}$
$\dfrac{\text{oz-in.}}{\text{r/min}}$	6.74×10^{-2}	newton-m/rad/s
$\dfrac{\text{oz-in.}}{\text{r/min}}$	6.74×10^{5}	dyne-cm/rad/s

Density

gm/cm³	10^3	kg/m³
lb/ft³	16.018	kg/m³

Length

in.	2.54	cm
ft	30.48	cm
cm	0.3937	in.
ft	12.00	in.
cm	3.281×10^{-2}	ft
in.	8.333×10^{-2}	ft

Energy

ergs	10^{-7}	joules
kWh	3.6×10^{6}	joules
calories	4.182	joules
ft-lb	1.356	joules
Btu	1055	joules
watt-sec	1.000	joules

Force and Weight

dynes	1.020×10^{-3}	gm (force)
dynes	10^{-5}	newtons
poundals	0.13826	newtons
lb (force)	4.4482	newtons
gm (force)	980.7	dynes

Inertia

gm-cm^2	10^{-7}	kg-m^2
gm-cm^2	5.468×10^{-3}	oz-in.^{2}
gm-cm^2	7.372×10^{-8}	slug-ft^2
oz-in.^{2}	1.829×10^2	gm-cm^2
oz-in.^{2}	1.348×10^{-5}	slug-ft^2
slug-ft^2	1.357×10^7	gm-cm^2
lb-ft-sec^2	7.419×10^4	oz-in^2
slug-ft^2	1.357	kg-m^2
lb-in.^{2}	2.925×10^{-4}	kg-m^2
oz-in.^{2}	1.829×10^{-5}	kg-m^2
oz-in.^{2}	2.59×10^{-3}	oz-in.-sec^2

Mass

gm	3.527×10^{-2}	oz
gm	10^{-3}	kg
slug	14.594	kg
oz.	28.35	gm

Power

erg/s	10^{-7}	watts
cal/s	4.182	watts
Btu/hr	0.2930	watts
joules/s	1.00	watts
hp	746	watts
ft-lb/s	1.356	watts
watts	1.341×10^{-3}	hp

Pressure

dynes/cm^2	10^{-1}	newton/m^2
psi	6.895×10^3	newton/m^2
atmospheres	1.013×10^5	newton/m^2
cm Hg	1333	newton/m^2

Torque

dyne-cm	1.416×10^{-5}	oz-in.
ft-lb	1.383×10^4	gm-cm
ft-lb	192	oz-in.
gm-cm	1.235×10^{-5}	ft-lb
gm-cm	1.389×10^{-2}	oz-in.
oz-in.	5.208×10^{-3}	ft-lb
oz-in.	72.01	gm-cm
oz-in.	7.0612×10^{-3}	newton-m
oz-in.	7.0612×10^4	dyne-cm

Torque
Error

$\dfrac{\text{oz-in.}}{\text{min}}$	0.0558	$\dfrac{\text{lb-ft}}{\text{rad}}$
$\dfrac{\text{lb-ft}}{\text{rad}}$	17.9	$\dfrac{\text{oz-in.}}{\text{min}}$

Velocity

ft/s	0.30480	m/s
miles/hr	0.44704	m/s
knots	1.152	miles/hr

Appendix B.

Decibel table and calculations

Voltage, Current and Gain Ratio Equivalent of Decibels				Decibel Equivalent of Voltage, Current, and Gain Ratio					
dB	Ratio	dB	Ratio	Ratio	dB	Ratio	dB	Ratio	dB
0.1	1.01	8.0	2.51	0.01	−40.00	0.80	−1.94	11.0	20.83
0.2	1.02	8.5	2.66	0.02	−33.98	0.85	−1.41	12.0	21.58
0.3	1.03	9.0	2.82	0.03	−30.46	0.90	−0.92	13.0	22.28
0.4	1.05	9.5	2.98	0.04	−27.96	0.95	−0.45	14.0	22.92
0.5	1.06	10.0	3.16	0.05	−26.02	1.00	0.00	15.0	23.52
0.6	1.07	11.0	3.55	0.06	−24.44	1.10	0.83	16.0	24.08
0.7	1.08	12.0	3.98	0.07	−23.10	1.20	1.58	17.0	24.61
0.8	1.10	13.0	4.47	0.08	−21.94	1.30	2.28	18.0	25.11
0.9	1.11	14.0	5.01	0.09	−20.92	1.40	2.92	19.0	25.58
1.0	1.12	15.0	5.62	0.10	−20.00	1.50	3.52	20.0	26.02
1.1	1.13	16.0	6.31	0.11	−19.17	1.60	4.08	22.0	26.85
1.2	1.15	17.0	7.08	0.12	−18.42	1.70	4.61	24.0	27.60
1.3	1.16	18.0	7.94	0.13	−17.72	1.80	5.11	26.0	28.30
1.4	1.17	19.0	8.91	0.14	−17.08	1.90	5.58	28.0	28.94
1.5	1.19	20.0	10.00	0.15	−16.48	2.00	6.02	30.0	29.54
1.6	1.20	25.0	17.8	0.16	−15.92	2.20	6.85	32.0	30.10
1.7	1.22	30.0	31.6	0.17	−15.39	2.40	7.60	34.0	30.63
1.8	1.23	35.0	56.2	0.18	−14.90	2.60	8.30	36.0	31.13
1.9	1.24	40.0	100.0	0.19	−14.42	2.80	8.94	38.0	31.60
2.0	1.26	45.0	177.8	0.20	−13.98	3.00	9.54	40.0	32.04
2.2	1.29	50.0	316	0.22	−13.15	3.20	10.10	42.0	32.46
2.4	1.32	55.0	562	0.24	−12.40	3.40	10.63	44.0	32.87
2.6	1.35	60.0	1,000	0.26	−11.70	3.60	11.13	46.0	33.26
2.8	1.38	65.0	1,780	0.28	−11.06	3.80	11.60	48.0	33.63
3.0	1.41	70.0	3,160	0.30	−10.46	4.00	12.04	50.0	33.98

Voltage, Current and Gain Ratio Equivalent of Decibels				Decibel Equivalent of Voltage, Current, and Gain Ratio					
dB	Ratio	dB	Ratio	Ratio	dB	Ratio	dB	Ratio	dB
3.2	1.44	75.0	5,620	0.32	− 9.90	4.20	12.46	55.0	34.81
3.4	1.48	80.0	10,000	0.34	− 9.37	4.40	12.87	60.0	35.56
3.6	1.51	85.0	17,800	0.36	− 8.88	4.60	13.26	65.0	36.26
3.8	1.55	90.0	31,600	0.38	− 8.40	4.80	13.62	70.0	36.90
4.0	1.58	95.0	56,200	0.40	− 7.96	5.00	13.98	75.0	37.50
4.2	1.62	100.0	100,000	0.42	− 7.53	5.50	14.81	80.0	38.06
4.4	1.66	105.0	178,000	0.44	− 7.13	6.00	15.56	85.0	38.59
4.6	1.70	110.0	316,000	0.46	− 6.74	6.50	16.26	90.0	39.08
4.8	1.74	115.0	562,000	0.48	− 6.38	7.00	16.90	95.0	39.55
5.0	1.78	120.0	1,000,000	0.50	− 6.02	7.50	17.50	100.0	40.00
5.5	1.88	130.0	3.16×10^6	0.55	− 5.19	8.00	18.06	10^3	60.00
6.0	1.99	140.0	10^7	0.60	− 4.44	8.50	18.59	10^4	80.00
6.5	2.11	150.0	3.16×10^7	0.65	− 3.74	9.00	19.08	10^5	100.00
7.0	2.24	160.0	10^8	0.70	− 3.10	9.50	19.55	10^6	120.00
7.5	2.37	170.0	3.16×10^8	0.75	− 2.50	10.00	20.00	10^7	140.00

For dB values not shown in left-hand part of table, follow this example.

Given 42 dB.

(1) Subtract 20, 40, 60, 80, or 100 dB ($= 10$, 100, 1000, 10,000, 100,000) from dB value given so that value left after subtraction is given in table: $(42 − 40)$ dB $= 2$ dB; 40 dB $= 100.0$.

(2) Find ratio corresponding to dB value left: 2 dB $= 1.26$

(3) Multiply the two ratio values found above: $1.26 \times 100 = 126$ gain ratio

Another example:

(1) 37 dB − 20 dB $= 17$ dB; 20 dB $= 10.0$

(2) 17 dB $= 7.08$ (3) $7.08 \times 10.0 = 70.8$ gain ratio

For ratio values not shown in right-hand part of table, follow this example.

Given gain ratio $= 1400$.

(1) Write ratio given in powers of ten: $1400 = 1.4 \times 10^3$

(2) Find dB value in table for new ratio value: 1.4 = 2.92 dB.

(3) Add dB value in (2) to 20 × power ten from (1): 2.92 dB + 20 × 3 dB = 62.92 dB

Another example:

$650 = 6.5 \times 10^2 = 16.26$ dB + 40 dB = 56.26 dB

CALCULATION OF DB ON SPECIAL SLIDE RULES

To find dB and equivalent gain ratio using a slide rule with a split square root scale: Post slide rules with R_1 and R_2 scales, K&E slide rules with $Sq1$ and $Sq2$ scales, and Pickett slide rules with $\sqrt{}$ (upper and lower) scales:

For values of dB from 1 to 10 (=gain ratio 0 to 3.16):

Set value of dB on logarithm scale L, and find ratio value on R_1, $Sq1$, or $\sqrt{}$ (upper) scale under hairline.

Example: 2 dB = ? gain ratio? Move hairline to 2 (actually .2) on L scale and read 1.26 on R_1, $Sq1$, or $\sqrt{}$ (upper) scale under hairline.

For values of dB from 10 to 20 (= gain ratio 3.16 to 10.00):

Set value of dB − 10.00 on logarithm scale L and find ratio value on R_2, $Sq2$, or $\sqrt{}$ (lower) scale under hairline.

Example: 17 dB = ? gain ratio? Move hairline to 7 (actually .7) on L scale and read 7.08 on R_2, $Sq2$, or $\sqrt{}$ (lower) scale under hairline.

To find ratios reverse the above method:

Example: Gain ratio 1.61 = ? dB? Move hairline to 1.61 on R_1, $Sq1$, or $\sqrt{}$ (upper) scale and read 4.14 dB (actually .414) on L scale under hairline.

Example: Gain ratio 5.60 = ? dB? Move hairline to 5.60 on R_2, $Sq2$, or $\sqrt{}$ (lower) scale and read 4.96 on L scale under hairline. Add (10 + 4.96) dB = 14.96 dB.

By using the same technique as shown above in directions for use of the table, extended values may be found on the slide rule.

Example: 54.65 dB = (40 + 14.65) dB. 40 dB = 100. Move hairline to 4.65 on L scale and read 5.40 on R_2, $Sq2$, or $\sqrt{}$ (lower) scale under hairline. Ratio = 5.40 × 100 = 540.

Example: Gain ratio 2740 = 2.74 × 10³. Move hairline to 2.74 on R_1, $Sq1$, or $\sqrt{\ }$ (upper) scale and read 8.76 on L scale under hairline. (8.76 + 3 × 20) dB = 68.76 dB.

Note the following *approximate* values:

Ratio	1.00	1.4	2.0	3.0	6.0	10.0
dB	0.0	3.0	6.0	9.5	15.5	20.0

Appendix C.
Vector conversion table

This table is used to find values of A, dB A, and θ when given values of ωT of the vector $1 + j\omega T$. The equations below apply:

$$1 + j\omega T = A\underline{/\theta}$$
$$1 - j\omega T = A\underline{/-\theta}$$
$$j\omega T - 1 = A\underline{/180° - \theta}$$
$$\frac{1}{\underline{/\theta}} = \underline{/-\theta}$$

Sample calculations:
(1) Given $1 + j5.1$, find A, dB A, θ. From the table,

$$A = 5.20, \quad \text{dB } A = 14.32, \quad \theta = 78.9°$$
$$\therefore 1 + j5.1 = 5.2\underline{/78.9°} = 14.32 \text{ dB}\underline{/78.9°}$$

(2) Given $3 + j4$, find A, dB A, θ.

$$3 + j4 = 3(1 + j1.33) = 3(1.665\underline{/53.1°}) = 5.00\underline{/53.1°} = $$
$$13.98 \text{ dB}\underline{/53.1°}$$

The calculation of dB A,

$$5.00 = 13.98 \text{ dB}$$

can be made by using this table, by using the table in Appendix B, or by using the slide rule (see Appendix B for instructions).

Note: This table was developed because no comparable table is available. Calculations were made by slide rule, and small errors may occur in the third or fourth figure. However, these errors are insignificant in control calculations.

ωT	A	dB A	$\theta°$	ωT	A	dB A	$\theta°$
0.01	1.000	0.00	0.6	0.41	1.081	0.68	22.3
0.02	1.000	0.00	1.1	0.42	1.085	0.71	22.8
0.03	1.000	0.00	1.7	0.43	1.089	0.74	23.3
0.04	1.001	0.01	2.3	0.44	1.093	0.77	23.7
0.05	1.001	0.01	2.9	0.45	1.097	0.80	24.2
0.06	1.002	0.02	3.4	0.46	1.101	0.84	24.7
0.07	1.003	0.02	4.0	0.47	1.105	0.87	25.2
0.08	1.003	0.03	4.6	0.48	1.110	0.91	25.7
0.09	1.004	0.03	5.1	0.49	1.114	0.94	26.1
0.10	1.005	0.04	5.7	0.50	1.118	0.97	26.6
0.11	1.006	0.05	6.3				
0.12	1.007	0.06	6.8	0.51	1.122	1.00	27.0
0.13	1.008	0.07	7.4	0.52	1.127	1.04	27.5
0.14	1.010	0.08	8.0	0.53	1.132	1.08	27.9
0.15	1.011	0.10	8.5	0.54	1.137	1.12	28.4
0.16	1.013	0.11	9.1	0.55	1.141	1.15	28.8
0.17	1.014	0.12	9.6	0.56	1.146	1.19	29.2
0.18	1.016	0.14	10.2	0.57	1.151	1.23	29.7
0.19	1.018	0.16	10.8	0.58	1.156	1.26	30.1
0.20	1.020	0.17	11.3	0.59	1.161	1.30	30.5
0.21	1.022	0.19	11.9	0.60	1.167	1.34	31.0
0.22	1.024	0.21	12.4	0.61	1.172	1.38	31.4
0.23	1.026	0.23	13.0	0.62	1.177	1.42	31.8
0.24	1.028	0.24	13.5	0.63	1.182	1.46	32.2
0.25	1.031	0.26	14.0	0.64	1.187	1.49	32.6
				0.65	1.192	1.53	33.0
0.26	1.033	0.28	14.6	0.66	1.198	1.57	33.4
0.27	1.036	0.31	15.1	0.67	1.203	1.61	33.8
0.28	1.038	0.33	15.6	0.68	1.209	1.65	34.2
0.29	1.041	0.36	16.2	0.69	1.215	1.69	34.6
0.30	1.044	0.38	16.7	0.70	1.221	1.74	35.0
0.31	1.047	0.40	17.2	0.71	1.227	1.78	35.4
0.32	1.050	0.42	17.7	0.72	1.233	1.82	35.8
0.33	1.053	0.45	18.3	0.73	1.238	1.86	36.1
0.34	1.056	0.48	18.8	0.74	1.244	1.90	36.5
0.35	1.060	0.51	19.3	0.75	1.250	1.94	36.9
0.36	1.063	0.53	19.8				
0.37	1.066	0.56	20.3	0.76	1.256	1.98	37.2
0.38	1.070	0.59	20.8	0.77	1.262	2.02	37.6
0.39	1.073	0.62	21.3	0.78	1.268	2.06	38.0
0.40	1.077	0.65	21.8	0.79	1.274	2.10	38.3

ωT	A	dB A	$\theta°$	ωT	A	dB A	$\theta°$
0.80	1.281	2.15	38.7	1.20	1.562	3.88	50.2
0.81	1.287	2.19	39.0	1.21	1.570	3.92	50.4
0.82	1.294	2.24	39.4	1.22	1.578	3.96	50.7
0.83	1.300	2.28	39.7	1.23	1.586	4.01	50.9
0.84	1.306	2.32	40.0	1.24	1.594	4.05	51.1
0.85	1.313	2.36	40.4	1.25	1.602	4.10	51.3
0.86	1.319	2.40	40.7				
0.87	1.325	2.45	41.0	1.26	1.610	4.14	51.6
0.88	1.332	2.49	41.3	1.27	1.617	4.18	51.8
0.89	1.339	2.54	41.7	1.28	1.625	4.22	52.0
0.90	1.346	2.58	42.0	1.29	1.633	4.26	52.2
0.91	1.352	2.62	42.3	1.30	1.641	4.30	52.4
0.92	1.359	2.66	42.6	1.31	1.649	4.34	52.6
0.93	1.365	2.71	42.9	1.32	1.657	4.39	52.9
0.94	1.372	2.75	43.2	1.33	1.665	4.43	53.1
0.95	1.379	2.79	43.5	1.34	1.673	4.47	53.3
0.96	1.386	2.84	43.8	1.35	1.681	4.51	53.5
0.97	1.393	2.88	44.1	1.36	1.689	4.55	53.7
0.98	1.400	2.92	44.4	1.37	1.697	4.60	53.9
0.99	1.407	2.97	44.7	1.38	1.705	4.64	54.1
1.00	1.414	3.01	45.0	1.39	1.713	4.68	54.3
				1.40	1.721	4.72	54.5
1.01	1.422	3.06	45.3	1.41	1.729	4.76	54.7
1.02	1.429	3.10	45.6	1.42	1.737	4.80	54.8
1.03	1.436	3.15	45.8	1.43	1.745	4.84	55.0
1.04	1.443	3.19	46.1	1.44	1.753	4.88	55.2
1.05	1.450	3.23	46.4	1.45	1.761	4.92	55.4
1.06	1.458	3.28	46.7	1.46	1.769	4.96	55.6
1.07	1.465	3.32	46.9	1.47	1.777	5.00	55.8
1.08	1.472	3.36	47.2	1.48	1.785	5.04	56.0
1.09	1.479	3.40	47.5	1.49	1.793	5.08	56.1
1.10	1.486	3.44	47.7	1.50	1.802	5.12	56.3
1.11	1.493	3.48	48.0				
1.12	1.501	3.53	48.2	1.51	1.810	5.16	56.5
1.13	1.508	3.57	48.5	1.52	1.818	5.20	56.7
1.14	1.516	3.62	48.7	1.53	1.826	5.24	56.8
1.15	1.524	3.66	49.0	1.54	1.835	5.28	57.0
1.16	1.532	3.70	49.2	1.55	1.843	5.32	57.2
1.17	1.539	3.74	49.5	1.56	1.851	5.36	57.3
1.18	1.546	3.79	49.7	1.57	1.860	5.40	57.5
1.19	1.554	3.83	50.0	1.58	1.869	5.44	57.7

ωT	A	dB A	$\theta°$	ωT	A	dB A	$\theta°$
1.59	1.877	5.48	57.8	2.00	2.235	6.99	63.4
1.60	1.886	5.52	58.0				
1.61	1.895	5.56	58.2	2.01	2.244	7.02	63.5
1.62	1.903	5.59	58.3	2.02	2.253	7.06	63.7
1.63	1.911	5.63	58.5	2.03	2.262	7.10	63.8
1.64	1.919	5.66	58.6	2.04	2.271	7.13	63.9
1.65	1.928	5.70	58.8	2.05	2.280	7.16	64.0
1.66	1.936	5.74	58.9	2.06	2.289	7.20	64.1
1.67	1.945	5.78	59.1	2.07	2.298	7.23	64.2
1.68	1.954	5.82	59.2	2.08	2.306	7.26	64.3
1.69	1.963	5.86	59.4	2.09	2.315	7.30	64.4
1.70	1.971	5.90	59.5	2.10	2.324	7.33	64.5
1.71	1.980	5.94	59.7	2.11	2.333	7.36	64.6
1.72	1.988	5.97	59.8	2.12	2.341	7.39	64.7
1.73	1.997	6.01	60.0	2.13	2.350	7.42	64.9
1.74	2.006	6.05	60.1	2.14	2.359	7.46	65.0
1.75	2.014	6.09	60.3	2.15	2.368	7.48	65.1
				2.16	2.377	7.52	65.2
1.76	2.022	6.12	60.4	2.17	2.386	7.55	65.3
1.77	2.031	6.16	60.5	2.18	2.395	7.59	65.4
1.78	2.039	6.19	60.7	2.19	2.404	7.62	65.5
1.79	2.048	6.23	60.8	2.20	2.413	7.66	65.6
1.80	2.056	6.26	60.9	2.21	2.422	7.69	65.7
1.81	2.065	6.30	61.1	2.22	2.431	7.72	65.8
1.82	2.074	6.34	61.2	2.23	2.440	7.75	65.8
1.83	2.082	6.38	61.3	2.24	2.449	7.78	65.9
1.84	2.091	6.41	61.5	2.25	2.458	7.81	66.0
1.85	2.100	6.45	61.6				
1.86	2.109	6.48	61.7	2.26	2.467	7.84	66.1
1.87	2.118	6.52	61.9	2.27	2.476	7.88	66.2
1.88	2.127	6.56	62.0	2.28	2.486	7.91	66.3
1.89	2.136	6.59	62.1	2.29	2.495	7.94	66.4
1.90	2.145	6.63	62.2	2.30	2.504	7.98	66.5
1.91	2.154	6.67	62.4	2.31	2.513	8.01	66.6
1.92	2.163	6.71	62.5	2.32	2.522	8.04	66.7
1.93	2.172	6.74	62.6	2.33	2.531	8.07	66.8
1.94	2.181	6.78	62.7	2.34	2.540	8.10	66.9
1.95	2.190	6.81	62.9	2.35	2.549	8.13	66.9
1.96	2.199	6.84	63.0	2.36	2.559	8.16	67.0
1.97	2.208	6.88	63.1	2.37	2.568	8.19	67.1
1.98	2.217	6.92	63.2	2.38	2.577	8.22	67.2
1.99	2.226	6.95	63.3	2.39	2.586	8.25	67.3

ωT	A	dB A	$\theta°$	ωT	A	dB A	$\theta°$
2.40	2.595	8.28	67.4	2.80	2.970	9.46	70.3
2.41	2.604	8.32	67.5	2.81	2.979	9.48	70.4
2.42	2.613	8.35	67.5	2.82	2.988	9.51	70.5
2.43	2.623	8.38	67.6	2.83	2.998	9.54	70.5
2.44	2.632	8.41	67.7	2.84	3.007	9.56	70.6
2.45	2.642	8.44	67.8	2.85	3.017	9.59	70.7
2.46	2.651	8.47	67.9	2.86	3.027	9.62	70.7
2.47	2.661	8.50	68.0	2.87	3.036	9.65	70.8
2.48	2.670	8.53	68.0	2.88	3.046	9.67	70.9
2.49	2.679	8.56	68.1	2.89	3.056	9.70	70.9
2.50	2.688	8.59	68.2	2.90	3.065	9.73	71.0
				2.91	3.075	9.76	71.0
2.51	2.698	8.62	68.3	2.92	3.084	9.79	71.1
2.52	2.707	8.65	68.4	2.93	3.094	9.82	71.2
2.53	2.717	8.68	68.4	2.94	3.103	9.84	71.2
2.54	2.726	8.71	68.5	2.95	3.113	9.87	71.3
2.55	2.735	8.74	68.6	2.96	3.124	9.90	71.3
2.56	2.744	8.77	68.7	2.97	3.135	9.93	71.4
2.57	2.753	8.80	68.7	2.98	3.145	9.96	71.5
2.58	2.762	8.83	68.8	2.99	3.156	9.98	71.5
2.59	2.771	8.86	68.9	3.00	3.167	10.01	71.6
2.60	2.780	8.89	69.0				
2.61	2.790	8.92	69.0	3.1	3.26	10.26	72.10
2.62	2.799	8.94	69.1	3.2	3.35	10.50	72.63
2.63	2.809	8.97	69.2	3.3	3.45	10.76	73.13
2.64	2.819	9.00	69.3	3.4	3.54	10.99	73.60
2.65	2.829	9.03	69.3	3.5	3.64	11.22	74.05
2.66	2.838	9.06	69.4	3.6	3.74	11.45	74.47
2.67	2.847	9.09	69.5	3.7	3.83	11.67	74.87
2.68	2.856	9.12	69.5	3.8	3.93	11.89	75.25
2.69	2.865	9.15	69.6	3.9	4.03	12.10	75.61
2.70	2.875	9.18	69.7				
2.71	2.885	9.21	69.7	4.0	4.12	12.30	75.96
2.72	2.895	9.24	69.8	4.1	4.22	12.51	76.29
2.73	2.904	9.27	69.9	4.2	4.32	12.71	76.60
2.74	2.914	9.30	70.0	4.3	4.41	12.89	76.90
2.75	2.924	9.33	70.0	4.4	4.51	13.08	77.19
				4.5	4.61	13.27	77.47
2.76	2.933	9.36	70.1	4.6	4.71	13.46	77.74
2.77	2.943	9.38	70.2	4.7	4.80	13.63	77.99
2.78	2.952	9.41	70.2	4.8	4.90	13.81	78.23
2.79	2.961	9.44	70.3	4.9	5.00	13.98	78.47

ωT	A	dB A	$\theta°$	ωT	A	dB A	$\theta°$
5.0	5.10	14.15	78.69	8.8	8.85	18.94	83.51
5.1	5.20	14.32	78.90	8.9	8.95	19.04	83.58
5.2	5.30	14.49	79.11				
5.3	5.39	14.64	79.30	9.0	9.05	19.14	83.65
5.4	5.49	14.79	79.50	9.1	9.15	19.23	83.72
5.5	5.59	14.95	79.69	9.2	9.25	19.33	83.79
5.6	5.69	15.10	79.88	9.3	9.35	19.42	83.86
5.7	5.79	15.25	80.05	9.4	9.45	19.51	83.93
5.8	5.88	15.39	80.21	9.5	9.55	19.60	83.99
5.9	5.98	15.54	80.37	9.6	9.65	19.69	84.05
				9.7	9.75	19.78	84.11
6.0	6.08	15.68	80.53	9.8	9.85	19.87	84.17
6.1	6.18	15.82	80.68	9.9	9.95	19.96	84.23
6.2	6.28	15.96	80.83				
6.3	6.38	16.10	80.96	10.0	10.05	20.05	84.29
6.4	6.47	16.23	81.10	11	11.04	20.86	84.78
6.5	6.57	16.36	81.25	12	12.04	21.61	85.22
6.6	6.67	16.39	81.37	13	13.04	22.30	85.58
6.7	6.77	16.62	81.50	14	14.04	22.95	85.90
6.8	6.87	16.74	81.62	15	15.03	23.54	86.09
6.9	6.97	16.87	81.75	16	16.03	24.10	86.42
				17	17.03	24.63	86.63
7.0	7.07	16.89	81.85	18	18.03	25.12	86.82
7.1	7.17	17.11	81.97	19	19.03	25.59	86.98
7.2	7.26	17.22	82.08	20	20.02	26.07	87.16
7.3	7.36	17.34	82.19	25	25.02	28.00	87.71
7.4	7.46	17.46	82.30	30	30.02	29.57	88.09
7.5	7.56	17.57	82.40	35	35.01	30.89	88.36
7.6	7.66	17.69	82.50	40	40.01	32.05	88.57
7.7	7.76	17.80	82.59	45	45.01	33.07	88.73
7.8	7.86	17.91	82.68	50	50.01	33.98	88.83
7.9	7.95	18.01	82.77	60	60.01	35.57	89.04
				70	70.01	36.91	89.18
8.0	8.05	18.12	82.86	80	80.01	38.07	89.28
8.1	8.15	18.22	82.95	90	90.01	39.09	89.36
8.2	8.25	18.33	83.04	100	100.0	40.00	89.43
8.3	8.35	18.44	83.13	150	150.0	43.52	89.62
8.4	8.45	18.54	83.21	250	200.0	46.02	89.72
8.5	8.55	18.64	83.29	250	250.0	47.96	89.77
8.6	8.65	18.74	83.36	500	500.0	53.98	89.88
8.7	8.75	18.84	83.44	∞	∞	∞	90.0

Appendix D.

Partial list of servomechanism component manufacturers

The bulletins, reference manuals, and catalogs of the manufacturers listed here are extremely valuable for the student, but they are expensive to produce, and the manufacturers will *not* send a complete set of material to each student. The best way to get these items is to have a committee of students send for literature. A class letter should be written *on school stationery* to the *sales manager* of each manufacturer telling him exactly what the literature will be used for. The letter should include the name and number of the course, the number of students, and the fact that during the course each student will design a servomechanism system, choosing his components from one or more manufacturer's catalogs. Ask the manufacturer to send his material to *your instructor*, and *give his name, his full title, and his address at the school.* Since all manufacturers listed may at times issue booklets of interest as well as catalogs, request in your letter "catalogs of servo components and systems plus technical information, such as design and application data and servo theory." Special manufacturer literature listed in the bibliography (Appendix E) should be requested by title when you write to the manufacturer.

Beckman Instruments, Inc., Helipot Division, Fullerton, Calif.; 92634.
Bowmar Instrument Corp., 8000 Bluffton Road, Fort Wayne, Ind.; 46809.
*Cedar Engineering Division, Control Data Corporation, 5806 West 36th Street, Minneapolis, Minn.; 55416.
Clifton Precision Products Division of Litton Industries, Clifton Heights, Penna.; 19018.
Harowe Servo Controls ████████ttown Rd. at West Chester Pike, West Chester, Penna.
*Inland Motor Corporation, 501 First St., Radford, Virginia; 24141.

257

*Kearfott Products Division, General Precision, Inc., Little Falls, N. J.

Kollsman Motor Corporation, Mill Street, Dublin, Penn.

Muirhead Instruments, Inc., 1101 Bristol Road, Mountainside, N. J.

Reeves Instrument Corporation, Roosevelt Field, Garden City, N. Y.

Singer Company, Diehl Division, Finderne Plant, Somerville, N. J.

*Superior Manufacturing and Instrument Corporation, 36-07 20th Avenue, Long Island City, N. Y.; 11105.

*Technology Instrument Corporation of California, 850 Lawrence Drive, Newbury Park, Calif.

*Weston Instruments, Inc., Transicoil Division, Worcester, Penna.; 19490.

Wright Machinery Company, Division of Sperry Rand Corporation, Durham, N. C.

* See Appendix E. Ask for these items by title when you write to the manufacturer.

Appendix **E.**
Selected bibliography

MAGAZINES

Electromechanical Design. This is a most valuable publication containing the latest industry practice and product information. The January and the July issues entitled "System Designer's Handbook" are encyclopedias of simplified theory, useful practice, and summarized component information. Subscriptions are free but rigidly restricted. Write on school stationery and ask for back issues of the "System Designer's Handbook" and a free subscription to the magazine for your instructor, giving his title and his address at your school. Send your request to

Mr. Harold G. Buchbinder, President
Benwill Publishing Co.
167 Corey Road
Brookline, Mass.; 02146

MANUFACTURER LITERATURE *

Direct-Drive Servo Design Handbook. Inland Motor Corporation. Very useful theory, practice, and catalog information—looseleaf.

Kearfott Technical Information for the Engineer No. 1; Motors, Motor-Generators, Synchros, Resolvers. Kearfott Division; General Precision, Inc. Very useful theory, practice, and catalog information.

Servo Engineer's Handbook. Weston Instruments, Inc.; Transicoil Division. Excellent book with well-developed component and system theory and practice information. The example problems in Chapter 5 were taken from Chapter 7 of this Handbook; it is worthwhile to compare the two approaches.

Servo Engineer's Handbook. Superior Manufacturing and Instrument Corporation. Very useful presentation of servo system theory and practice.

Techniques for Achieving Servo System Stability. Cedar Engineering Division; Control Data Corporation. Interesting pamphlet.

TICOC Potentiometer Handbook. Technology Instrument Corporation of California. Valuable potentiometer information and catalog—looseleaf.

* See Appendix D for addresses of manufacturers.

259

BOOKS—SERVOMECHANISM COMPONENTS

W. R. Ahrendt and C. J. Savant, Jr., *Servomechanism Practice*, McGraw-Hill Book Co., New York, second edition, 1960.

Sidney A. Davis and Byron K. Ledgerwood, *Electromechanical Components for Servomechanisms*, McGraw-Hill Book Co., New York, 1961.

John E. Gibson and Franz B. Tuteur, *Control System Components*, McGraw-Hill Book Co., New York, 1958.

BOOKS ON THEORY—GENERAL

Harold Chestnut and Robert W. Mayer, *Servomechanisms and Regulating System Design*, Volume I, John Wiley and Sons, New York, second edition, 1959.

John J. D'Azzo and Constantine H. Houpis, *Feedback Control System Analysis and Synthesis*, McGraw-Hill Book Co., New York, second edition, 1966.

Benjamin C. Kuo, *Automatic Control Systems*, Prentice-Hall, Englewood Cliffs, N. J., 1962.

BOOKS ON THEORY—EMPHASIS ON ROOT LOCUS

Robert N. Clark, *Introduction to Automatic Control Systems*, John Wiley and Sons, New York, 1962.

L. Dale Harris, *Introduction to Feedback Systems*, John Wiley and Sons, New York, 1961.

BOOKS ON THEORY—ADVANCED BUT USEFUL

George J. Thaler and Robert G. Brown, *Analysis and Design of Feedback Control Systems*, McGraw-Hill Book Co., New York, second edition, 1960.

HANDBOOKS

John G. Truxal, Editor, *Control Engineers' Handbook*, McGraw-Hill Book Co., New York, 1958. An encyclopedia. A little out of date but still very useful.

Floyd E. Nixon, *Handbook of Laplace Transformation*, Prentice-Hall, Englewood Cliffs, N. J., second edition, 1965. An excellent book with a table of over 300 transform pairs at the end. The Laplace transforms in the table are given in both the $(s + a)$ and the $(1 + sT)$ forms. When using the tables be sure to read the coding system on pages 45 and 46 (Section 3.30).

Paul A. McCollum and Buck F. Brown, *Laplace Tables and Theorems*, Holt, Rinehart and Winston, New York, 1965. Large table of transform pairs. Read the preface for the key to the organization of the tables.

Answers to selected problems

Note: Answers are given for numerical problems but not for graphical problems.

2.1. $\dfrac{sT}{sT+1}$; $T = RC$

2.3. $\dfrac{sT_1+1}{sT_2+1}$; $T_1 = R_2C$, $T_2 = (R_1 + R_2)C$

2.5. $\dfrac{R_2}{R_1+R_2} \dfrac{1}{sT+1}$; $T = \dfrac{L}{R_1+R_2}$

2.7. $\dfrac{sT_1+1}{sT_2}$; $T_1 = \dfrac{L}{R_1}$, $T_2 = \dfrac{L}{R_2}$

2.9. $\dfrac{R_2}{R_1+R_2} \dfrac{sT_1+1}{sT_2+1}$; $T_1 = R_1C$, $T_2 = \dfrac{R_1R_2C}{R_1+R_2}$

2.11. $\dfrac{R_2(sC_1R_1+1)}{R_1(sC_2R_2+1)+R_2(sC_1R_1+1)}$; if $R_1C_1 = R_2C_2$ the answer becomes $\dfrac{R_2}{R_1+R_2}$

4.2. $\dfrac{16.0}{s(1+0.076s)} = \dfrac{16.0}{s(1+s/13.16)}$

4.4. $\dfrac{50.6}{s(1+0.076s)} = \dfrac{50.6}{s(1+s/13.16)}$

4.6. (a) $\dfrac{27.9}{s(1+0.0312s)} = \dfrac{27.9}{s(1+s/32.1)}$

261

4.8. (a) $\dfrac{10.92}{s(1 + 0.01778s)} = \dfrac{10.92}{s(1 + s/56.2)}$

4.14. $\dfrac{49.9(1 + j10\omega)}{j\omega(1 + j4.2\omega)(1 + j120\omega)} = \dfrac{49.9(1 + j\omega/0.1)}{j\omega(1 + j\omega/0.238)(1 + j\omega/0.00833)}$

4.16. $\dfrac{100.8}{j\omega(1 + j0.03\omega)} = \dfrac{100.8}{j\omega(1 + j\omega/33.3)}$

4.18. $\dfrac{100.8(1 + j0.03\omega)}{j\omega(1 + j0.03\omega)(1 + j0.003\omega)} = \dfrac{100.8}{j\omega(1 + j0.003\omega)} = \dfrac{100.8}{j\omega(1 + j\omega/333)}$

5.1. (a) 89,   (b) 0.026°

5.3. (a) 0.03°

(b) $\dfrac{119.2}{j\omega(1 + j0.08\omega)} = \dfrac{119.2}{j\omega(1 + j\omega/12.5)}$

(c) $\dfrac{119.2}{j\omega(1 + j0.08\omega) + 119.2} = \dfrac{119.2}{j\omega(1 + j\omega/12.5) + 119.2}$

$= \dfrac{1490}{1490 + j12.5\omega - \omega^2}$

5.4. $M_m = 1.67 = 4.45$ dB; $\omega_m = 37.6$ rad/sec;   phase   angle   at $\omega_m = -58.2°$; $\omega_b = 58.8$ rad/sec.

5.7. $\dfrac{38}{j\omega(1 + j0.0153\omega)} = \dfrac{38}{j\omega(1 + j\omega/65.4)}$

5.11. $\dfrac{19.87}{j\omega(1 + j0.01467\omega)} = \dfrac{19.87}{j\omega(1 + j\omega/68.2)}$

5.13. (b) $\dfrac{119.2(1 + j0.5\omega)}{j\omega(1 + j0.08\omega)(1 + j10\omega)} = \dfrac{119.2(1 + j\omega/2)}{j\omega(1 + j\omega/12.5)(1 + j\omega/0.1)}$

5.15. (b) $\dfrac{119.2(1 + j0.045\omega)}{j\omega(1 + j0.08\omega)(1 + j0.0045\omega)} = \dfrac{119.2(1 + j\omega/22.2)}{j\omega(1 + j\omega/12.5)(1 + j\omega/222)}$

5.17. (a) $\omega_{c_1} = 1$ rad/sec; $\omega_{c_2} = 5$ rad/sec; $\omega_{c_3} = 100$ rad/sec
$K_{vm} = 52.4$; $K_v/N = 120$

(b) $\dfrac{120(1 + j0.2\omega)}{j\omega(1 + j\omega)(1 + j0.01\omega)} = \dfrac{120(1 + j\omega/5)}{j\omega(1 + j\omega)(1 + j\omega/100)}$

(e) Similar to lag network compensated system.

5.19. $\dfrac{119.2}{j\omega(1 + j0.16\omega)} = \dfrac{119.2}{j\omega(1 + j\omega/6.25)}$

6.1.

z	Max. Over- shoot (% of Initial Step)	No. of Oscilla- tions to Settle to 5%	ω_n	Time to Max. Over- shoot π/ω_d	One Period $2\omega/\omega_d$	Time of Settling Time to 5% Band	ω_d	ω_b	ω_m
			Uncompensated system						
0.1619	0.598	2.91	38.6	0.825	0.1649	0.480	38.1	58.8	37.6
			Rate generator system						
0.926	0.004	0.1943	36.8	0.226	0.453	0.0880	13.88	26.4	None
			System with load inertia						
0.1144	0.696	4.14	27.3	0.116	0.232	0.960	27.1	41.3	27.0

6.2. (a) $\dfrac{1490}{1490 + j12.5\omega - \omega^2} = \dfrac{1490}{1490 + 12.5s + s^2}$

(b) $\dfrac{1}{s\left(\dfrac{s^2}{(38.6)^2} + \dfrac{2(0.1619)s}{38.6} + 1\right)}$

6.5. (a) $f(t) = 1 + 1.013e^{-6.25t} \sin(38.1t - 99.3°)$

(b) First maximum $= 1 + e^{-0.515} = 1.598$

First minimum $= 1 - e^{-1.03} = 0.643$

6.7. (a) $i = 20e^{-4000t} \sin(1273 \times 2\pi t)$

7.1. $\dfrac{-\frac{1}{2}}{s + 2} + \dfrac{\frac{1}{2}}{s + 4}$

7.3. No roots in RHP, $\therefore$ not absolutely unstable (factors into $(s + 1)^2(s + 2)$).

7.5. Roots in RHP, $\therefore$ absolutely unstable (factors into $(s + 3)(s^2 - 2s + 17)$).

7.7. No roots in RHP, $\therefore$ not absolutely unstable.

7.9. Roots in RHP, $\therefore$ absolutely unstable.

7.11. (a) $\dfrac{K_r}{s(s + 12.5)}$

(b) $\dfrac{K_r}{s^2 + 12.5s + K_r}$

(c) $s^2 + 12.5s + K_r = 0$

(d) $s_1 = -6.25 + \sqrt{39.06 - K_r}$, $s_2 = -6.25 - \sqrt{39.06 - K_r}$

(e) (1) $s_1 = 0$, $s_2 = -12.5$
   (2) Any value of $K_r < 39.06$
   (3) $s_1 = s_2 = -6.25$; $K_r = 39.06$
   (4) Any value of $K_r > 39.06$

7.12. (d) $K_r = 119.2 \times 12.5 = 1490$

(e) $\omega_n = 38.6$ rad/sec; $\omega_d = 38.1$ rad/sec;   angle $= 80.7°$;
   $z = 0.1619$; maximum overshoot $= 1.598$

7.15. $\dfrac{K_r}{s^2 + 68.2s + K_r}$

7.17. (a) 0, -2, -3; (b) 3; (c) -1; (d) between 0 and -1 and between -2 and -3; *not* between -1 and -2; (e) $\pm 90°$; (f) -2; (g) -2.47

7.19. (a) $\dfrac{K_r(s + 2)}{s(s + 0.1)(s + 12.5)}$

(b) Asymptote angles $= \pm 90°$
   Asymptotes intersect real axis at -5.3
   Breakaway at about -3.4

(d) Original problem 5.13(b): $K_v/N = 119.2$, $K_r = 74.5$; if you raised the gain of this system you will have a different K_v/N and K_r.

7.21. (a) $\dfrac{K_r(s + 22.2)}{s(s + 12.5)(s + 222)}$

(b) Asymptote angles $= \pm 90°$
   Asymptotes intersect real axis at -106.15
   Breakaway at -105

(d) Original problem 5.15(b): $K_v/N = 119.2$, $K_r = 14,900$; if you raised the gain of this system you will have a different K_v/N and K_r.

7.23. (a) $\dfrac{K_r(s + 5)}{s(s + 1)(s + 100)}$

(b) Asymptote angles $= \pm 90°$
   Asymptotes intersect real axis at -48
   Breakaway at -47.5

Index of symbols and abbreviations

Subnumbers after a variable—K_3, p_2, ω_{c1}—are specific values of the variable: ω_c is any corner frequency; ω_{c2} is one value of ω_c. Similarly the subscripts ${}_{\text{in}}$ and ${}_{\text{out}}$; for example, θ_{in} and E_{out} are input and output values of the variables.

Symbol or Abbreviation	Quantity or Term	Units or Value	Defined on Page
A	amplifier gain	volts/volt	4
ac	alternating current		
ASA	American Standards Association		
B	viscous damping (or viscous friction)	$\dfrac{\text{dyn-cm}}{\text{rad/sec}}$	94
B'	viscous damping—catalog value	$\dfrac{\text{dyn-cm}}{\text{rad/sec}}$	100
b	root locus breakaway point		222
B_{Lr}	reflected viscous damping	$\dfrac{\text{dyn-cm}}{\text{rad/sec}}$	155
C	capacitance	microfarads	
c or c/s	frequency	cycles/sec	
CR	synchro control receiver		81
CT	synchro control transformer		83
CX	synchro control transmitter		81
CX-CT	synchro CX and CT pair		83
d	denominator factor = pole		218
dB	decibels		26
dB A	decibel gain or magnitude		46
dc	direct current		
e or $e(t)$	voltage—time function		28, 33
E or $E(s)$	voltage—Laplace function		28, 33
e	base of natural logarithms	2.71828	
$e^{i\theta}$	rotating operator	degrees or radians	187, 189

Symbol or Abbreviation	Quantity or Term	Units or Value	Defined on Page
$e^{j\omega t}$	rotating operator		188
$e^{\sigma t}$	exponential term		190–191
$e^{(\sigma+j\omega)t}$	rotating plus exponential operator		191–193
e^{st}	operator; equals either $e^{j\omega t}$ or $e^{(\sigma+j\omega)t}$		190–193
f	frequency	cycles/sec	27, 71
$f(t)$	time function		27
$F(s)$	Laplace function		27
$G(j\omega)$	frequency function		27
G	general system function (usually KG, which see)		
H	feedback function	1 = 100% in this book	127
i or $i(t)$	current—time function		28, 33
I or $I(s)$	current—Laplace function		28, 33
I_0	current at time $t = 0$		186
IDSM	inertia-damped servomotor		152
j	operator rotating phasor 90°		49, 57
J	moment of inertia	gm-cm²	97
J_{Lr}	reflected load inertia	gm-cm²	155
K	any constant gain value		55, 56
K_a	amplifier gain constant	volts/volt	84
K_d	demodulator constant	dc volts/ac volts	85–86
K_g	rate generator constant	volts/1000 r/min	108
K_m	modulator constant	ac volts/dc volts	85–86
K_r	root locus system constant		205
K_s	CX-CT synchro pair constant	volts/rad or volts/degree	83
K_t	system torque constant $(= K_s K_a K_{tm})$	dyn-cm/rad	127
K_{tm}	servomotor torque constant	dyn-cm/volt	97
K_{tm}'	servomotor torque constant —catalog value	dyn-cm/volt	102
K_v	system velocity constant $(= K_s K_a K_{vm})$	sec⁻¹	126
K_{vm}	servomotor velocity constant	$\frac{\text{rad/sec}}{\text{volt}}$ or $\frac{\text{rad}}{\text{V-sec}}$	99
K_{vm}'	servomotor velocity constant —catalog value	$\frac{\text{rad/sec}}{\text{volt}}$ or $\frac{\text{rad}}{\text{V-sec}}$	100
kc	frequency	kilocycles/sec	7
KG	open-loop system transfer function		127

Symbol or Abbreviation	Quantity or Term	Units or Value	Defined on Page
$\dfrac{KG}{1+KG}$	closed-loop system transfer function		128
L	inductance	henries	30
L	torque	dyn-cm or oz-in	91
L_s	servomotor stall torque	dyn-cm or oz-in	91
LHP	left half-plane		199
M_m	maximum closed-loop system magnitude or gain		132–133
n	numerator factor = zero		218
N	reciprocal of gear train transfer function		106–107
R	resistance	ohms	27
RHP	right half-plane		197
s	Laplace transform variable		27
SAE	Society of Automotive Engineers		123
t	time function variable	sec	27
T	time constant	sec	29–30, 99
T'	time constant—catalog value	sec	100–101
T_m	servomotor time constant	sec	116
X	reactance	ohms	27
Y	admittance	mhos	29
z	damping factor or relative damping		170–171
Z	impedance	ohms	28

Greek Symbols

β	audio amplifier feedback ratio		7
σ	real part of s		27, 190–191
θ	phase shift	degrees	4, 47–51
θ	angular position	degrees or radians	98, 126–127
ω	angular velocity	rad/sec	27, 47
ω_b	closed-loop system bandwidth	rad/sec	131–132, 181
ω_c	corner frequency	rad/sec	52–53
ω_d	damped frequency	rad/sec	173
ω_f	free speed or no-load speed	rad/sec or r/min	91–92
ω_m	frequency of M_m	rad/sec	132
ω_n	natural frequency	rad/sec	170–171

Subject index

ASA C85.1 (1963) "Terminology for Automatic Control," 15, 23-24, 123-124

Admittance transform, 29, 31, 33

Algebra, 25, 29

American Standard: "Terminology for Automatic Control" (ASA C85.1 (1963)), 15, 23-24, 123-124

Amplifier, audio, 2-10
  feedback, 10-12, 24
  frequency response of, 2-10, 24
  gain of, 124-125, 200-201
  servo, 84-85, 87

Amplitude, 5
  ratio, 6

Angle value table, 251-256

Angular measure conversion factors, 243

Angular velocity conversion factors, 243

Answers to selected problems, 261-264

Asymptotes, Bode diagram gain curves, 46-48, 52-55
  Bode diagram phase curves, 52-53
  root locus, 221-222, 230-231, 236, 239

Automatic control, 1
  theory, 1

Automobile, automatically steered, 15-22

Bandwidth, 7
  closed-loop (ω_b), 130-133, 181-183
  motor, 101-102

Bibliography, 259-260

Block diagrams, 13-15, 21-22

Bode, H. W., 46

Bode diagram, 25, 42-71, 136-138
  building blocks, 55-59, 61
  construction, 50-54
  initial slope, 62, 64

Books, 259-260
  control theory, 260
  handbooks, 260
  servomechanism components, 259-260

Branch point, 14

Breakaway point of root locus, 209, 214, 231-232, 236, 239-240
  rules for finding, 222-224

Breakaway voltage, 87, 124-125

Breakpoint, 52, 71

Bridge, potentiometer, 76-81

Bridged T network, 110

Calculus, 25, 175

Characteristic equation, 195-209
  complex roots, 197-212
  positive real roots, 197-199
  roots in RHP (right half-plane), 197-199
  roots = poles of the closed-loop system, 200

269

Circuit elements (table), 32
Closed loop, 7–12, 20–24
  frequency analysis advantages, 133
  frequency response, 126–133
  gain and phase diagrams, 126–133
    from open-loop data, 159–167
  peak, 132
  plot, 126–133, 159–167
  system, bandwidth, ω_b, 130–133, 181–183
    maximum magnitude, M_m, 132–133, 164, 180–183
    peak frequency, ω_m, 132–133, 180–183
  transfer function from open-loop transfer function, 126–128
Cogging, 87, 124
Compensation, 69–70, 118–119, 140–154, 158
Compensator, 107
Complex frequency plane (or s plane), 189–193, 200
Complex numbers, 49–50
Complex roots, 197–212
Conditionally stable system, 147, 154
Control, automatic, 1
Control components, impedance, 74–75
Control synchro, 81
Control system, 10, 15, 24, 34, 41, 45, 46, 70, 72–73
Control theory, 1
Control transformer, 83
  sensitivity, 124–125
Conversion factors, 243–246
Corner frequencies, IDSM, 152
Corner frequency, 52, 71
cosine ωt, 186–194
Course recorder, 73–74, 121–122

dB A, calculation and table, 251–256
Damped cosine wave, 186–196
  frequency, 173–183
  sine wave, 172
  sinusoid, 173
Damping, 94–95, 103, 212
  conversion factors, 244

Damping, critical, 171
  factor, z, 171–183
  overdamped, 171
  underdamped, 171
Dead band, 123–125, 158, 164–166, 213
Decade, 51–52
Decibel, 7, 26–27, 46–47,
  approximate values, 50, 250
  magnitude (dB A) values, 251–256
  slide rule calculations, 248–250
  table and calculations, 247–250
Delay, 53
Demodulator, 86
Density conversion factors, 244
Differentiation, 33
Directly controlled system, 24
Disturbance, 24
Double sideband suppressed carrier, 80

Energy conversion factors, 244
Envelope of a sinusoid, 173
Error detector, 24
Excitation function, 80
Experimental or laboratory method, 136
Euler's formula, 188

Feedback, 7, 9, 12, 69, 135, 140–143
  amplifier, 10–12, 24
  negative, 24
  oscillator, 9–11
  positive, 9
First-order system, 201–204
  root locus characteristics of, 204
Force and weight conversion factors, 244
Forward control elements, 24
Forward part of the closed-loop system, 7
Four-terminal network, 34–41, 46, 50–54
Free speed, 91
Frequency, 26–27, 37, 45
  damped, ω_d, 173–183
  function, 45
  natural, ω_n, 171–183

Frequency, of maximum magnitude or gain, ω_m, 132, 159
  response, 2–10, 15–24, 25, 37, 45, 167
    closed-loop data, 180–183
    of amplifier, 2–10
    transfer function, 46
Friction coefficient, 103

Gain, 3–4, 6–7, 12, 17–19, 22, 26, 46–47, 200–241
  asymptote, 71
  crossover, 71
  crossover frequency, 69–71, 137–138, 153–154, 158
  curve, 71
  in decibels, 46–47, 70–71
  margin, 71
  -phase plot, 164
Gear ratio for maximum acceleration, 155–156
Gear train, 106–107
  friction, 124
  transfer function, 107
Generator, rate, 140–144

Horizontal axis intercept = root, 208
Hunting, 133

IDSM (inertia-damped servo motor), 238–241
Impedance of control components, 74–75
Impedance transform, 28–32, 34
Impulse, 186
Inductor, 30–31
Inertia conversion factors, 245
Inertia-damped servo motor (IDSM), 111–116, 152–154, 218–219, 238–241
Initial conditions, 28
Input voltage, 3
Instability, absolute, 197–199
  amplifier, 10
Instrument servomechanisms, 70, 72–74, 121
Integrating circuit, 42–45

Integration, 33
Intercept, horizontal axis, = root, 208
Inverse Laplace transform, 29–30

LHP (left half-plane), 199
Lag network, 109
  compensation by, 118–119, 145–148, 230–234
Laplace transfer functions, 45–46
Laplace transform, 24–37, 42–43, 169–173
  algebraic operation, 29
  of rotational quantities, 98
  operations, 33
  pairs, 28
  procedures, 31
  pronunciation, 25
Lead network, 110
  compensation by, 149–150, 235–237
Left half-plane (LHP), 199
Length conversion factors, 244
Linear, 1
  circuit, 45
  control systems, 72
  element, 2
  system, 1
  velocity conversion factors, 246
Load inertia, reflected, 155–157
Locus (of roots), 209
Logarithms, 25–27
Log magnitude, 46–47

Magazines about servomechanisms, 259
Magnitude, 46–47
  ratio, 70–71
Manufacturer literature, 259
Manufacturers of servomechanism components, 257–258
Mass conversion factors, 245
Mathematical approach, 136–137
Mathematical model, 24
Mathematical operator, 187–188
Maximum, magnitude, M_m, 132, 159
  overshoot, 177–183, 212
    time to, 179–183
  points of transient curve, 175–178

Modulator, 85
Motor starting voltage, 124–125

Natural frequency, 138, 171–183, 211–212
Negative feedback, 9, 24
Network, ac, 110
    dc, 109
    "mechanical," 152
    phase-lag, 109, 145–148, 230–234
    phase-lead, 110, 149–150, 235–237
    R-C, 50–54, 74–75, 145, 149–150
    servo compensating, 109, 118, 145
Network functions, 27–45, 50–54
Nichols chart, 159
Node, 14
No-load speed, 91
Nonlinear element, 2
Nonlinear system, 2
Number of oscillations to settle, 180–183, 212

Ohm's law experiment, 45–46
One-line block diagrams, 13–15
Open loop, 7–9, 13, 17–20, 69
Open-loop vs. closed-loop frequency response, 135–138
Operator, mathematical, 187–188
Oscillations, 12, 17, 186
    damped, 186
Oscillator, 9–10, 69
Output amplitude/input amplitude, 12
Output/input ratio, 3, 18
Output voltage, 3
Overshoot, maximum, 177–183

Partial fractions, 195–196
Period of a damped sine wave, calculation, 173–177
Phase angle, 70–71
    curve, 52–54, 71
    values, table, 251–256
Phase curve, 52–54, 71
Phase lag, 4
    compensating network, 109, 145–148, 230–234

Phase lead, 4
    compensating network, 110, 149–150, 235–237
Phase margin, 69–71, 137, 158
Phase shift, 4, 6–8, 12, 17–19, 22
    curves, 52–54, 71
Pole, 197–239
    position in a third-order equation, 218–220
Poles of the closed-loop system = roots, 200
Pole-zero "cancellation" in third-order system, 218–220
Positive feedback, 9
Positive real part (of a complex number), 197–199
Positive real roots, 197–199
Potentiometer, 123
    bridge, 76–81, 123
    precision, 75
Power conversion factors, 245
Pressure conversion factors, 245
Pulse, 168
    integrator, 43–44

R-C circuit, 27–30, 34–41, 42–45, 50–54
R-C network, 50–54, 74–75, 145, 149–150
RHP (right half-plane), 197–199
R-L circuit, 30–31, 37–41
Ramp, 168
Rate generator, 107–109
    compensation, 140–144, 214–215
    transfer function, 109, 116
Reciprocal time, 27
Relative damping, z, 171–183
Resonant peak, 22
Response function, 80
Right half-plane, (RHP) 197–199
Rise time, 125
Root locus, 195–242
    asymptotes: angles and real-axis intercepts, 221–222, 230–231, 236, 239
    branches, 209, 214, 220, 230, 236, 239

Root locus, breakaway from real axis, 209, 214, 222–224, 231–232, 236, 239–240
  first-order system, 201–204
  gain constant, K_r, 227–228, 232–234, 237, 240
  on real axis, 220, 230, 236, 239
  path of characteristic equation roots, 200–201
  points off the real axis, 224–227
    circle, 232, 239–240
  poles and zeros, 201–202, 205–206, 214–215, 218, 220, 230, 236, 239
  rules for construction, 220–228
    examples of rules applied, 230–241
  second-order system, 205–215
  third-order system, 217–241
  transfer function form, 201, 205, 214, 220, 230, 235, 239
Roots in the right half-plane, 197–199
Roots of the closed-loop system, 200–201
Rotor, inertia, 97–100
  resistance, 90–91
  servomotor, 87
Routh array, 198–199
Routh test, 197–199

s land, 27
s plane, 189–193, 200
SAE (Society of Automotive Engineers), 123
Second-order system, 170, 205–215
  root locus, characteristics, 209
  transient equation, 169–194
Semilog graph paper, 47
Servo amplifier, 84
  ac, 84
  dc, 84–85
  impedance, 85–87
Servomechanism, instrument, 70, 72–74
Servomechanism component manufacturers, 257–258
Servomechanism conversion factors, 243–246
Servomechanisms, 72–73

Servomotor, 86–104, 111–116
  ac, 86–104
  cogging, 87, 124
  dc, 86
  control-phase winding, 86–90
  fixed-phase winding, 86–90
  inertia damped (IDSM), 111–116, 152–154, 218–219, 238–241
  rotor, 87
    inertia, 97–100
    resistance, 90–91
  size, 123
  starting voltage, 87, 124–125
  transfer function, 90–104, 111–116
    linearizing, 92–93
  transient response, 114–115
  viscous-damped, 111–112
Servo networks, 109–110, 118–119
  ac, 100
  dc, 109
  phase-lag, 109, 145–148, 230–234
  phase-lead, 110, 149–150, 235–237
Settling time, 114–115, 125, 179–183, 212
Signal generator, 2–4
Sine wave, 2, 168
Sine wave input, 2, 17, 22
Singularity, 220
Slope at gain crossover, 137, 158
Speed of response, 227
Spirule, 227
Stability, 68–70, 118, 126, 171
  conditional, 147, 154
Stall torque, 91
Standards, ASA C85.1 (1963), 15, 24
  SAE, 123
Steady state, 167
  analysis, 168
Step, unit, 28
  voltage, 28–29, 168
Step input, 169–173
Storage, 53–54, 69
Straight-line approximations for Bode diagrams, 46–48, 52–55
  gain curve, 54–55
  phase curve, 52–53
Summing point, 14, 24

Suppressed carrier, double sideband, 80
Synchro, 81–84
    CX-CT pair, 83, 123, 128
        transfer function, 83–84, 128
    control, 81
    control transformer, 83–84
    receiver, 81–82
    torque, 81
    transmitter, 81–84
System, control, 10, 24
    linear, 1
System accuracy, 125
System transfer function, 101, 117–119

Tachometer, *see* Rate generator
Third-order system transient response, 217–220
Time, settling, 179–183
Time constant, 29–31, 53–54, 99–100, 145, 149–150, 156
Time delay, 53–54
Time domain, 193
Time function, 28–31, 33, 37, 41–45, 169
Time of one period, 173, 180
Time response, 16
Time to maximum overshoot, 179–183
Torque, 95–99
    constant, 96–97, 99
    conversion factors, 246
Torque/error conversion factors, 246
Torque synchro, 81
Transducer, 75
Transfer function, 13–15, 34–41, 45–46, 70
    ac servomotor, 90–104, 116
    amplifier, 84, 116
    demodulator, 86, 116
    development from catalog values, 100–104, 128–129
    gear train, 106–107, 116
    inertia-damped servomotor (IDSM), 111–115, 116
    modulator, 86, 116

Transfer function, potentiometer bridge, 80–81, 116
    root locus form, 201, 205, 214, 220, 230, 235, 239
    servo network, 109–110, 116
    synchro pair, CX-CT, 83–84, 116
Transform, Laplace, 24–37
    algebraic operation, 29
    inverse, 29
    operations, 33
Transient, 42–45, 167
Transient analysis, 168–194
Transient response, 16
    curve, 173–183, 187–194
        maxima and minima, 175–178
        maximum overshoot, 177–183; time to, 179–183
        plotting, 173–177
        settling time, 179–193
Twin T network, 110

Unit step, 28, 168–173
    Laplace transform, 28, 170

Vector conversion table, 251–256
    calculations, 251
Velocity (angular) conversion factors, 243
Velocity constant, 99, 129, 132–133
Velocity error coefficient, 125, 132–133, 144, 158
Velocity lag error, 125, 132–133, 144, 158
Velocity (linear) conversion factors, 246
Viscous-damped servomotor, 111–112
Viscous damping, 94–95, 140–142
Viscous friction, 155
Voltage divider, 35–37
Voltage step, 28–29

Weight conversion factors, 244

Zero, 197–239